Principles of Regeneration

ACADEMIC PRESS   New York and London

Academic Press, Inc.
111 Fifth Avenue, New York, New York 10003

United Kingdom Edition published by
Academic Press, Inc. (London) Ltd.
Berkeley Square House, London W.1

Library of Congress Catalog Card Number: 68-26636

Printed in the United States of America

Principles of Regeneration

RICHARD J. GOSS

Brown University
Providence, Rhode Island

Illustrated by Louise Russell

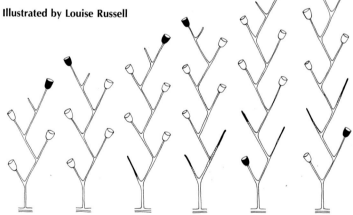

Preface

Two centuries ago, an Italian biologist, Lazzaro Spallanzani (1729–1799), published his famous "Prodromo di un Opera sopra la Riproduzioni Animali." To this day this remarkable book stands as the foundation upon which our subsequent research on regeneration has been based.

The topics included in the present volume have been selected with a view to the basic principles they exemplify. Each chapter will attempt to illustrate a different aspect of the phenomenon of regeneration. It is hoped that students of developmental biology, anatomy, and evolution will find here information about postembryonic morphogenesis beyond the immediate subject of regeneration. In addition, teachers and researchers in the fields of biology and medicine in general may find some new and provocative approaches to some old and persistent problems.

In any discussion of regeneration, considerable attention must be devoted to the straightforward description of what it is that is regenerated. If this description is to go beyond what is visible, experiments calculated to reveal the roles played by various components of the system as they interact with one another in the course of development must be performed. Since regeneration is a physiological process, the restoration of function is emphasized along with the restoration of structure.

The subject of regeneration lends itself especially well to analysis. So well in fact, that one must constantly be on guard against the pitfalls of teleological thinking. No one would seriously contend that regeneration evolved to fulfill some preordained purpose in life. No one would deny, however, that once evolved it is not a useful attribute.

Ernest Hemingway once noted that the hardest thing about writing a story was deciding what to leave out. I have intentionally omitted many things for which my colleagues will not easily forgive me. Whole phyla, for example, have gone unmentioned, and more than one man's lifetime of research has been totally disregarded. What is more, many great discoveries of the past have been relegated to the public domain without crediting those who made them. It is in the nature of things, I suppose, that classic discoveries should by definition find their tribute in such anonymity. The most regrettable omissions, however, are solutions to the still-unsolved problems of regeneration, problems which will be resolved only if we continue to question and experiment.

RICHARD J. GOSS

August, 1968

Contents

vii

Principles of Regeneration

1 Introduction

IF there were no regeneration there could be no life. If everything regenerated there would be no death. All organisms exist between these two extremes. Other things being equal, they tend toward the latter end of the spectrum, never quite achieving immortality because this would be incompatible with reproduction.

It is by reproducing that organisms regenerate themselves and their species. At this level of organization everything regenerates. Likewise at the molecular level. In between, some things regenerate and others do not. This is particularly true of whole fractions of the body and of such appendages as may protrude from it. It is here, then, that our attention shall be focused, but not to the extent that regeneration at other levels of organization is overlooked.

There are many kinds of regeneration. In the broadest sense regeneration is synonymous with reproduction, especially vegetative reproduction—in which case the prefix becomes redundant. Yet nothing new can be made without generating additional units of structure. To make a cell, new organelles must be produced: this in turn requires the synthesis of molecules.

All organisms, of course, can synthesize molecules. Without this constant biochemical turnover, cells could never adapt to the changing physiological demands of their existence. All living things can also make new cells, some better than others. They can also heal wounds, renew tissues, indulge in compensatory hypertrophy, and reproduce. So important are these phenomena that they have undergone little or no decline in the course of evolution.

What has declined is the capacity to regenerate substantial parts of the body, or appendages thereof. To achieve this requires more than just making more molecules and cells. To be sure, these units must be multiplied, but they must also be put together in the right way. Cells have to be assembled into tissues, and tissues into organs, because what is produced will be of no use unless it is organized into something that works.

Hence, the sheer morphological complexities at these higher levels of organization, not to mention the even greater complexities of the mechanisms by which they developed, have evidently posed problems too great for many animals to solve. Most creatures certainly might have solved these problems if the importance of regeneration had warranted it. However, the fact that higher animals have often not retained the regenerative capacities of their ancestors suggests that the strategy of evolution has been to select against regeneration, not for it. This implies that other advantages of greater importance must have been gained in the bargain. We can only guess what these advantages might have been, but they have obviously worked out very well judging from the success of highly evolved, but nonregenerating animals like ourselves.

Aside from the phylogenetic aspects of regeneration, consider the mechanism by which amputated structures are replaced. There are many ways to regenerate a structure. Usually the initial stimulus is the injury of amputation, but in at least some cases regeneration is a spontaneous event. Loss of the part to be replaced may be the effect instead of the cause of renewed growth. This is usually accompanied by autotomy, whereby old parts are shed by the animal itself. Wherever there is the capacity for autotomy, there are often provisions for regeneration.

In order to replace a missing structure, something must be left behind as a source of new building materials. Regeneration can replace a part, but never a whole, and one of the most perplexing problems facing us today is to explain how the boundaries of a regeneration territory are marked out. If an appendage is amputated at increasingly proximal levels the point is eventually reached when no regeneration ensues. At this level, all the territory of the appendage has been removed and no tissues remain from which renewed growth can proceed. Yet we still do not know what properties enable the cells in a territory to participate in regeneration while neighboring cells outside the territory are incompetent to respond to amputation in this way.

It takes more than amputation, however, to initiate regeneration. Amputation sets up the opportunity for renewed growth by exposing an appropriate cross section of tissues to injury and by initiating wound healing. But these factors alone do not necessarily stimulate the replacement of what was once there. In many instances, regeneration is dependent upon physiological agencies not of local origin. Such influences may be neural or hormonal in nature, and in some cases may even be triggered by environmental conditions. Yet if diverse examples of regeneration are compared in this respect, a common pattern emerges. In protozoans, the nucleus is indispensable for regeneration; eye regeneration in flatworms is stimulated by the brain; arthropods fail to grow new appendages unless they can molt; various extremities in the vertebrates require an adequate nerve supply; the newt lens cannot be replaced in the absence of the neural retina; antlers grow in response to changes in day length. Again and again, the initiation of regeneration is linked to physiological conditions which vary from animal to animal but which always relate to the function to be performed by the structure being replaced. Hence, there is a utilitarian imperative which assures that developmental efforts shall not be expended in the production of useless structures. In this sense, regeneration is to be regarded primarily as a device by which functional competence is recovered. Morphological restitution is only a means to this end.

This is not to say that morphogenetic mechanisms are not important. They dominate every aspect of regeneration and pose some of the most formidable problems in biology today. First and foremost, there can be no regeneration without cells available to undergo differentiation and morphogenesis appropriate to the organ being completed. Sometimes morphogenesis may be achieved simply by reorganizing the old tissues directly into the new without augmenting the number of cells orginally present in the stump. This is the process of morphallaxis, which involves the rearrangement of remaining parts so as to remodel an amputated structure into an integrated morphological whole. For obvious reasons, morphallaxis is feasible only in relatively simple regenerating systems.

Usually there intervenes a proliferative phase between amputation and reconstruction. The new cells may be locally produced or may be immigrants from elsewhere. They may be derived from formerly differentiated tissues or may be part of a reserve population of undifferentiated cells. In any case, they aggregate at the amputation site, where they form an undifferentiated bud, or blastema. Here the cells multiply profusely. They also organize into the various tissues of the developing regenerate.

How the blastema becomes organized is the most baffling problem of all. Not only must each and every missing part be reproduced, but the parts have to be put together in precisely the correct spatial relationships to give rise to a reasonable replica of what was there in the first place. Unless the morphology of the regenerate corresponds exactly to that of the stump from which it was produced, the resulting structure will be as functionally useless as it is anatomically shapeless. The mechanisms of morphogenesis, therefore, can leave nothing to chance. The number, size, orientation, and polarity of the regenerate must coincide with the corresponding characteristics of the stump, and when the final structure has been completed then growth must cease. In all, the precision of this development reflects the orderly communication of information to the blastema from the stump, but the language of such messages remains to be deciphered.

No discussion of regeneration would be complete without seriously considering why it is that some animals can replace missing parts and others cannot. Perhaps it is more to the point, however, to ask why regeneration can take place in some parts of a given organism but not in others. The answer, of course, lies in the existence of regeneration territories, by which the limits of reproducibility for any particular structure are defined. In certain lower forms, practically any part of the organism can give rise to a whole new animal. Here there is a single all-inclusive territory, nearly any part of which contains enough information to replace the entire body. With increasing complexity, however, regenerative ability has become restricted to subfractions of the body. The somatic blueprint was subdivided into a number of territories. Thus, the directions for forming a particular structure became less and less widely distributed in the body. Ultimately, such information came to lie only within its own structure. When this happened, no longer could the front end of an animal regenerate a hind end, and vice versa, but a limb could give rise only to a limb and a tail only to a tail. This compartmentalization created a specificity of potentialities within the resultant regeneration territories such that the cells in one region could not actively participate in the regenerative ventures of other regions. That is, limb tissues could not become part of a tail regenerate, nor tail tissues part of a jaw, and so forth. Within any given territory, however, a cell could still become incorporated into any part of its own kind of regenerate. Hence, a cell formerly situated in the upper arm could become relocated in the wrist or the digits in the course of regeneration. Carried to the extreme, however, continued restriction of potentialities might reduce the boundaries of a regeneration territory to the vanishing point. This is what evidently happens in the metamorphosing tadpole as it loses its capacity to regenerate legs. Maybe something comparable occurred during the evolution of reptiles, birds and mammals to account for the extinction of their potential to regenerate limbs.

What is it that happens when a structure loses the capacity to regenerate either during ontogeny or phylogeny? One can see no meaningful differences between the cells and tissues inside a regeneration territory and those outside. Yet they are not the same with regard to their developmental potentialities. When regenerative ability is lost in an appendage, is some essential ingredient absent altogether, or does the ability still persist in a latent form? If the latter explanation is correct, regenerative potential could theoretically be restored by discovering what is inhibiting it and then finding a way to eliminate the inhibition. Should something necessary for regeneration be missing altogether, the task of reviving regeneration after it is gone would be more formidable indeed.

In the latter case, there is assumed to be a deficiency which would have to be made good. Depending upon the nature of what might be lacking—and there could be more than one factor—the job of restoration would range from difficult to impossible. For example, one of the stimulatory agents, such as nerves or hormones, could be inadequate to promote regeneration. These can and have been experimentally augmented with results that are encouraging but still short of perfection. Otherwise, the deficiency could lie within the reacting tissues themselves, rendering them unresponsive to the above stimulating factors or perhaps just incapable of carrying out some essential step in the regenerative mechanism.

Presumably the deficiency has as its basis a genetic mutation— either an error of omission or an error of commission. If an essential gene is missing completely, then we might as well abandon all hope of ever replacing it, at least for a long time to come. If it is simply masked, then the possibility of activating it again is not inconceivable. In the event that the loss of regeneration might be due to the presence of a gene serving to block renewed development, we might someday learn how to inactivate that part of the DNA or its product in order to remove the inhibition.

Discussions along these lines raise the problem of just how genetics is bound up with regenerative ability. Are the same genes that direct the original ontogeny also utilized to regenerate an appendage? There seems to be little reason to believe otherwise. With rare exceptions, what regenerates is a duplicate of the original. And even when it is not, as in the case of the lizard tail, the differences can be explained in terms of the histological conditions existing in the adult tail which might alter the outcome from what it was originally in the embryo.

Assuming that the same genes are used over again in regeneration, and that they operate, as they must, at the level of the cell, is it logical to seek purely genetic explanations of regeneration? Surely there is no such thing as a gene for regeneration, despite the fact that regenerative capacity has been subject to natural selection. It seems that regeneration is not necessarily adaptive, but that it has disappeared or persisted as other more important physiological attributes evolved with which it may or may not have been incompatible. Hence, before any intelligent attempt can be made to restore regeneration where it does not naturally take place, it will first be necessary to learn what physiological advantages took precedence over regeneration in the course of natural selection. Only than can we decide if the gain was worth the loss, and what, if anything, can be done about it.

GENERAL REFERENCES

ABELOOS, M. 1932. "La Régénération et les Problèmes de la Morphogenèse." Gauthier-Villars, Paris.

BARR, H. J. 1964. Regeneration and natural selection. *Am. Naturalist* **98:** 183–186.

BERRILL, N. J. 1961. "Growth, Development, and Pattern." W. H. Freeman, San Francisco.

FLICKINGER, R. A. 1967. Biochemical aspects of regeneration. *In* "The Biochemistry of Animal Development" (R. Weber, ed.), Vol. 2, pp. 303–337. Academic Press, New York.

HAY, E. D. 1966. "Regeneration." Holt, Rinehart and Winston, New York.

KIORTSIS, V. and H. A. L. TRAMPUSCH (eds.). 1965. "Regeneration in Animals and Related Problems." North-Holland Publ. Co., Amsterdam.

KORSCHELT, E. 1927. "Regeneration und Transplantation," Vol. I: Regeneration. Borntraeger, Berlin.

MORGAN, T. H. 1901. "Regeneration." Macmillan, New York.

NEEDHAM, A. E. 1952. "Regeneration and Wound Healing." Methuen, London.

NEEDHAM, A. E. 1961. Evolution of regeneration, and its possible bearing on philosophy. *Nature* **192:** 1255–1256.

RUDNICK, D. (ed.). 1962. "Regeneration" (20th Growth Symposium). Ronald Press, New York.

SCHMIDT, A. J. 1968. "Cellular Biology of Vertebrate Regeneration and Repair." University of Chicago Press, Chicago.

SINGER, M. 1958. The regeneration of body parts. *Sci. Am.* **199** (4): 79–88.

SPALLANZANI, L. 1768. "Prodromo di un Opera sopra la Riproduzioni Animali." Modena.

SPILSBURY, R. J. 1961. Evolution of regeneration, and its possible bearing on philosophy. *Nature* **192:** 1254–1255.

THORNTON, C. S. (ed.). 1959. "Regeneration in Vertebrates." University of Chicago Press, Chicago.

VORONTSOVA, M. A. and L. D. LIOSNER. 1960. "Asexual Propagation and Regeneration." Pergamon Press, London.

WADDINGTON, C. H. 1956. "Principles of Embryology," Chapter 14, pp. 302–324. Allen and Unwin, London.

WEISS, P. 1939. "Principles of Development," pp. 458–478. Henry Holt, New York.

2   The Mermaid's Wineglass

*In common language, we describe the nucleus as the administrator of
the cell. It shares two attributes with more familiar administrators: It tends to
perpetuate its kind, and it defies so successfully all efforts to learn what
it is doing that only by trying to get along without it can we satisfy ourselves
that it is working at all.*

D. Mazia
AIBS Bull. **12**(1), 5 (1962)

IF Nobel prizes were awarded to experimental organisms instead of
to the people who work on them, *Acetabularia* would be a richly
deserving laureate. It is given to few living things to play a more
important role than has this unicellular marine alga in our quest
for explanations of regeneration and morphogenesis. Endowed with
morphological complexities approaching those of many higher organisms, yet containing but a single nucleus to manage its extensive
cytoplasmic household, *Acetabularia* combines in one plant a set of
attributes more unique than we might ever have dared to hope for.

Equally unique are the experimental opportunities it offers us, opportunities which have been pressed with advantage in recent years.

Acetabularia lives in the warm waters of shallow tropical seas, where it may be found attached to the surfaces of submerged rocks. Anchored to the substrate by a cluster of rhizoids, its slender stem rises to a length of several centimeters and is capped by an umbrella of radially arranged gametangia. This cap is the most distinctive feature of the alga, for its shape varies with the species. In *A. mediterranea*, its form reminds us of a wineglass, while in *A. crenulata*, which inhabits the Caribbean, it consists of an irregular profusion of sausage-shaped rays.

It is in the mature cap that gametes are produced by meiosis. When released, these biflagellate gametes fuse in pairs and the resulting zygote begins to develop into a new plant. In doing so, it first grows the rhizoids from which the stalk then sprouts. As the stalk elongates it puts out several whorls of "sterile hairs" which die off as new ones are formed above. When its full height is achieved, as determined in inverse proportion to the intensity of illumination, the stalk develops

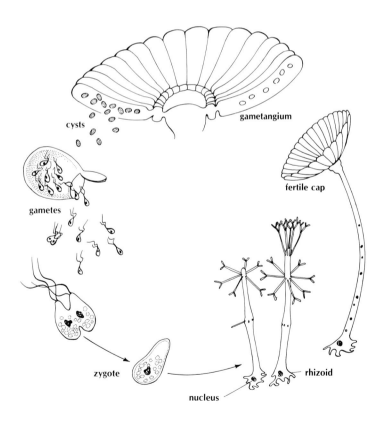

Fig. 1 **Life cycle of** *Acetabularia*. **The fertile cap (top) develops numerous cysts in which gametes are produced by meiosis. After their release the gametes fuse to reestablish the diploid condition in the zygote. The germinating plant sprouts several transient sets of sterile hairs before finally producing the mature gametangia of the fertile cap. The single nucleus in the rhizoid then proliferates into numerous daughter nuclei which stream up the stem to populate the cap and eventually give rise to more gametes.**

cysts

gametangium

gametes

fertile cap

zygote

nucleus

rhizoid

the apical cap characteristic of the mature alga. The whole period of development may last the entire season of several months.

Up until maturity, the plant has only a single nucleus located in one of the rhizoids at the base. Not until it gets ready to reproduce does the nucleus begin to proliferate. The resulting daughter nuclei than swarm up the stem to the cap where they become segregated from each other by cell walls. It is inside these cysts that gametogenesis occurs. The gametes, like the mature alga, contain chloroplasts.

What makes *Acetabularia* so interesting and useful to the biologist is that it can develop such a large and complicated morphological structure under the guidance of only one nucleus. This nucleus, moreover, can be removed or transplanted between individuals by relatively simple operative procedures. Add to these advantages the fact that the amputated cap is capable of regeneration, and we have a system ideally suited to challenge the curiosity of the experimental biologist. Joachim Hämmerling of the Max Planck Institute deserves credit for first recognizing the immense possibilities of *Acetabularia* as an experimental system in which to study regeneration. It may take quite a few weeks for the cap to regenerate, but the wait is worth it because its morphology can tell us a great deal about how the genetic messages from the nucleus are translated into the structure of the organism.

Here, then, it is possible to analyze the regeneration of part of a whole organism in terms of cytological events. This is an important advantage because the organ and tissue levels of organization which normally intervene between organism and cell are dispensed with. The resulting reduction in complexity allows us to ask questions of a less ambiguous nature than is possible in multicellular forms. It means that we can approach regeneration with the precision of the cytologist and with the analytical methods of the biochemist.

Clearly, the nucleus must play a dominant role in cap regeneration, a role that has been intensively investigated by a variety of ingenious techniques. But before exploring these fascinating experiments, let us first become better acquainted with the nucleus itself and how it guides the life history of the plant.

Nature of the Nucleus in Acetabularia The nucleus is very large and contains relatively enormous nucleoli. The latter are elongate structures which are twisted around within the nucleus, taking up the lion's share of the volume. In contrast, the DNA is so diffusely distributed in the spaciousness of the nucleus that it can hardly be demonstrated cytochemically until the plant matures and the nucleus begins to divide. It is significant, however, that the nucleoli should dominate the nucleus, for the RNA derived from them is probably the key to many of the extraordinary things that *Acetabularia* can do.

When it comes time for the nucleus to divide in preparation for reproduction, its proliferation can be postponed by cutting off the cap. This process can be repeated over and over as long as it is desired to prevent the production of daughter nuclei. Not until a new cap is subsequently allowed to regenerate and mature will the nucleus again prepare for division. The opposite trick can also be played on the nucleus by grafting a mature cap onto an immature plant, whereupon premature mitoses are made to take place. This means, of course, that the presence of a fully developed cap triggers nuclear proliferation, but the exact nature of the feedback message is unknown.

Not only are certain nuclear activities dependent upon the rest of the cell, but it comes as no surprise that the cell is dependent upon the nucleus. What is surprising, however, is how much less dependent *Acetabularia* is on its nucleus than are other kinds of cells. The vast majority of cells cannot long survive the loss of their nuclei, mammalian erythrocytes being the most conspicuous exception. These cells, however, cannot synthesize hemoglobin for much more than 24 hours or so after nuclear extrusion, after which their days are numbered. And whether they live for several weeks, as in the mouse, or several months, as in man, they are hardly more than robots capable of little if any independent activity. *Acetabularia*, on the other hand, can go on living for over two months without a nucleus, during which time it continues to synthesize proteins for growth and differentiation. Thus, the influence of the nucleus can be felt long after it is gone.

It can also be felt over a long distance, for the nucleus in the rhizoid is several centimeters away from the cap it controls. In fact, there is reason to believe that the cap automatically develops at that point farthest removed from the nucleus (while rhizoids are induced closest to the nucleus). In the normal course of development, the cap will form even after the rhizoid containing the nucleus is cut off. But if an already formed cap is amputated, it will not regenerate from the stem unless the nucleus is present (Fig. 2). Under these conditions, however, the nucleus is needed for only a short time. After a few days, it can be removed from the capless *Acetabularia* and regeneration of a new cap will proceed normally. During this interval the nucleus produces something necessary for the successful initiation of regeneration. This morphogenetic substance, as Hämmerling called it,

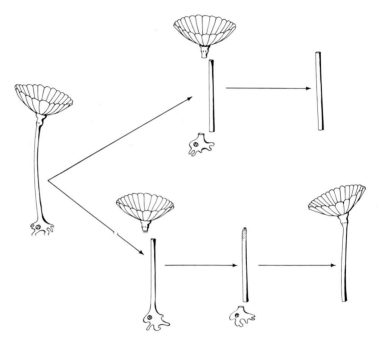

Fig. 2 **Regeneration depends on the nucleus. If a length of stem is simultaneously isolated both from its cap and its nucleated rhizoid (top row) it will grow neither a cap nor a rhizoid. But if enucleation is postponed for several days after decapitation (bottom row) enough time is allowed for the re-establishment of a new apical bud which can then regenerate a cap in the absence of the nucleus.**

accumulates at the amputation stump where regrowth is going to occur. Development of the cap therefore depends on the presence of this important apical region of the stem, for it is here that the morphogenetic memory from the nucleus is stored.

Since the nucleus is necessary, although indirectly so, for the differentiation of the cap, one might logically ask how specific this influence is. A provident nature has placed at our disposal different species of *Acetabularia* with caps of varying configurations. These have been used to test the species-specificity of the nuclear effects on cap morphogenesis. Fortunately, it is possible to graft segments of two plants together by telescoping the cell wall of one over that of the other. As shown in Fig. 3, this technique may be used, for example, to graft a rhizoid (containing its nucleus) of one species to the enucleated stem of another species. This is something like replacing the manager in a Ford factory with one from a Chevrolet plant to see if the automobiles subsequently produced are Fords or Chevrolets. Those currently on the assembly line turn out to be a combination of the two.

When the rhizoid of *A. mediterranea* is amputated to get rid of its nucleus, and is replaced with the rhizoid of *A. crenulata*, the effect of the new nucleus on morphogenesis depends on whether the host plant has not yet developed a cap or already has one which must be amputated. In either case, cap development will take place, but in the former situation the cap that is produced will be of the *mediterranea* type, or a combination of *mediterranea* and *crenulata*. The reason is that in the immature capless plant the apical region of the stem already contains morphogenetic substances derived from its original nucleus. Hence, the cap that develops reflects such influences even though a different kind of nucleus may now be present at the base. To the extent that morphogenetic substances from the new nucleus are allowed to augment those from the old one, the shape of the cap will be a hybrid of the two sources of information. It is a curious thing that such intergrade plants cannot successfully reproduce, presumably owing to nucleocytoplasmic incompatibilities.

In situations in which the host alga already has a mature cap which must be amputated at the time of nuclear substitution, cap regeneration will invariably be of the nuclear type. The reason is that no apical region of the stem is present under these conditions to provide messages from the former nucleus. Therefore, the results of such experiments depend entirely on whether or not there remains a

Fig. 3 **Interspecific grafts between** Acetabularia mediterranea **(white) and** A. crenulata **(black). When a** crenulata **nucleus is transplanted to a** mediterranea **stalk with an immature apical bud (upper row) the latter generally develops into a cap of mixed type expressing characteristics of both the former nucleus and the currently present one. Should this be amputated, however, the resulting regenerate turns out to be pure** crenulata. **If nuclei are switched between mature stalks (lower row), regeneration of the cap is under complete control of the new nucleus.**

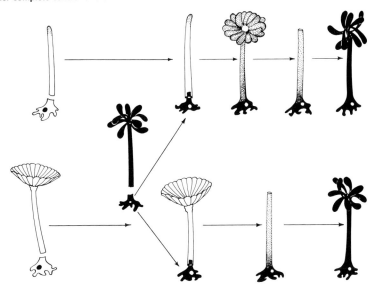

backlog of commands from the ex-nucleus when the new one takes charge of the organism.

Bearing this in mind, it is not difficult to predict what would happen under other combinations of nuclear transplantations. Instead of substituting one nucleus for another, one can graft nucleus-containing fragments of two species together. When made to regenerate in the presence of both *mediterranea* and *crenulata* nuclei, the resulting morphology of the cap will be a cross between the two species. And if two nuclei of one kind are added to one of the other, then the cap that regenerates will still be an intermediate type, but will favor the species with the double dose of nuclei. No matter how such experiments are done, the nucleus will eventually make its presence felt. What is unique about *Acetabularia* is that this nuclear influence can last for such a long time.

Enzyme Effects   Nuclear effects persist at the molecular as well as the morphological level of organization, for protein synthesis goes on for a long time after the loss of the nucleus. Enzymes are the cell's most important protein, and their responses to various experimental manipulations of *Acetabularia* nuclei have been extensively analyzed by Konrad Keck. In the case of some enzymes (e.g., aldolase, invertase, phosphorylase) there may be considerable increases in their activities as growth of the alga continues after enucleation. Other enzymes, such as acid phosphatase, may decrease slowly but still remain detectable for some weeks. In the case of the latter enzyme, as well as certain esterases, different kinds of algae have been found to contain different isozymes, that is, enzymes acting specifically on the same substrates but which occur in different forms that can be separated by electrophoresis.

When *Acetabularia mediterranea* was compared with the closely related genus *Acicularia schenckii,* their esterase and acid phosphatase isozymes proved to be distinguishable by grinding up plants of the two genera in tiny glass homogenizers and subjecting them to starch gel electrophoresis. Subsequent histochemical staining revealed that the isozymes of *Acetabularia* had greater electrophoretic mobility than did those from *Acicularia*. Thus, isozymes can be separated from each other in this way even in mixed homogenates of two species of plants.

Now, when nuclei are exchanged between *Acetabularia* and *Acicularia,* the esterase isozymes of the host cytoplasm eventually become replaced by those characteristic of the transplanted nuclei. If both kinds of nuclei are combined in one plant, a mixture of the two isozymes appears. In the case of acid phosphatase, however, a more puzzling situation is encountered.

When a nucleated rhizoid of *Acetabularia mediterranea* is grafted to an enucleated *Acicularia* plant, the latter type of acid phosphatase isozyme disappears within five days instead of remaining detectable for over a month as in enucleated algae. *Acetabularia* phosphatase begins to appear on the second day in the *Acicularia* host, and its concentration increases thereafter. The presence of the *Acetabularia* nucleus is somehow responsible for the precocious loss of *Acicularia* phosphatase.

The reciprocal experiment yields even more surprising results. Enucleated *Acetabularia mediterranea* stalks with *Acicularia* nuclei do not acquire *Acicularia* phosphatase. Rather, the *Acetabularia* isozyme persists in the cytoplasm. Even if rhizoids from both kinds of algae are grafted together, only *Acetabularia* phosphatase is produced, although the cap that forms is morphologically intermediate between the two kinds of nuclei. Can we explain this paradox by the conversion of *Acicularia* phosphatase to the *Acetabularia* type? Possibly; but we have no direct proof. Electrophoretically, an intermediate type of acid phosphatase has been detected in mixed homogenates of the two kinds of cytoplasm incubated *in vitro*, but this has never been supplanted by the *Acetabularia* type of isozyme. In grafts between fragments of living plants, however, the final step in the conversion apparently does take place. As the *Acicularia* phosphatase disappears, the intermediate type becomes detectable, which is in turn replaced by the *Acetabularia* isozyme. Thus, in these particular species (but not necessarily in other combinations), one kind of enzyme dominates the other, perhaps by promoting its conjugation with other molecules bearing negative charges and thereby increasing its electrophoretic mobility. It is a curious thing that there should exist such a molecular conversion, when the morphogenetic effects, in contrast, are produced equally by both kinds of nuclei. Apparently nucleo-cytoplasmic relationships are not as straightforward as we sometimes assume them to be.

The Role of Ribonucleic Acid in Morphogenesis The phenomena thus far mentioned depend upon the existence of nuclear-derived instructions in the cytoplasm. It is not difficult to venture an educated guess as to the nature of this material. Evidence from Jean Brachet's laboratory at the Free University of Brussels points strongly in the direction of RNA. It will be remembered, for example, that the nucleus of *Acetabularia* is unusual in that it contains exceptionally large nucleoli, the major source of RNA. According to staining experiments, this RNA, once it leaves the nucleus, becomes concentrated at the tip of the growing stalk in immature or regenerating plants. This is where the morphogenetic potential for cap formation exists. The expression of this potential under diverse experimental conditions is outlined in Table 1.

Nucleic acids are sensitive to irradiation. Exposure to X-rays or ultraviolet light inhibits morphogenesis in *Acetabularia*. Ordinarily, an enucleated stalk of *A. crenulata* will grow a cap, but not if it has been exposed to UV light. If an unirradiated nucleus from *A. mediterranea* is transplanted to an enucleate *A. crenulata* stalk, the cap that develops will be intermediate between the two species only if the host stalk has not been exposed to UV light. Otherwise, the morphogenetic influence of the nucleus prevails.

Less circumstantial evidence derives from experiments with ribonuclease, which specifically degrades RNA. As long as algae are exposed to this enzyme, they cannot synthesize proteins, nor can they grow new caps. Unlike the effects of irradiation, however, RNase inhibition is reversible after withdrawal of the enzyme. In otherwise intact plants in which existing RNA may have been destroyed, new RNA can be made afterward by the nucleus. If enucleate stalks are subjected to RNase, the inhibitory effects are permanent because the source of genetic information, upon which RNA regeneration depends, is missing.

Actinomycin exerts somewhat different effects. It blocks the synthesis of RNA, rather than destroying that which has already formed as in

Table 1 *Effects of various experimental treatments on growth and cap formation in vegetative* Acetabularia *with nucleus intact, following enucleation, and after decapitation of growing tip*[a]

	Control	UV	RNase	Actinomycin	Puromycin
Nucleus present	+	−	−+	+	−+
Nucleus absent	+	−	−	+	−+
Tip of stalk decapitated	+	−	−+	−+	−+

[a] *Symbols:* + *regeneration of cap;* − *no regeneration;* −+ *reversible inhibition.*

the case of RNase. Hence, enucleate stems of *Acetabularia* will still form new caps on their ends in the presence of actinomycin, but decapitated plants fail to do so because their cytoplasmic RNA is lost and the nucleus cannot make any more so long as they are exposed to the drug. Antibiotics which interfere with protein synthesis also prevent cap formation. Puromycin, for example, inhibits morphogenesis reversibly irrespective of whether the alga contains a nucleus or not.

Being a green plant, *Acetabularia* must have light in order to carry out many of its life processes, including cap regeneration. Kept in total darkness, the alga not only fails to grow or undergo morphogenesis, but its nucleus and nucleoli shrink to a fraction of their normal sizes. Under such starvation conditions, however, not all physiological processes cease. Indeed, the all-important synthesis and release of RNA by the nucleus continues in the absence of photosynthesis as shown by regeneration studies in light versus darkness. As previously mentioned, simultaneous decapitation and enucleation are not followed by regeneration because there is neither a pre-existing supply of RNA nor a source of new RNA to direct specific protein synthesis for cap morphogenesis. On the other hand, delayed enucleation permits cap regeneration owing to the replenishment of RNA. If algae are maintained in the dark during the interval between decapitation and enucleation, and then illuminated at the time the nucleus is removed, cap regeneration takes place successfully. Therefore, all RNA involved had to be made during the dark period, although it could not implement morphogenesis until reilluminated. Evidently the energy supplied by photosynthesis is required to carry out protein synthesis as specified by RNA, but not to activate genes for RNA transcription.

In conclusion, we have in *Acetabularia* a true natural curiosity, not because it is unicellular, not because its single nucleus presides over a complex cytological structure, not even because a specialized part of that structure can regenerate. Other cells are equally extraordinary. Its claim to fame lies in how long it can live and grow without a nucleus, a feat made possible by the unusually long survival of the messenger RNA in its cytoplasm. In bacteria, as in most other cells, the turnover rate of messenger RNA is notoriously rapid. These molecules enjoy life spans measured in minutes or only a few hours at best. There are a few kinds of cells, such as reticulocytes, lens fibers, or the cells in avian down feathers, in which messenger RNA may remain active for as long as a day. These exceptions to the general rule are adaptations to the loss or inactivation of the nucleus before differentiation has gone to completion. But in *Acetabularia* the nucleus remains healthy, yet its RNA is stable for weeks or months. There must be a reason why this unique attribute has survived evolutionary selection, but its advantage to *Acetabularia* remains as elusive as it is intriguing.

It is axiomatic that regeneration cannot occur unless there remains something to regenerate from—some part of the organism to provide the right genetic information for morphogenesis. In the case of *Acetabularia*, RNA fulfills this role. It is also true that the replacement of lost parts generally depends upon physiological factors responsible for the proper functioning of those parts after they are replaced. In this regard also, *Acetabularia* is exceptional, for its cap is a reproductive organ essential for gametogenesis. Yet we have seen that it can regenerate even in the absence of a nucleus when all hope for reproduction has been abandoned. One wonders how such apparent inefficiency could have evolved since it is obviously of no use in perpetuating the species. The answer lies in the inexplicable longevity of messenger RNA, a phylogenetic luxury to *Acetabularia,* and an experimental bonus to students of cellular regeneration.

REFERENCES

BRACHET, J. L. A. 1965. Acetabularia. *Endeavour* **24:** 155–161.

GIBOR, A. 1966. Acetabularia: A useful giant cell. *Sci. Am.* **215** (5): 118–124.

HÄMMERLING, J. 1963. Nucleo-cytoplasmic interactions in Acetabularia and other cells. *Ann. Rev. Plant Physiol.* **14:** 65–92.

KECK, K. 1960. Nucleo-cytoplasmic interactions in the synthesis of species-specific proteins in *Acetabularia. Biochem. Biophys. Res. Commun.* **3:** 56–61.

KECK, K. and E. A. CHOULES. 1963. An analysis of cellular and subcellular systems which transform the species character of acid phosphatase in *Acetabularia. J. Cell Biol.* **18:** 459–469.

STICH, H. and W. PLAUT. 1958. The effect of ribonuclease on protein synthesis in nucleated and enucleated fragments of *Acetabularia. J. Biophys. Biochem. Cytol.* **4:** 119–121.

3   Stentor: Morphogenetic Magician

THE ultimate in regeneration is to grow an entire organism from a single cell. When the ovum does this, the distinction between reproduction and regeneration disappears. When single-celled organisms do it, the distinction hardly exists in the first place. In *Stentor coeruleus*, a large ciliate protozoan, reproduction is achieved by dividing in half transversely. The way each half reconstitutes itself is essentially the way it regenerates following surgical bisection. Thus, reproduction in this organism is tantamount to regeneration, and *vice versa*.

Stentor has no embryology because it is not so complex that it must segregate germ cells. Strictly speaking, it is not even unicellular. The many nuclei of its soma, instead of being partitioned between cell walls, are collected together in a macronucleus believed to contain all the genomes. In this sense, *Stentor* may be regarded as an acellular organism.

Owing to its large size, this ciliate has long been the animal of choice for experimental studies on regeneration in protozoans. It is a giant in a Lilliputian world, measuring 0.5 mm from stem to stern, but capable of stretching out to five times that length. Yet for all its enormity relative to other protozoans, it still remains a very tiny organsim on an absolute scale, as anyone who has tried to operate on it soon discovers. Those few investigators who have successfully mastered such manipulative techniques have done so by a combination of ingenious trouble-shooting, a steady hand, and stubborn determination. The perseverance of such investigators as Vance Tartar of the University of Washington and Paul Weisz at Brown University has yielded a wealth of information on how ciliates reproduce, reorganize, and regenerate.

The anatomy of *Stentor* is deceptively simple. Its most conspicuous feature is the pattern of pigmented stripes alternating with rows of

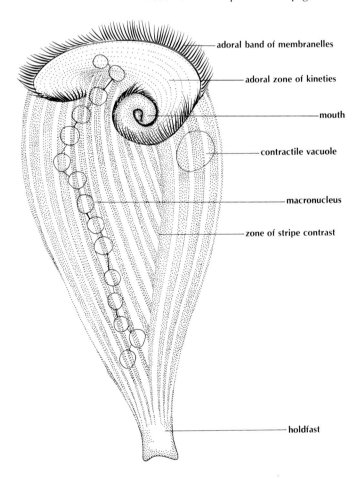

— adoral band of membranelles

— adoral zone of kineties

— mouth

— contractile vacuole

— macronucleus

— zone of stripe contrast

— holdfast

Fig. 4 **Ventral aspect of** *Stentor* **showing the zone of stripe contrast on the animal's left and the chain of macronuclear nodes on its right. Not shown are the rows of cilia, or kineties, which alternate with the pigment stripes.**

cilia which adorn its surface. There may be as many as one hundred stripes, longitudinally oriented, and reflecting the bilateral asymmetry of the animal. *Stentor* is usually viewed in the ventral aspect as determined by the position of its mouth, in which case the widest stripe is situated a bit to the left of center. The stripes become increasingly narrow as they are traced to the animal's left, around the back to the ventral midline again. The junction of the thinnest and the thickest pigment stripes will turn out to be a most important region of the body for morphogenetic reorganization, as we shall see later on.

Stentor also has front and back ends. Posteriorly, it terminates in a holdfast by which it is anchored to the substrate. Here the pigment stripes converge like lines of longitude coming together at the South Pole. At the front end the morphology is organized around the mouth, which is little more than a spiral-shaped funnel. Circling out to the left of this, and encompassing the whole anterior end of the organism, is an adoral band of membranelles. Each membranelle is made up of a number of cilia organized in the same plane and operating as a unit. The membranelles beat in waves so as to sweep food particles toward the gullet. The area of the animal circumscribed by the adoral band is filled with numerous curved rows of cilia also beating in the direction of the buccal cavity.

The cilia deserve special attention because their pattern of distribution can be used as an important indication of developmental events in reorganization, reproduction and regeneration. The cilia are arranged in rows, which over most of the cell surface are oriented between and parallel to the longitudinal pigment stripes. Like the latter, they have a left-right asymmetry such that the various structures associated with them in the cortical cytoplasm are situated to the right of the cilia themselves, in accordance with the so-called "rule of desmodexy." This infraciliature consists of a kinetosome (equivalent to the basal body and presumably a derivative of the centriole) at the base of each cilium, and a kinetodesma extending to the animal's right from each kinetosome. The kinetodesma is a fiber which turns anteriorly to join with those from behind and ahead of it. This row of kinetodesmas, together with the associated kinetosomes and cilia, are collectively referred to as a kinety. There are as many kineties as there are pigment stripes, and their orientation is highly polarized so that the cilia all beat in the same direction.

Internally, *Stentor* contains many of the ubiquitous organelles one would expect to find in any cell. In addition, it has a contractile vacuole located next to the oral region. Its most prominent internal structure, however, is the macronucleus. Shaped like a string of beads with lobes numbering in the teens, this important organ twists its way from one end of the animal to the other and exerts profound influences on the structure and function of the rest of the body. There are also micronuclei present, but their activities, in this species at least, seem to be limited to conjugation behavior and not to be related to the developmental events we are concerned with here.

Reorganization and Reproduction One of the strangest events in *Stentor* is reorganization, a process the animal goes through in response to various crises such as those of injury, chemical irritation, starvation, or overcrowding. Apparently any situation that disturbs the integrity or size relationships of the oral apparatus in particular will set off the phenomenon of reorganization. There first occurs an extensive disorganization of the existing adoral organelles, followed by the redifferentiation of a new set of mouth parts to replace those which have disappeared. The organism, like an architect, apparently finds it easier to begin construction with a clean slate than to remodel pre-existing, but imperfect, structures.

Accompanying these events are some interesting nuclear changes. There is no mitotic activity, as in the case of reproduction, unless the micronuclei have been reduced in number. For example, one way to induce reorganization experimentally is to excise some of the macronuclear nodes. Since this cannot ordinarily be done without also removing the adherent micronuclei, the latter tend to be replaced by endomitosis among the residual micronuclei during the course of subsequent reorganization.

Whatever may be the stimulus to reorganization, the macronucleus contracts its nodes to a single mass in the center of the cell. After reorganization is complete, renodulation of the macronucleus restores its normal moniliform configuration.

The process of reproduction illustrated in Fig. 5 has much in common with reorganization, except that in the former case micronuclear mitoses occur, the macronucleus separates into two parts, and dedifferentiation is confined to those kineties around the waistline where fission takes place. The original buccal cavity and adoral zone are preserved intact and passed on to the anterior descendant, which has only to form a new basal holdfast. The posterior half of the animal, in order to survive, must regenerate a whole new oral apparatus, as well as another contractile vacuole.

The entire reproductive episode may require no more than six hours from start to finish, the actual process of cleavage being the

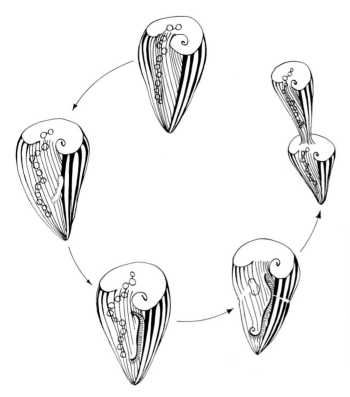

Fig. 5 **Sequence of events in the reproduction of** *Stentor* **by fission. Duplication of parts takes place before, not after, division. Not until the new oral primordium and and contractile vacuole have formed, and the macronucleus has condensed, does the fission line begin to cut across the lateral pigment stripes and kineties. Some of the latter become incorporated into the adoral zone of the posterior daughter cell.**

last act in the sequence of events. The earliest sign of impending fission is the elaboration of a second oral primordium half way down the ventral side of the animal to the right of the zone of stripe contrast. When the new feeding apparatus has taken shape, the macronuclear nodes begin to condense into a compact mass in the center of the cell. Then, as the cleavage furrow materializes, the nucleus again elongates, whereupon it is bisected by the constriction that separates the two daughters. Renodulation of the nucleus ensues, with the production of just as many nodes in each descendant as was present in the parent animal. Tracer studies with radioactive phosphorus have revealed that during condensation there is a thorough mixing of macronuclear material which becomes evenly distributed among the nodes of the next generation.

Since binary fission gives rise to two individuals of diminutive dimensions, there follows a period of adjustment in which each must grow back to normal size. The macronucleus, for example, reconstitutes the original number of nodes, but they are only half as big as they should be and must ultimately grow to normal dimensions. Similarly, the length of each kinety has to be restored following their transection along the line of fission. Elongation of such kineties can presumably be achieved only by reproduction of the kinetosomes from pre-existing ones and the subsequent development of new cilia and kinetodesmas from them.

Regeneration Regeneration is an indispensable part of reorganization and reproduction in *Stentor*, for in both of these processes new structures must be formed to replace those which have been lost by dedifferentiation or fission. Virtually the same mechanisms enable the organism to regenerate after fragmentation.

For successful regeneration to occur, two major prerequisites must be satisfied. The cut piece must contain at least part of the macronucleus, and it must also include a portion of the cortical ectoplasm with its constituent kinetosomes. Naturally, some of the intervening cytoplasm has to be present too. Neither macronucleus nor kinetosomes can be formed from anything but themselves, and if either one is missing from a fragment the reconstruction of a complete organism is impossible. But as long as each of them is represented, a tiny fragment less than one-one hundredth of the total animal can reconstitute itself. Portions of *Stentor* lacking either macronucleus or kinetosomes survive only for a short time.

Although the nucleus is essential for regeneration, its influence on morphogenesis is mediated through the kinetosomes. The latter structures are directly responsible for the elaboration of the various specialized cortical organelles characteristic of the species, but they cannot do this in the absence of a macronucleus. One exception to this rule, however, is the holdfast. Curiously enough, an enucleated anterior piece of a stentor can quickly reorganize a new holdfast on its posterior end, perhaps because this structure does not require kinetosomal replication and tends to form wherever the posterior ends of the kineties converge. The contractile vacuole is in the same category, for it too can be regenerated in the absence of the nucleus. Wounds in the ectoplasm can also heal in enucleate pieces, and pigment stripes can reconnect their cut ends. Except for these relatively minor readjustments, however, regeneration cannot occur in the absence of the nucleus. In fact, if the macronucleus is removed from a fragement of a stentor in the process of regenerating an oral primordium, development can continue for only a couple of hours. Enucleation of an early regenerate, however, brings morphogenesis to a halt sooner than the same operation in more advanced regenerates.

It is as though the protein synthesis required for regeneration were completed before overt morphogenesis, with the result that once this stage has been reached development can coast to completion even without the nucleus.

As in other systems (e.g., *Acetabularia*), RNA probably mediates the influence of the macronucleus on ectoplasmic morphogenesis. Regeneration can be blocked reversibly by various antimetabolites, as well as by ribonuclease. It might be expected, therefore, that any process directly dependent on the synthesis of specific proteins should be inhibited by enucleation. Experimental results in support of this view have revealed that enucleate stentors can eat and defecate, but cannot digest their food. Unable to synthesize digestive enzymes, such animals starve to death with ample food in their vacuoles.

The length of time required for regeneration depends on what must be replaced, and in part on the size of the fragment. When a stentor is cut in half transversely, an operation that simulates fission, the wound sites promptly seal themselves off. Within a couple of hours the anterior portion of the animal will have reconstituted its holdfast, thereby completing itself qualitatively at least. There is no immediate attempt on the part of its macronucleus to contract or restore its original number of nodes.

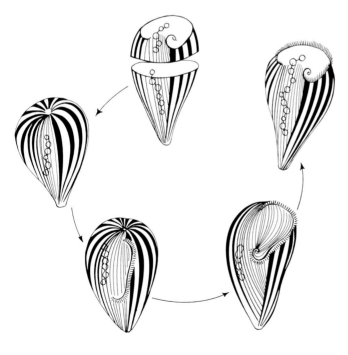

Fig. 6 **Steps in the process of anterior regeneration by the posterior portion of a bisected stentor. Following closure of the wound, a new oral primordium appears along the zone of stripe contrast. Segments of many thin pigment stripes are subsequently incorporated into the new adoral zone. Meanwhile, the macronuclear remnant condenses and renodulates, augmenting its number of lobes as it does so.**

The posterior half of the stentor, however, has farther to go and takes longer to get there. For the first few hours there is little or no visible indication that any steps are being taken to make good the loss of its feeding apparatus. It is during this period however, that there are set in motion those important but invisible reactions which will culminate in the morphogenetic phenomena soon to begin in the ectoplasm. Finally, after some three or four hours, the first suggestions of an oral primordium can be detected taking shape in the fine-line zone to the right of the widest pigment stripe (Fig. 6). While the mouth parts grow in length and complexity, the macronucleus condenses, though not so much as in reorganization or reproduction. Not until eight or ten hours after amputation is the new feeding apparatus fully formed, complete with buccal cavity, adoral band of membranelles, and adoral zone of kineties. By this time the macronucleus has recovered its lobulation, often augmenting its number of nodes in the process. These events may also be accompanied by micronuclear mitoses, perhaps to maintain some balance with the amount of macronuclear substance. Again and again it is possible for a single animal to regenerate when subjected to daily subdivision. Eventually, however, it gets too small to contain the requisite macronuclear material to support morphogenesis. Unable to regenerate a mouth, it dies of starvation.

Nevertheless, extremely small but complete stentors can be produced by the regeneration of tiny fragments. From such miniature creatures some important facts are to be learned, not the least of which relate to the problem of organelle size-determination.

Maintenance of Organelles When the bulk of the organism as a whole is reduced or increased manyfold, how do its component parts accommodate to the change? Do they in turn undergo corresponding reductions or increases in size, or do they change numerically? Since the dimensions of most cellular organelles are remarkably immutable, quantitative changes are generally achieved by shifts in their populations.

In dwarf stentors, for instance, there are fewer pigment stripes than normal, but their widths are not much reduced. The macronuclear nodes are of normal dimensions but are fewer in number. The membranelles on the adoral band are as long as those on a large animal, but there are fewer of them. Many kinds of organelles have fixed sizes which are probably dictated by the spatial relationships of their constituent macromolecules. It follows that when the cell or organism alters its mass, there must be a shift in how many organelles of a given kind shall be represented. Ribosomes, mitochondria, chloroplasts, cilia—these and others all adjust their numbers to cell size and/or physiological state. Perhaps their production and destruction may be controlled by functional demands. Or maybe there is an inherent ratio of organelle number to cytoplasmic mass which is maintained regardless of physiological influences. Of these two alternatives, the case for functional demand is the easier to prove.

In the case of the macronucleus, both the size and number of nodes have been shown to depend upon physiological conditions. Factors which increase metabolic rate, such as high temperatures, abundant oxygen and ample nutrition, all tend to promote the formation of more nodes of smaller size, obviously an adaptation to increase the macronuclear surface area. The opposite conditions yield fewer but larger nodes.

The macronucleus is also subject to control by ectoplasmic structures, particularly the feeding apparatus. Condensation of the macronucleus so regularly follows the formation of a new oral primordium that the relationship is almost certainly a causal one. When stentors with two mouths are experimentally produced (see below) they also acquire double macronuclear chains. These chains become single again when the single-mouthed condition is restored. The stripe pattern also affects the nucleus, for when the wide and narrow stripes are experimentally reversed, the position of the macronuclear chain is likewise backwards. Thus, the nucleus not only regulates morphogenesis in the ectoplasm, but like a wise administrator, responds to changes in that which it governs.

It is difficult to imagine what functional demands, if any, might be responsible for determining the number of cilia or membranelles. Perhaps it is the overall size of the cell, rather than physiological conditions *per se*, that dictates how many of these organelles shall develop. Whatever the stimulus might be, once a cilium starts to develop it always grows to a fixed length regardless of how small or large the cell is.

Cilia and flagella, incidentally, are also capable of regeneration in such diverse systems as mammalian oviducts, sea urchin embryos, ciliates, and flagellate protozoans. Sea urchin embryos can be deciliated by exposure to hypertonic sea water, whereupon new ciliary growth commences after a lag of only about ten minutes. Elongation takes place at the rate of 10–15 μ per hour, so only several hours are required for the entire organelle to be regenerated. Flagella can be amputated from various species of protozoans by agitation or pH shock. In either case, after a half-hour lag period, they grow back, in a matter of hours (Fig. 7), a process which can be directly observed in cultures, as illustrated in Fig. 8. But just how do cilia grow and regenerate? Are they spun out from the basal bodies by some kind of extrusion process, or do they elongate by apical addition like a bean shoot? Autoradiographic studies of flagella allowed to regenerate in the presence of tritium-labeled leucine, which marks the newly formed protein, indicate the presence of an apical growth zone. Thus, flagella grow by terminal addition. The next thing we must learn is how they know when to stop adding on to their ends.

The body parts of Stentor can be classified as either primary or derivative, depending on whether they are formed *sui generis* or *de novo*. The most important organelles are in the former category, organelles which are produced exclusively from pre-existing entities of their own kind. The kinety is a case in point. If Stentor is called upon to augment its complement of kineties, as when it has been cut in half longitudinally, it can make new ones only from those it already possesses. Although never directly observed, the dogma of the genetic continuity of the kinetosome suggests that the kinety replicates by the duplication of its constituent kinetosomes, which then elaborate new cilia and kinetodesmas.

Similarly, the adjacent pigment stripe reproduces by splitting in two like a zipper, starting at its anterior end. New thin stripes are thus formed from the thickest one. These gradually become wider as they are displaced to the right by succeeding generations of thinner ones. Newly forming thin stripes do not run the full length of the body. There is a so-called "ramifying zone" on the ventral surface of Stentor, where thin stripes appear to branch off the thickest one all along its

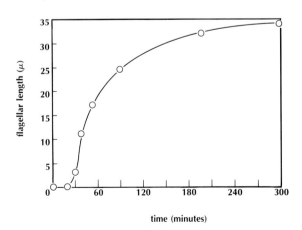

Fig. 7 **Rate of flagellar regeneration in** Euglena gracilis **following amputation by agitation in a homogenizer. Visible growth commences after a half hour's delay, and nears completion in several hours.** (After Rosenbaum and Child, 1967.)

Fig. 8 Regeneration of flagella
in Euglena gracilis (A) immediately after their amputation, (B) during the lag
phase, (C) at the onset of
flagellar regeneration, and
(D) when new flagella are
half grown. (From Rosenbaum
and Child, 1967.)

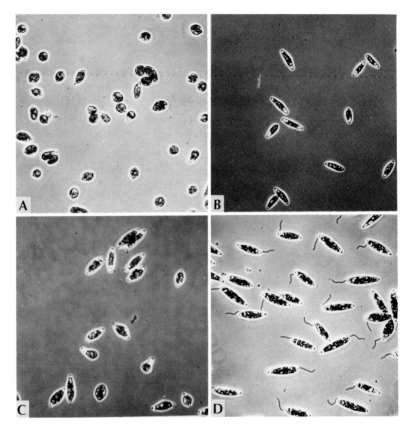

Fig. 8 Regeneration of flagella in Euglena gracilis (A) immediately after their amputation, (B) during the lag phase, (C) at the onset of flagellar regeneration, and (D) when new flagella are half grown. (From Rosenbaum and Child, 1967.)

length. The shortest and thinnest pigment stripe is therefore located immediately to the right of the anterior end of the thick stripe.

Kineties, or rather the kinetosomes from which they originate, are strictly self-generating. This mode of regeneration they share in common with such other intracellular organelles as nuclei, mitochondria and chloroplasts, which, like centrioles, all contain DNA. It is a bit surprising, therefore, that pigment stripes should also be produced only from their own kind. However, it turns out that their pigmentation is contained within many small granules, each about 1 μ in diameter. Available evidence suggests that these granules may actually be mitochondria. If true, then the genetic continuity of pigment stripes is not so anomalous after all.

The feeding apparatus is the most highly organized part of the ectoplasm. It is also the most important, for in its absence the organism starves to death. This structural complex forms only and always in association with the region where the widest and narrowest pigment

Fig. 9 **If a sector of** Stentor **containing thin stripes is inserted into the region of wide stripes, an accessory zone of stripe contrast is established, which will induce an extra mouth if the animal is made to regenerate.**

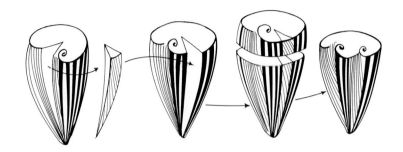

stripes are in juxtaposition. At this locus, an oral primordium develops whenever the original one is missing, either because of its dedifferentiation prior to reorganization or its loss by amputation or fission. In fact, the original oral structure need not even be absent for a new one to be induced, provided there is a permanent interruption in the longitudinal continuity of the zone of thick and thin stripe contrast. Transected kineties will ordinarily rejoin across the gap if they can. But should healing be precluded by injuries too extensive for the severed ends to find each other, then an oral primordium may develop at the anterior end of the posterior kinetal segment. Conversely, a new holdfast will form at the posterior ends of the anterior segments.

Extra oral primordia can be experimentally induced by appropriate grafting experiments as illustrated in Fig. 9. If a region of thin striping is transplanted amongst thicker ones there will be set up a new zone where narrow and wide stripes are artificially adjacent. If the front end of such a stentor is now amputated, the rear half will regenerate two mouths, one at each locus of stripe contrast. The resulting animal usually remains as a doublet for some time, but eventually reorganizes to restore its normal anatomical integrity.

Grafting Experiments Grafting experiments of various kinds are of value in revealing the morphogenetic limitations of Stentor. It is one thing to replace lost parts, but it is quite another thing to do away with extra parts. Errors of omission can be corrected by ordinary regenerative processes, but errors of commission require the coordination of both destructive and constructive events.

There is hardly any restriction to the variety of grafting experiments that can be performed except those imposed by the imagination of the experimenter and the limits of his technical skill. Cut pieces of Stentor tend to heal their exposed surfaces with inconvenient alacrity. Therefore, it is necessary to join the pieces together without delay if they are to become properly fused.

In this way entire organisms can be conjoined to produce all sorts of parabiotic combinations. Doublets and triplets eventually reorganize themselves to singles again. Larger stentorian masses experience increasing difficulty in regaining their individuality. Incapable of reorganizing into a single giant organism, yet equally incapable of subdividing by fission (in a multipolar system, how to tell front from back?), these compound creatures find themselves in a bind from which there is no escape. Their unnatural dimensions also create problems of gas exchange between inside and out, a problem they attempt to solve by adopting various elongate and contorted shapes to increase the ratio of surface to volume.

Parabiotic stentors have been especially useful in attempts to understand the mechanisms by which morphogenesis is controlled. Mouthparts, for example, do not form except under the circumstances described above. Is this process initiated as the result of a stimulatory message, or does an oral primordium form whenever the normal inhibitory influences abate? Partial answers have been obtained by grafting regenerating fragments onto intact organisms. The outcome of such experiments depends on which parabiont is the larger. If the intact stentor is larger than its regenerating partner, then the latter discontinues its regeneration to be resorbed into the dominant normal organism. In the reciprocal combination, outlined in Fig. 10, the larger regenerating partner completes its own development, but the smaller intact one undergoes reorganization too. The morphogenetic events in the big animal are thus communicated across to the little one, where a vicarious episode of mouth formation is initiated. Meanwhile, the

Fig. 10 **Induced reorganization in a normal small stentor grafted to a regenerating large one. Whatever factors promote the differentiation of an oral primordium in the regenerate also cause the resorption of mouthparts in the graft to be replaced by new ones that develop in synchrony with those in the regenerate.**

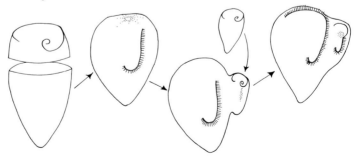

development of the oral primordium in the large regenerating partner slows down until its smaller counterpart catches up with it, whereupon they both go to completion simultaneously. Hence, there must be morphogenetic messages passed back and forth between both members, but their effectiveness depends upon the relative sizes of the instigating and reacting systems.

Comparable experiments can be carried out between dividing and nondividing organisms in order to probe the mysteries of mitotic stimulation. In general, a recently divided stentor is considerably smaller than one about to enter fission. Now, if two such animals are grafted together side by side, it is found that the impending fission of the larger partner is usually reversed and its partly formed oral primordium regresses. Thus, nondividing stentors exert an inhibitory influence on dividing ones. On rare occasions, however, the opposite may happen. If the dividing partner is considerably larger than the nondividing one, and is in the appropriate stage of fission, then it may actually induce division in the smaller animal to which it is grafted. In such cases, fission in the larger partner is postponed, but when it finally does occur, the smaller stentor also divides. As in naturally occurring syncytia, it is the rule that when one nucleus divides they all divide. Again we see evidence for reciprocal influences. It seems quite likely that reproduction in *Stentor* may be under the control of stimulatory and inhibitory factors, and that mitogenesis occurs when the former outbalance the latter.

Thus far we have considered two basic operative techniques by which morphogenesis can be investigated. Parts of the organism can be removed to promote regeneration, or extra ones can be added to induce reorganization. Still a third approach, involving a combination of both techniques, can tell us even more about how *Stentor* extricates itself from embarrassing situations. By having the parts of its body disarranged in various ways, *Stentor* can be forced to reorganize itself, but in doing so it has to decide which portion shall reorganize which. Perhaps the simplest operation along these lines is that by which the anterior half of the body is rotated 180° on the posterior half. In such cases, one part must be resorbed while the other regenerates a replacement which is correctly oriented. But first there must go on within the organism a contest between the two halves to decide which one is going to dominate the other. There is no room for compromise, for coexistence of disoriented halves is incompatible with survival. Invariably it is the larger fraction of the animal which dictates what the "correct" orientation shall be.

Even more drastic disruptions of the body seldom present a morphogenetic challenge which cannot be solved by the stentor's amazing ability to disentangle its own scrambled anatomy. Whole organisms can be minced, for example, and put back together randomly. Yet the various pieces reorient their stripe patterns in harmony with their neighbors, and in due course a new mouth is produced at one end and a holdfast at the other. One begins to wonder if there is any limit to the animal's regulatory abilities.

There is a limit, however, and one of the most interesting ways to exceed it is to reverse the animal's normal bilateral asymmetry. This is not easy to do, but sometimes it happens more by accident than design when the organism is cut into quarters and reassembled backwards. In favorable cases, it turns out that the zone of stripe contrast is a mirror image of the normal arrangement—that is, the fine stripes are to the *left* of the thickest one. When an oral primordium forms, it does so in the usual place next to the widest pigment stripe. But since it now develops to the left instead of to the right of the wide stripe, its symmetry is correspondingly reversed and the curvature of the buccal cavity now turns in the opposite direction. Probably it would make no difference at all if such a stentor were a true mirror image of the usual kind, but it is not. Although the major details of its anatomy are reversed, the ciliature is not. Hence, when the new feeding apparatus forms, its membranelles beat away from the mouth instead of toward it! This intolerable situation triggers a new reorganization in which another oral primordium is produced. But like its predecessor, this feeding apparatus is also defective. Again and again the animal regenerates imperfect mouthparts, and finally it starves to death after many futile attempts to correct the incorrigible.

This case illustrates the chink in the stentor's morphogenetic armor. There is practically no abnormality it cannot repair so long as its homeostatic mechanisms are operating. But there must always be a point of reference—some part of the organism where the morphogenetic blueprints are stored. The macronucleus is the most likely candidate for the job of "morphostat." It detects abnormalities in the morphology and initiates the development of replacement parts. In stentors with reversed asymmetry there is nothing wrong with the nucleus; it repeatedly gives orders to regenerate new oral primordia. The trouble is in translating these orders into structural end products. Somewhere along the line (presumably in the disharmonious patterns of stripes and kineties) the nuclear message is mistakenly interpreted and the error persistently repeated.

The lesson we learn from this is that there are two kinds of pathological situations. Most things that go wrong elicit appropriate corrective reactions on the part of the organism, reactions which depend upon the operation of negative feedback mechanisms. Such physiological adaptations form the basis of the several morphogenetic events for which *Stentor* is famous, as well as comparable homeostatic phenomena in all other organisms. There is another kind of disorder, however, which by definition cannot be repaired. This is a lesion in the adaptive mechanism itself. For such a "disease" there can be no hope of recovery since there is no logical provision for repairing the repair mechanism. Nature, in her infinite wisdom, has never overcome this impasse, not even in *Stentor*.

REFERENCES

AUCLAIR, W. and B. W. SIEGEL. 1966. Cilia regeneration in the sea urchin embryo: Evidence for a pool of ciliary proteins. *Science* **154:** 913–915.

BALAMUTH, W. 1940. Regeneration in Protozoa: A problem of morphogenesis. *Quart. Rev. Biol.* **15:** 290–337.

BONNER, J. T. 1958. "The Evolution of Development." Cambridge University Press, London and New York.

de TERRA, N. 1966. Leucine incorporation into the membranellar bands of regenerating and non-regenerating stentor. *Science* **153:** 543–545.

ELLWOOD, L. C. and R. R. COWDEN. 1966. RNA metabolism during regeneration in *Stentor coeruleus. Cytologia* **31:** 80–88.

JAMES, E. A. 1968. Regeneration and division in *Stentor coeruleus:* the effects of microinjected and externally applied actinomycin D and puromycin. *Develop. Biol.* **16:** 577–593.

ROSENBAUM, J. L. and F. M. CHILD. 1967. Flagellar regeneration in protozoan flagellates. *J. Cell Biol.* **34:** 345–364.

TARTAR, V. 1960. Reconstitution of minced *Stentor coeruleus. J. Exptl. Zool.* **144:** 187–207.

TARTAR, V. 1961. "The Biology of Stentor." Pergamon Press, London.

TARTAR, V. 1966. Induced division and division regression by cell fusion in Stentor. *J. Exptl. Zool.* **163:** 297–310.

TARTAR, V. 1967. Morphogenesis in Protozoa. *In* "Research in Protozoology" (T. Chen, ed.), Vol. 2, pp. 1–116. Pergamon Press, London.

WEISZ, P. 1951. An experimental analysis of morphogenesis in Stentor coeruleus. *J. Exptl. Zool.* **116:** 231–258.

WEISZ, P. 1954. Morphogenesis in Protozoa. *Quart. Rev. Biol.* **29:** 207–229.

WEISZ, P. 1956. Experiments on the initiation of division in Stentor coeruleus. *J. Exptl. Zool.* **131:** 137–162.

WHITSON, G. L. 1965. The effects of actinomycin D and ribonuclease on oral regeneration in *Stentor coeruleus. J. Exptl. Zool.* **160:** 207–214.

4   **Turnover in Hydroids**

THE year was 1740. Abraham Trembley was on the verge of making a startling discovery. This young Swiss had been living in Holland as tutor to the sons of Count Bentinck. On the latter's estate not far from The Hague he spent much of his spare time, as was his wont, in the study of natural history. Trembley's curiosity had been aroused by some small green plant-like organisms he had fished out of a nearby canal.

Unaware that these polyps, as he called them, had already been discovered by the great Dutch microscopist van Leeuwenhoek back in 1702, Trembley was intrigued by the dilemma of deciding whether they were plants or animals. Like plants, these strange creatures had branches, were green in color, and preferred the light; like animals they devoured tiny aquatic arthropods, contracted when touched, and even "walked" the way an inch-worm does. He reasoned that if they were cut in half and both pieces lived and grew, then they must be plants. If they died, they were animals. So on November 25, 1740 he put one of his polyps to the test. The top half bearing the ring of tentacles soon recovered and resumed feeding. The bottom half, however, became inactive, though it betrayed its live condition by contracting when stimulated. Not until December 4 did Trembley get the first inkling of what was going on, for on that date he noticed that several small buds were present on the upper end of the basal half of the polyp. In a few more days these had grown into a ring of tentacles, and the significance of Trembley's discovery swept over him.

Never before had anyone experimentally produced two animals from one. As news of the discovery spread, and its validity was confirmed, Trembley found himself something of a celebrity among the scientists of his day. He continued to carry out one remarkable experiment after another on his polyps for some years. Even more important, he stimulated an interest in regeneration that has lasted for over two centuries. Nowadays we know a lot more about regeneration, and our advanced instrumentality permits ever more sophisticated investigations. But I doubt that many of us, were we living in the eighteenth century, and knew no more than they knew then, could have done what Abraham Trembley did.

Despite the outcome of his regeneration experiment, Trembley correctly chose to consider his polyps as animals instead of plants. Their green color was due to the presence of symbiotic algae living in the hydra we now call *Chlorohydra viridissima*. Other species lacking such algae are not green. Except when they are producing asexual buds, hydras are single individuals. They are thus distinguished from colonial hydroids, such as the marine *Tubularia* or the fresh water *Cordylophora*, in which numerous hydranths are interconnected by extensively ramifying coenosarcs. All such hydroids regenerate well, as do other coelenterates (e.g., sea anemones), but our attention will be focused on the former because we know more about them.

Regeneration in Hydra It is no accident that many of the key discoveries in hydroid regeneration have been made on *Hydra*. Its various species exhibit such a high degree of morphological simplicity that they make ideal experimental animals. Although they are not colonial, they may appear to be so during vegetative reproduction when a number of lateral buds develop on the sides of the parent. It was this many-headed condition that prompted Trembley to compare the animal to the mythological Hydra slain by Hercules. In the legend, two heads

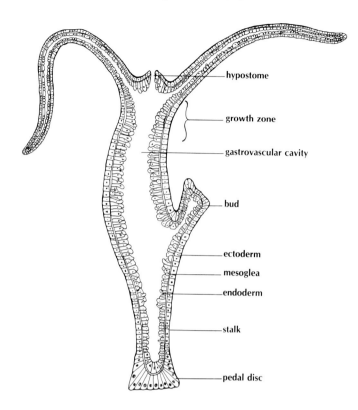

hypostome

growth zone

gastrovascular cavity

bud

ectoderm

mesoglea

endoderm

stalk

pedal disc

Fig. 11 Anatomy of Hydra. The organism's form is maintained by the turnover of cells originating in a growth zone just below the ring of tentacles around the hypostome. These cells migrate distally into the tentacles and proximally to the pedal disc, where they are eliminated. Asexual budding occurs in a region intermediate between the head and foot.

grew back for each one cut off, unless the stump was cauterized by fire. In the real hydra, only one head grows back, but each amputated head can reconstitute an entire organism.

Hydras are capable of sexual reproduction, which they indulge in as a result of such adverse conditions as overcrowding, stagnant water, lowered temperatures and/or a rise in CO_2 tension. In response to these conditions, gonads develop along the sides of the animal. Eggs are fertilized by sperm (usually from a different parent), and the zygote develops directly into a new polyp. Sexual reproduction may be permanently bypassed, however, by rearing hydras under constant optimal conditions, in which case they multiply indefinitely by asexual budding.

Budding has much in common with regeneration. It takes place by a straightforward outpocketing of both ectoderm and endoderm from the lateral body wall. As the bud enlarges it differentiates its own hypostome and ring of tentacles. All the while, its point of attachment to the parent hydra shifts downward. When it nears the base, it is detached to become a free-living individual. The whole process may take only a few days, and, since several buds in consecutive stages of

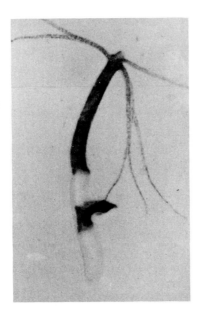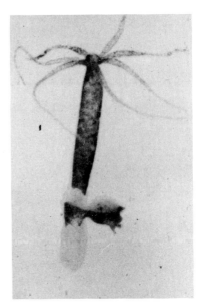

Fig. 12 **Bud migration experiment in** Hydra viridis. **Upper halves of green individuals were grafted to lower halves of white ones. Then the two-toned segment in the middle bearing a green bud was excised, inverted and grafted back (left). On right, the same individual after one day showing how the originally all green bud has migrated upward onto white region, becoming half white in the process.** (From Shostak, 1967. Copyright 1967 by The American Association for the Advancement of Science.)

development may be arranged *seriatim* along the body of one parent, budding is a remarkably efficient means of expanding the population.

How the direction of this bud migration is controlled has recently been investigated by Stanley Shostak at the University of Pittsburgh. By grafting bud-bearing segments of hydras back into the organism upside down, he has been able to show that the buds now migrate upward instead of downward with respect to the animal as a whole. This means that shifts in the location of buds along the axis of the animal are polarized by local factors in the surrounding tissues, and are not to be explained by the possibility that the upper region of the animal simply grows away from the buds below. Indeed, other evidence indicates that bud development is achieved largely by the morphogenetic movements of cells, rather than by cell proliferation in a zone of growth. Cell division is more or less evenly distributed throughout the bud and the parent hydra, and mitotic inhibition does not prevent lateral buds from elongating.

No matter how it is cut up, *Hydra* can regenerate from practically any fragment of itself with the possible exception of the tentacles. Distal parts can regenerate proximal ones, and vice versa. Longitudinal slices produce two individuals, or double-headed ones if the cut is incomplete and the separated halves are kept from growing together again. Even very tiny pieces of *Hydra* can give rise to qualitatively complete individuals.

It is also possible to destroy the morphological organization of hydras completely, without abolishing their capacity for getting themselves back into shape. For example, if an animal is cut up into many tiny fragments and all the pieces are allowed to grow together again, they usually reconstitute a whole organism. In fact, vital staining experiments have shown that each part ends up approximately where it was in the original anatomy. Evidently each region of the animal exhibits a selective affinity for tissues from like regions. If more than one hydra is minced, the fused pieces may reassemble into compound organisms in which the number of hydranths formed is a function of the mass of tissue in the reorganizing clump. Mechanisms seem to be operating to control the size of the organism as well as its shape.

Experiments such as these take advantage of the capacity of pieces of *Hydra* to grow together. The first successful grafting experiments in hydra, or in any other animal for that matter, were carried out by Trembley in 1742. He inserted one animal inside another, and in some cases they actually grew together. Nowadays, segments are routinely grafted by impaling them on hairs or thin wires inserted through their gastrovascular cavities. In a matter of hours the fragments fuse with one another. If the pieces come from the same species, they generally remain permanently attached provided the morphological integrity of the animal is not too seriously violated. If parts of different species are grafted together the resulting chimera usually comes apart after some days or weeks. How these tissues recognize each other as foreign we do not know.

One of the most curious stunts *Hydra* can perform is to turn itself inside out. Again, it was Trembley who first studied this phenomenon. Using nothing but a wild boar's bristle as a tool, he managed to push the foot of a hydra out through its mouth. Some of the everted creatures died, but others survived by turning themselves right side out again. Down through the years there has been a controversy about whether they do this by rolling their stomachs back in through their mouths, or by a more subtle migration of endoderm and ectoderm cells past one another through the mesoglea. Probably they can do it either way.

The case of the inside out hydra was made even more intriguing as a result of certain studies on the feeding habits of these animals. It seems that *Hydra* will eat only living material; this means that its swallowing mechanism is linked to a recognition system whereby nonliving food is rejected. When given a superabundance of food in the form of a substratum of yeast, the hydra literally does everything it can to put itself on the outside of all this food, which is far more than it can possibly swallow. Eventually, its mouth opens so wide that the endoderm rolls through it to the outside of the animal. Further studies have revealed that the swallowing reaction may occur in response to the release of glutathione from captured prey. Hydras can now be induced to evert their stomachs (in an apparent effort to swallow themselves) simply by adding glutathione to the water in which they live.

For all the amazing contortions which *Hydra* can perform, it always seems capable of reverting to its original morphology. This necessitates the existence within it of information as to what it normally should be, not to mention the means of becoming just that. This is the essence of regeneration.

When *Hydra* regenerates, there is no blastema, or aggregate of undifferentiated cells, produced as in higher animals. It reconstitutes itself by the process of morphallaxis. This is the process by which missing parts may be remodeled out of pre-existing tissues with little or no cellular dedifferentiation or proliferation. The cells near the cut end reorganize themselves into whatever is needed to complete the morphological integrity of the animal. This is best illustrated in a hydra from which the hypostome and its ring of tentacles has been cut off.

The first thing to happen after amputation, of course, is closure of the wound, which may be completed in only a few hours. If the hydra is treated with sufficient doses of colchicine at this time, regeneration will not occur. Apparently there must be some build-up of cells before subsequent morphogenesis can proceed, but the actual necessity for cell division remains problematical in view of the occurrence of regeneration even after treatment with X-rays or nitrogen mustard, both of which inhibit mitosis.

The severed stalk is sealed by the inward migration of endodermal cells across the opening. It is from these cells that the new hydranth is destined to develop. The outermost layer of these former endoderm cells gives rise to the new ectoderm and the two layers then go on to sprout tentacles. But before this can take place it must be determined how many tentacles shall be produced, and where they shall develop. These decisions apparently involve the synthesis of specific nucleic acids and proteins. Analogues of purines, pyrimidines or amino acids interfere with the synthesis of these molecules. Treatment with these substances during this phase reduces the number of tentacles to be formed later in the regenerate.

Presumably tentacles can form anywhere around the distal circumference of the amputated hydra. But the fact that they form only in limited numbers and at specific locations suggests that any given tentacle anlage once it is established may inhibit the production of any others in its immediate vicinity. This inhibitory influence may be mediated by the nervous system since the application of nerve drugs (chloretone, xylocaine, cholinesterase inhibitors) tends to increase the average number of tentacles regenerated.

All these events go on without any overt signs that development is in progress. Not until hours later do the first grossly visible indications of morphogenesis become evident. Cell migration plays an important role in this constructive phase of regeneration, which continues until the definitive shape and size of the new hydranth is achieved.

Interstitial Cells Of the 100,000 or so cells that make up a hydra, there are only about half a dozen different kinds represented. Those associated with digestive activities (mucous and gland cells) are found in the endodermal layer lining the gastrovascular cavity. Others, such as epitheliomuscular cells, are characteristic of the ectoderm. In addition, there are nerve cells which form a network throughout the body, plus those specialized cells of offense, the cnidoblasts. Yet the most ubiquitous type of cell in *Hydra* is the most important of all. It is the interstitial cell.

Interstitial cells are remarkable, among other things, for their lack of distinguishing characteristics, except that their cytoplasm is unusually rich in RNA. Situated in among the cells of the ectodermal layer, they are said to constitute a reserve population of multipotent cells from which replacements for various differential cell types can be recruited. Notable among these are the cnidoblasts which represent a terminal state of cytological differentiation. Once they have discharged their functional responsibilities, and their contents, they are discarded and must be replaced. Hence, interstitial cells constantly differentiate into cnidoblasts in the tentacles and await their chance for self-immolation.

The true nature of the interstitial cell is still not completely understood. It appears to play the role of stem cell from which other kinds of cells are descended, and without which the organism cannot long survive. It is not indispensable for the process of regeneration, although its deployment within the organism seems to parallel the distribution of regenerative potentialities. For example, the number of interstitial cells decreases basally, as does the incidence of regeneration; and their absence altogether from the tentacles is correlated with the lack of regeneration there. Nevertheless, it is possible for a hydra to regenerate even in the total absence of interstitial cells.

By taking advantage of their vulnerability to X-rays or nitrogen mustard, it has been possible to deplete hydras of their entire interstitial cell populations without doing serious damage to other cell types. Destined to die in a matter of weeks, such animals are still capable of repeated regenerations as long as they survive. This suggests that regeneration in *Hydra* may rely as much on the reorganization of pre-existing differentiated cells (morphallaxis) as on the differentiation of new ones from multipotent interstitial cells.

The occurrence of regeneration in amputated hydras is not unexpected. What makes this animal unique, however, is the fact that the entire organism is regenerating itself constantly. The discovery of this remarkable phenomenon marked a milestone in the natural history of *Hydra* and has profoundly influenced our interpretation of all other developmental events in hydroids ever since.

By an ingenious combination of vital staining and grafting experiments, Paul Brien, at the University of Brussels, showed that there is a so-called growth zone in *Hydra* just below the ring of tentacles, distinguished by the presence of a large number of interstitial cells. When this part of an animal is selectively stained and grafted back into the hydra, it is possible to trace the fate of the labeled cells (Fig. 13). Instead of staying where they are put, they gradually move downward from their original location. In due course, the stained cells become situated in the basal stalk of the hydra and within a few weeks disappear after being incorporated into the pedal disc. Other cells migrate out into the tentacles where they are eventually escalated off the distal ends. Under normal conditions, therefore, a hydra is dying apically and basally, but is being ceaselessly reborn by the emigration of cells from the growth zone.

Although the growth zone may be the locus from which cells else-

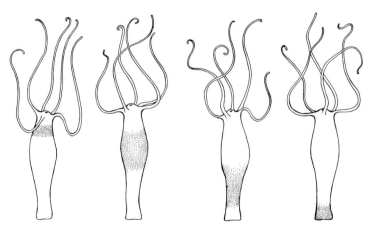

Fig. 13 When the sub-hypostomal growth zone is vitally stained and grafted back in place, its cells can be traced during subsequent migration downward toward the pedal disc. Thus, Brien demonstrated the role of cell turnover in maintaining the anatomical integrity of *Hydra*.

where in the body are ultimately derived, and may well be the source of growth-regulating substances too, it is apparently not the site of heightened mitotic activity it was once thought to be. According to the analyses of Richard Campbell at the University of California, proliferation among various cell types in *Hydra* is seldom confined to any one region of the body, least of all to the so-called growth zone. Cells can be found in division practically everywhere along the body column except in the tentacles and the pedal disc. Since the growth zone is not growing mitotically any more than anywhere else, Campbell prefers to call it a "stationary region" because it is the point of equilibrium between distally and proximally directed cell migrations.

Hydra maintains itself by a combination of polarized cell migrations and widespread cell divisions. As long as the birth and death rates are in balance, the organism remains stabilized at the size and shape we refer to as normal. It follows that if the kinetics of this system were upset, the hydra would be in serious trouble. This is exactly what happens in an animal exposed to X-irradiation or nitrogen mustard. Although the cells are not necessarily killed, nor prevented from differentiating or functioning, their division is inhibited. This in effect turns off the fountain of youth. When the current generation of cells grows old and dies within a few weeks, the organism is gradually phased out of existence. This dramatically emphasizes the absence of aging in *Hydra*, at least as we are accustomed to think of it. Here it is not the organism that ages, but the individual cells of which it is composed.

Other organisms possess renewing tissues, and all living things undergo turnover at various levels of organization. But the hydra is the only creature that constantly regenerates its entire body at the histological level. This perpetual rejuvenation explains why it can survive indefinitely without sexual reproduction. Sex is ordinarily necessary to offset the death rate, and is reserved in *Hydra* for those occasions when the organism's survival is in jeopardy. But as long as the environment is sufficiently salubrious to permit the hydra to remain forever ageless, its sex life is relinquished as the price to be paid for immortality.

The definitive shape of any organism is the morphological resultant of subtle physiological processes responsible for maintaining a developmental steady state. This is especially true in *Hydra*, where not only is the entire population of cells in a state of dynamic equilibrium, but the kinetics of their production, migration, differentiation and death is presided over by stimulatory and inhibitory factors. The morphology of *Hydra* at each moment is a function of the interacting influences of these growth regulating substances, and much of today's

Fig. 14 **Five hydras grafted head-to-tail still preserve their individualities. Beginning at the back and working forward, new heads and feet are reconstituted as each one of the original animals re-establishes itself.** (After Tardent, 1960.)

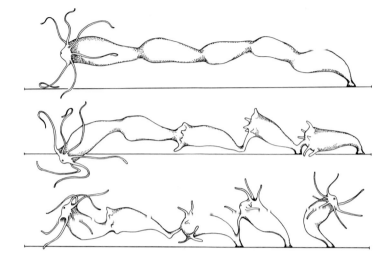

research along these lines is designed to determine the existence, biological activity, and chemical nature of these elusive molecules. Allison Burnett and his colleagues at Case Western Reserve University have made particularly important contributions to our understanding of such problems.

It has long been known that *Hydra* is a highly polarized animal. So rigidly imposed is this polarity that even the tiniest fragments of the organism will regularly regenerate heads and feet from the original distal and proximal ends, respectively. Even when several hydras are grafted together *in tandem*, their individual polarities are not subordinated to any overall head-to-foot gradient in the series (Fig. 14). Each one of the polymerized polyps simply excuses itself from the queue by regenerating a new hydranth and pedal disc, thus re-establishing its individuality. This happens simultaneously all along the line if neither of the two end hydras has a hydranth or a pedal disc. But if the terminal ones are allowed to retain a head in one case and a foot in the other, then individuation will begin at the back of the line farthest removed from the hydranth. Detachment then proceeds forward, the front hydra being the last to separate.

This latter phenomenon demonstrates the interesting fact that the presence of a hydranth apparently suppresses the development of any other structures of its own kind. Or rather, when a new hydranth must form it does so as far away from any others as it possibly can. This has given rise to the hypothesis that hydras produce something that inhibits their own development. In fact, the water in which hydras live accumulates material which will arrest the growth of other hydras placed in it, or block the regeneration of amputated ones. A note of caution is in order, however. Some recent investigations by Lary Davis of the University of Hawaii have revealed that cell-free homogenates of hydranths (but not stems) from the colonial hydroid *Corymorpha palma* will inhibit hydranth regeneration not only in its own species, but in various species of hydra as well. Further analysis traced the inhibitory factor to the nematocyst toxin which contains tetramethylammonium as its active ingredient.

Where there is an inhibitor, there is usually a stimulator. Extracts from homogenized hydras, when applied to segments cut from the body, will promote excessive tentacle regeneration. This substance can also cause hydranths to regenerate on the proximal ends of fragments, thus inverting the original polarity. In point of fact, there is reason to believe that the polarity in *Hydra* is nothing more than the gradient in stimulator concentration. Produced in the hypostome, this substance

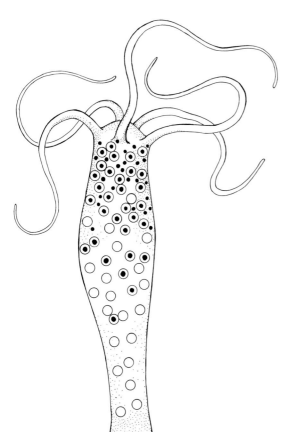

Fig. 15 **Distribution of growth regulating substances in** *Hydra*. **Stimulators (open circles) and inhibitors (black dots) are both in high concentration in the growth zone where the inhibitors inactivate the stimulators (dots in circles). About half way down the stalk the inhibitors disappear, leaving the stimulators free to promote the growth of buds. Farther down toward the base the stimulator concentration also declines. Hence, the budding region is defined by a relative excess of stimulators over inhibitors, and the pedal disc develops where the concentration of stimulators is minimal.**

diffuses proximally and becomes increasingly dilute toward the base of the hydra. The inhibitor, presumably produced in the subhypostomal growth zone, also distributes itself down the length of the hydra. Unlike the stimulator, which remains bound to cells, the inhibitor is an extracellular agent which constantly leaks out of the organism. It works by inactivating the stimulatory material. Hence, the pattern of growth is affected by the combined actions of these two factors as diagrammatically represented in Fig. 15. It is the ratio of stimulator to inhibitor that chemically controls the growth and therefore the shape in each region of the hydra.

Colonial Hydroids

Hydra is a unipolar organism, but other kinds of Hydrozoa are colonial and multipolar. On the end of each branch is an individual hydranth, the form of which varies with the species. In some cases they may even differ from one part of the colony to another. Hydranths are linked together via interconnecting branches variously referred to as stolons, coenosarcs or hydrocauli. In many species these branches are invested in a noncellular sheath, called the perisarc, from which only the hydranths protrude. In their manner of growth and regeneration, colonial hydroids have much in common with *Hydra*. They also show some interesting differences.

The hydranths of a colonial hydroid such as *Tubularia* are equipped with two rings of tentacles between which is a region bearing gonophores. When such a hydranth is amputated, its replacement (Fig. 16) is foreshadowed by the distal migration of cells in the hydrocaulus. As

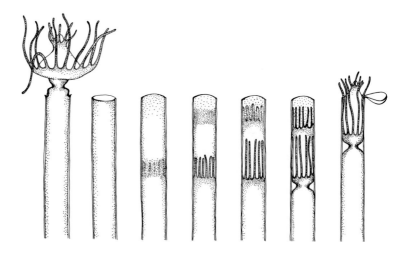

Fig. 16 **Successive steps in the regeneration of** *Tubularia*. **Following amputation of the hydranth, new rings of tentacles develop on the hydrocaulus within the perisarc. When fully formed, the regenerated hydranth unfolds as it pushes its way out of the perisarc.** (*After Fig. 1, in Tardent and Tardent, 1956.*)

a result, the terminal region of the stem immediately behind the level of amputation appears to darken where the new rings of tentacles are destined to develop. Pinched off from the sides of the hydrocaulus as a series of longitudinal pleats, the newly forming tentacles incorporate both ectoderm and endoderm. They remain folded snugly against the stem until the entire regenerate is extruded from the end of its enveloping perisarc.

Some of the same questions asked about the regenerating hydra are applicable to colonial hydroids, but the answers will not always be the same. Consider the problem of polarity. As in *Hydra*, the amputated hydrocaulus of *Tubularia* exhibits distal dominance, but in this case it is more easily reversed. A length of stem normally regenerates a new hydranth only at its distal end. If the stem is cut up into a number of smaller segments, each one grows its own hydranth, typically in the original distal direction. Hence, hydranth potentiality is present all along the stem, but is expressed only when the hydrocaulus distal to a given level is removed. Clearly, a hierarchy is set up by inhibitory influences emanating from the end of the stem where a hydranth is already present or is in the process of developing. There are ways, however, of suppressing hydranth formation distally and also of inducing it elsewhere along a segment of hydrocaulus (Fig. 17).

Distal hydranth formation can be experimentally prevented by encapsulating the end of the stem in a glass tube. The same result may be achieved by ligating the perisarc terminally. When this is done, a hydranth may now be made to develop at the other end of the hydrocaulus where regeneration is normally suppressed. Apparently the distal end can exert its dominance over the portion of the stem below it only when it is actually producing a new hydranth. If the distal end is prevented from regenerating, then the other end of the hydrocaulus takes over.

Proximal regeneration can also be induced by a number of other experimental methods. For example, if the piece of hydrocaulus is extra long, hydranth regeneration may take place on both ends. Here the proximal end is so far away from the distal end that it escapes the inhibitory effects of the latter. Conversely, much the same effect occurs if the piece of stem is too short for an adequate inhibitory gradient to be established. If the two ends of the stem are so close together that each is exposed to practically equal inhibitory influences, then both of them may develop a hydranth simultaneously. This kind of exception tends to prove the rule that there is indeed an inhibitory effect of the distal end of a stem on its more proximal portions.

It is relatively easy to block the passage of this influence down the

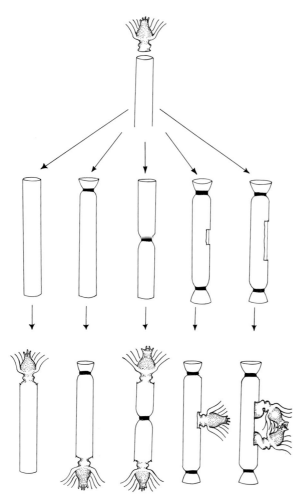

Fig. 17 **Hydranth regeneration normally occurs distally in a piece of hydrocaulus (left), but can be induced proximally by ligating the distal end, or on either end by tying off the middle. If both ends are ligated and a hole is cut in the side of the perisarc, Zwilling showed that a hydranth will now grow out through the opening. From larger holes, two hydranths may regenerate.**

hydrocaulus. By simply ligating a piece of stem in the middle it is possible to promote hydranth regeneration at both ends. Other studies have shown that any obstruction in the gastrovascular cavity (e.g., an oil droplet or air bubble) is sufficient to block the inhibitor and permit regeneration from either end. It must be concluded that the influence is transported in the lumen of the hydrocaulus, and not necessarily through the tissues. Attempts to isolate the hydranth inhibitor have proved successful in some cases, for extracts of hydranths, or water in which they have been kept, can be shown to prevent regeneration from the stems of *Tubularia*. Whether this inhibitor represents anything more than nematocyst toxins, as noted earlier, is a problem for the future to solve.

A stimulator principle has not been found in the tissues of colonial hydroids as it has in *Hydra*. What, then, stimulates hydranth development at the end of a hydrocaulus? There have been a few revealing experiments which have given us some clues as to the nature of "distal dominance" in hydranth initiation. It has already been mentioned that if the distal end of a hydrocaulus is sealed off in one way or another, no hydranth forms. Could it be that a hydranth regenerates at the *end* of a stem because that is the only region not covered by the perisarc? Apparently so, for Edgar Zwilling discovered that if a small window is cut in the perisarc to expose the side of the hydrocaulus, then a hydranth regenerates there. And if an even larger hole is made in the perisarc, two hydranths may develop in mouth-to-mouth orientation.

Results of experiments along these lines suggest that distal dominance may be nothing more than the high point in a metabolic gradient. Wherever the hydrocaulus is exposed to the surrounding medium, there its tissues will enjoy a greater abundance of metabolites. This may be enough to give that part of the stem a head start in hydranth development, whereupon all other potential sites of regeneration are automatically inhibited. The reason why the distal end of a stem should be dominant in the first place may simply be due to the fact that it is the part of the hydrocaulus originally open to the environment.

Over and above this, however, there exists an intrinsic gradient along the hydrocaulus as revealed by regenerative abilities at different levels. The rate of hydranth development increases at progressively distal levels of amputation, and the regenerated structures grow to greater dimensions. Correlated with this is a rise in oxygen consumption toward the distal end of the hydrocaulus. Perhaps the most meaningful correlation, however, is the gradient in interstitial cell population. This is an interesting facet of the problem which has been worked out by Pierre Tardent at the University of Zurich. As was true in *Hydra*, the number of such cells also decreases basally in *Tubularia* (Fig. 18). We do not yet know which of these correlations are causal and which are derivative, but interstitial cells probably play a key role in regeneration. These are the cells which have been observed to participate in the distal migration of tissues during the incipient phases of regeneration shortly after amputation. On the other hand, when a stem is compelled to regenerate many times in a row by repeated amputations of each newly formed hydranth, the hydrocaulus ultimately becomes very thin and depleted of all cell types, interstitial and otherwise. This may be taken to indicate that regeneration evidently involves the participation of all kinds of cells, with interstitial cells probably serving as a source of replacement.

Fig. 18 **Gradients in inter-**
stitial cell populations in
Hydra **(left) and** *Tubularia*
(right). In both cases the
greatest density of interstitial
cells is immediately behind
the ring of tentacles on the
hydranth. More proximally
their concentrations
steadily decline.

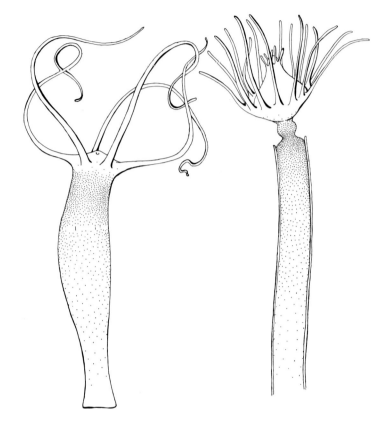

Once hydranth development has been initiated, the next problem
to be solved is how not to produce too many hydranths. This it does
by means of the inhibitory influences mentioned above. Yet there must
also be some provision to insure that the growth of a given hydranth
shall not be arrested by its own inhibitory agents. To guarantee its
"self-immunity," the hydranth has established a temporal gradient in
its sensitivity to the inhibitor which is the reciprocal of its capacity for
inhibitor production. These principles, according to a comprehensive
series of experiments carried out in Tardent's laboratory, can best be
illustrated by grafting hydranths of varying degrees of development
together in all possible combinations in order to learn which will
inhibit which.

When a recently amputated hydrocaulus that has not yet begun to
regenerate has a hydranth grafted in reversed polarity onto its proximal
end, its own potentiality for hydranth formation is suppressed. No
matter what the age of the grafted hydranth, regeneration will be
prevented. But if two recently amputated hydrocauli are combined,

neither will dominate the other and both will therefore give rise to a hydranth (Fig. 19).

Now, if a similar series of grafts is made to older stems with hydranth regeneration already in progress, the results depend upon the relative ages of the two regenerates. A graft will inhibit or delay regeneration only in stems less advanced than itself (Fig. 19) and will in turn be inhibited only by older regenerates. When the two segments are the same age, regeneration in both continues uninterrupted. Thus, as a hydranth regenerates it produces more and more inhibitor, but becomes less and less susceptible to it. This inverse temporal relationship assures the normal regeneration of only one hydranth at a time.

Spatial relationships are also important. S. Meryl Rose of Tulane University has extensively explored the polarization of inhibitory influences in *Tubularia* hydranth regeneration. Why is it, he wondered, that proximal tentacles do not form unless distal ones are present? What if a very early hydranth regenerate were cut into proximal and distal halves? Would each piece go on to develop into what it would have become in the first place? The distal part does, but the proximal part does not. Instead of regenerating into proximal tentacles, the hind piece now gives rise to distal tentacles. But if proximal primordia are cultured in the presence of distal extracts, the development of distal tentacles is suppressed. The obvious conclusion is that the distal region normally inhibits more of the same proximal to it. The polarity

Fig. 19 **Diagram of Tardent's experiments on the effects of relative ages of grafted hydranth regenerates on each other's development in** *Tubularia.* **Arrows point distally. When two segments of hydrocauli at the same stage of development are grafted together in opposite directions (left), both go on to form hydranths together. When one piece of stem is more advanced than the other (right), the latter's regeneration is delayed until the first one completes its development.**

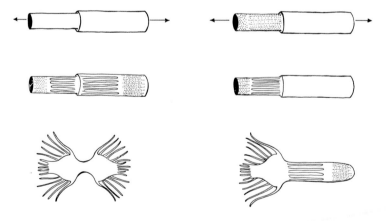

of the system may even be oriented along a bioelectric gradient. The proximal ring of tentacles, it seems, is low man on the totem pole. It develops only when its aspirations for a more distal status are frustrated because of its inferior position in the hydrocaulus.

The inhibitory influence of distal structures works in only one direction. Tardent showed that a hydranth regenerate can arrest development of a less advanced one grafted onto it proximally. Rose has demonstrated, however, that if incipient regenerates are grafted together *distal* to each other, that is, in a head-on orientation (Fig. 20), then each develops independently, neither one inhibiting the other. It is only when the grafted parts are upstream from each other's disto-proximal flow of inhibitor that two rings of distal tentacles can exist in juxtaposition.

Regeneration in hydroids is more than just an emergency measure. It is an integral part of the animal's existence. In colonial forms, hydranths have limited life spans. They are periodically resorbed in most species, and in a few cases are regularly autotomized. In *Campanularia*, for example, Sears Crowell of Indiana University has shown that hydranths are produced at the ends of dichotomously

Fig. 20 **Simplified outline of Rose's analysis of how polarity affects development of regenerating hydranth grafts in** *Tubularia.* **Horizontal arrows indicate distal direction. On the left, the proximal ring of tentacles of one regenerate is grafted onto an intact regenerate in a distal-to-distal orientation. Part of the proximal graft now reorganizes independently into distal tentacles, and two hydranths are produced facing each other. On the right, similar regenerates are grafted together facing in opposite directions. The smaller graft bearing only a ring of distal tentacles is sometimes inhibited by its proximity to the larger piece, but may occasionally reorganize into both distal and proximal rings of tentacles. In this case, two complete hydranths may develop back-to-back.**

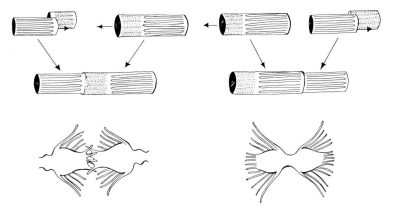

Fig. 21 **Sequence of hydranth turnover in** *Campanularia,* **as analyzed by Crowell (1953). Hydranths tend to be resorbed in the same order in which they developed. After a few days new ones sprout from the same stems where the old ones disappeared. The colony grows by the terminal addition of hydranths, but maintains itself by producing successive waves of hydranth generations.**

branching stems. Each one lives only a few days to a week, after which it degenerates. Then, from the end of the hydrocaulus where it was resorbed, there regenerates a new hydranth. Bernard Strehler of the University of Southern California recognized in this system of hydranth succession an example of localized aging in which the impending death of the cells is foreshadowed by excessive numbers of lysosomes rich in acid phosphatase. The programmed mortality of hydranths, however, may not necessarily signal the demise of all their component cells. If regressing hydranths are isolated, not only may they organize into short stolons, but these may even give rise to new hydranths.

As the colony grows, it is constantly rejuvenated by the successive rounds of loss and regeneration of its hydranths. This process goes on in an orderly sequence in *Campanularia*, with the oldest hydranth in the colony being the first to disappear and to be replaced. Others follow suit according to the sequence in which they first developed. This process is diagrammatically outlined in Fig. 21. In *Tubularia* the hydranths are not resorbed, but are shed bodily from the hydrocaulus, whereupon new ones regenerate to take their places.

Like *Hydra*, colonial hydroids depend upon regeneration for their very existence. They differ from *Hydra* in that the renewal of their hydranths occurs periodically, not continuously. In both cases, however, the organisms cannot survive except by the turnover of their tissues. Indeed, it is their irrepressible urge to regenerate, whether there is anything to replace or not, that keeps these improbable animals perpetually young and practically immortal.

REFERENCES

BAKER, J. R. 1952. "Abraham Trembley of Geneva. Scientist and Philosopher, 1710–1784." Edward Arnold and Co., London.

BARTH, L. G. 1940. The process of regeneration in hydroids. *Biol. Rev. Cambridge Phil. Soc.* **15**: 405–420.

BERRILL, N. J. 1957. The indestructible Hydra. *Sci. Am.* **197** (6): 118–125.

BRIEN, P. 1960. The fresh-water Hydra. *Am. Scientist* **48**: 461–475.

BURNETT, A. L. 1961. The growth process in Hydra. *J. Exptl. Zool.* **146**: 21–83.

BURNETT, A. L. 1966. A model of growth and cell differentiation in Hydra. *Am. Naturalist* **100**: 165–189.

CAMPBELL, R. D. 1967. Tissue dynamics of steady state growth in *Hydra littoralis.* I. Patterns of cell division. *Develop. Biol.* **15**: 487–502.

CAMPBELL, R. D. 1967. Tissue dynamics of steady state growth in *Hydra littoralis.* II. Patterns of tissue movement. *J. Morphol.* **121**: 19–28.

CLARKSON, S. G. and L. WOLPERT. 1967. Bud morphogenesis in Hydra. *Nature* **214**: 780–783.

CROWELL, S. 1953. The regression-replacement cycle of hydranths of *Obelia* and *Campanularia. Physiol. Zool.* **26**: 319–327.

CROWELL, S. 1961. Developmental problems in Campanularia. *In* "The Biology of Hydra and of Some Other Coelenterates" (H. M. Lenhoff and W. F. Loomis, eds.), pp. 297–316. University of Miami Press, Coral Gables.

DAVIS, L. V. 1966. Inhibition of growth and regeneration in Hydra by crowded culture water. *Nature* **212**: 1215–1217.

DAVIS, L. V. 1967. The source and identity of a regeneration-inhibiting factor in hydroid polyps. *J. Exptl. Zool.* **164**: 187–194.

DIEHL, F. A. and A. L. BURNETT. 1965. The role of interstitial cells in the maintenance of Hydra. IV. Regeneration of hypostome and tentacles. *J. Exptl. Zool.* **158**: 299–318.

HAM, R. G. and R. E. EAKIN. 1958. Time sequence of certain physiological events during regeneration in Hydra. *J. Exptl. Zool.* **139**: 33–54.

LENTZ, T. L. 1966. "The Cell Biology of Hydra." John Wiley, New York.

MOOKERJEE, S. and S. BHATTACHERJEE. 1966. Cellular mechanics in hydroid regeneration. *Arch. Entwicklungsmech. Organ.* **157**: 1–20.

ROSE, S. M. 1957. Polarized inhibitory effects during regeneration in Tubularia. *J. Morphol.* **100**: 187–206.

ROSE, S. M. and J. A. POWERS. 1966. Polarized inhibitory control of regional differentiation during regeneration in *Tubularia.* I. The effect of extracts from distal and proximal regions. *Growth* **30**: 419–427.

SHOSTAK, S. 1967. Bud movement in Hydra. *Science* **155:** 1567–1568.

SINHA, A. K. 1966. Experimental determination of polarity in Hydra. *Arch. Fntwicklungsmech. Organ.* **157:** 101–116.

STREHLER, B. L. 1961. Aging in coelenterates. *In* "The Biology of Hydra and of Some Other Coelenterates" (H. M. Lenhoff and W. F. Loomis, eds.), pp. 373–398. University of Miami Press, Coral Gables.

TARDENT, P. 1960. Principles governing the process of regeneration in hydroids. *In* "Developing Cell Systems and Their Control" (D. Rudnick, ed.), pp. 21–43. Ronald Press, New York.

TARDENT, P. 1963. Regeneration in the Hydrozoa. *Biol. Rev. Cambridge Phil. Soc.* **38:** 293–333.

TARDENT, P. and T. TARDENT. 1956. Wiederholte Regeneration bei *Tubularia. Pubbl. Staz. Zool. Napoli* **28:** 367–396.

ZWILLING, E. 1939. The effect of the removal of perisarc on regeneration in Tubularia crocea. *Biol. Bull.* **76:** 90–103.

5   Flatworms and the Regeneration Blastema

FEW animals challenge the experimental ingenuity of zoologists more then do planarian worms. Their amazing powers of survival and regeneration following almost every imaginable mutilation pose questions that are difficult to resist trying to answer. Generations of biologists have risen to this challenge, but in truth it must be admitted that the secrets of how the flatworm regenerates are in no immediate danger of being discovered.

Not all flatworms regenerate, but of those that do, the relationship to asexual reproduction is undeniable. Some of the turbellarians, which are nonparasitic inhabitants of marine, fresh water or terrestrial environments, can pinch in two just behind the pharynx, whereupon each half develops into an entire worm. In the case of tape worms, regeneration is a constant and essential aspect of the parasite's life cycle. Attached to the mucosal lining of the host's intestine, the mature worm is capable of turning out an unending rib-

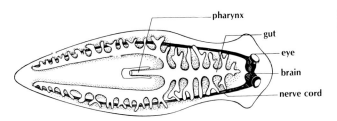

pharynx
gut
eye
brain
nerve cord

Fig. 22 **Generalized body plan of a flatworm.**

bon of proglottids. The terminal ones are detached by autotomy, or self-amputation, and are eventually shed from the host to become a source of eggs for subsequent generations. This assembly-line production of reproductive segments, each being an exact replica of all others, takes place in a growth zone located immediately behind the head of the worm. It is a unique form of regeneration in which amputation is the result of growth, instead of the other way around.

When a planarian is cut in half, regeneration is initiated at both wound surfaces. The front end grows a new tail, and the tail produces a new head. This is not so different from what we have already seen happen in still lower animals, except that in planarians the missing parts develop from a blastema, which is an accumulation of undifferentiated cells at the site of amputation. It is an alternative to morphallaxis, whereby new parts are organized directly out of pre-existing differentiated tissues.

Morphallaxis is an ideal mode of regeneration provided the specialized state of the tissues involved does not preclude their changing into different morphological structures. In hydroids, for example, hydranths could form by rearranging the various cell types already present. Regeneration was simply a matter of creating a new form without the necessity of differentiating new kinds of cells. The greater histological complexity of the planarian body, however, makes it impossible for regeneration to occur solely by having old tissues turn into new ones. Therefore, flatworms have had to resort to undifferentiated cells as a source of new heads and tails.

Neoblasts There are two ways to acquire undifferentiated cells. One is to make them by the dedifferentiation of already specialized cells; the other is to hold over a permanent reserve of pluripotent cells from embryonic stages. Planarians may do the latter. Distributed throughout their bodies are numerous undifferentiated cells distinguished mainly by the abundance of RNA in their cytoplasm (Fig. 23). These neoblasts,

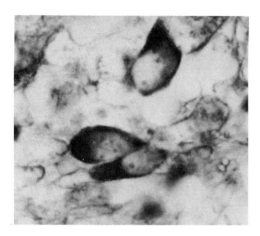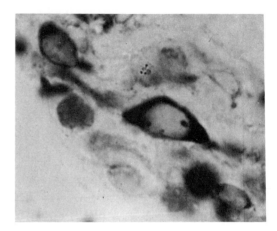

Fig. 23 **Neoblasts of** *Planaria vitta.* **Their cytoplasm becomes deeply stained with azur A, while the nuclei remain relatively clear.** (*From Pedersen, 1959.*)

as they are known, are believed to give rise to the blastema when part of the worm's body has been amputated.

Some investigators, not without good reason, deny the existence of neoblasts as such, believing that the regeneration blastema is derived from dedifferentiated cells rather than from reserve cells that were never differentiated in the first place. In order to be consistent with the bulk of the available literature, however, we shall assume in the present account that neoblasts really do exist, bearing in mind that the general consensus in this matter may change as new evidence is brought to light.

It takes only a few days to produce a blastema on a bisected flatworm, and little more than a week or two for a new head or tail to differentiate completely. In regeneration of the anterior region of the body from a posterior half, the blastema cells differentiate in several different directions depending upon their respective locations. Those situated near the middle of the blastema become nerve cells which give rise to a new brain. Others differentiate into eyes, muscle, intestine, or components of the excretory and reproductive systems. A few may remain undifferentiated, against the day when they may be called upon to form still another blastema. If it were not for the remarkable versatility of these neoblasts, planarians might never have been able to regenerate at all. There are some species, however, which cannot regenerate even though neoblasts are present.

Evidence in favor of the indispensable role of neoblasts in regeneration derives from the discovery that these cells are selectively susceptible to the deleterious effects of X-rays. Following exposure of the whole worm to 5000 r the neoblast population declines, and all capacity for regeneration is destroyed. Decapitation of such X-rayed planarians results in death within a few weeks. However, Dubois showed that if just the anterior half of a worm is irradiated while the rest of the body is shielded with lead (Fig. 24), then regeneration can occur even though the zone immediately behind the level of amputation has been X-rayed and hence depleted of its neoblasts. Under these circumstances, the onset of regeneration is delayed (from a few days to a few weeks or months) in proportion to the width of the irradiated zone. Histological studies have shown that the irradiated area first loses its neoblasts, but later on becomes recolonized by new ones presumably derived from the healthy parts of the body. From

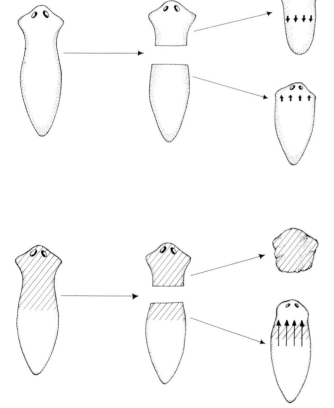

Fig. 24 **Above: Normal regeneration of bisected planarian illustrating the local source of blastema cells (short arrows). Below: Experiment by Dubois in which a partially X-rayed worm is cut across through the irradiated (crosshatched) region. The totally exposed head degenerates for lack of healthy cells from which to regenerate. The tail piece belatedly grows a new head, presumably from unirradiated neoblasts which traverse the X-rayed zone.**

these results it has been assumed that neoblasts from the unirradiated parts of the body must migrate across the X-rayed region toward the wound surface before a blastema can be produced; the farther they have to go the longer the delay.

Although neoblasts may indeed migrate over considerable distances to reach a wound surface under the conditions of the above experiments, there is evidence that they do not ordinarily do so. For example, if a piece of radioactively labeled tissue is grafted into a planarian which is later amputated nearby, the labeled cells of the graft do not necessarily become incorporated into the subsequent regenerate. This argues for the strictly local origin of neoblasts (except when they may have been locally destroyed). Furthermore, it has been shown that the size of the body fragment has little or nothing to do with the rate at which a new head grows. Small pieces regenerate just as fast as large pieces, despite the fact that they contain fewer neoblasts. Furthermore, no correlation has been found between the distribution of neoblasts in different regions of flatworms and their capacity for regeneration at different levels. Some species regenerate equally well no matter where they are amputated. Others can regenerate better anteriorly than posteriorly. Yet these and other patterns of regenerative abilities do not necessarily follow the variations in neoblast concentrations throughout the worm. Finally, observations of neoblast behavior *in vitro* have revealed strong affinities for each other resulting in a tendency to aggregate wherever intervening differentiated cells have been lost. This explains the propensity of neoblasts to cluster into blastemas at wound sites where other tissues have been injured and destroyed. It does not argue in favor of their ability to migrate over long distances, however.

It would be premature to contend categorically that neoblasts constitute the exclusive source of regenerative material in flatworms. Indeed, Knud Pedersen, at the University of Copenhagen, has uncovered evidence that planarians may be capable of some regeneration by morphallaxis if the usual pathways are blocked. When treated with triethylene melamine, an anti-cancer drug, flatworms fail to produce blastemas after amputation because their neoblasts can no longer proliferate. Unable to regenerate in the conventional way, they resort to morphallaxis. Nondividing neoblasts gradually turn into brain and eyes. Sometimes, if the dose was not too great, some neoblasts may regain mitotic competence and give rise to the other tissues needed to restore the decapitated worm to normal. If not, the partially reorganized worm eventually succumbs to a generalized regression of its entire body.

There is every reason to believe that the neoblasts in one part of the body are developmentally equivalent to those in any other region. That is, all of them are equally pluripotent. What they are to become depends on the direction in which the blastema is to differentiate, as well as on their position within the blastema. In the case of the partially irradiated flatworm, neoblasts from the posterior part of the body move forward from their original locations to take part in the construction of a new front end that would otherwise have developed at the expense of neoblasts from the anterior region of the worm. Actually, neoblasts become what the remaining part of the organism dictates. For example, when a planarian is cut in half transversely, each wound surface is bordered by subjacent neoblasts that were originally intermingled. Yet from this subdivided population of cells there develops a head in one case and a tail in the other. Of one thing we can be certain, that neoblasts stand ready, undifferentiated and undetermined, to mobilize at the site of amputation. Singly they remain unfulfilled. Only en masse do they express their potentialities.

The Problem of Polarity To answer the question of how the destinies of neoblasts are determined, our attention must turn to the blastema as a whole and the intriguing problem of head versus tail development. The polarity of the organism is so indelibly imprinted upon the blastema that only under the most unusual of circumstances can it be reversed. One such circumstance, pictured in Fig. 25, is realized by cutting a transverse segment of a planarian so thin that there is not enough room to establish a proper anterior-posterior gradient. Sometimes, in Janus-like fashion, these pieces may regenerate heads in both directions. This can happen only when neither end enjoys an advantage over the

Fig. 25 **Left: Two heads facing in opposite directions may be produced from a thin slice too narrow for a head-tail gradient to be established. Right: If second cut is delayed, an equally thin slice now forms a typical worm because the time lag has allowed an anterior-posterior gradient to be set up.**

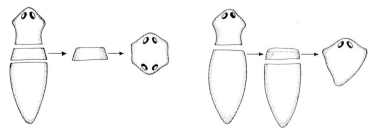

other, however. If a worm's head is amputated, and after only a short delay a narrow slice of the stump is severed from the rest of the body by a second transverse cut, then the bipolarity that might have occurred is never established owing to the head start of the anterior wound surface.

Still another way to reverse the polarity relies upon upsetting the metabolic differential between front and rear. One theory of head formation holds that the greater metabolic activity of the anterior end of a planarian fragment determines the site of head regeneration, while tails are produced under the reverse conditions at the opposite pole. Since the metabolic rate varies along the length of the worm anyway, it is not the absolute level of metabolism that matters, but the *relative* difference between two ends of a fragment that establishes polarity. It follows that if the metabolism of the anterior end of a planarian should be artificially reduced below that of the posterior region, then the latter should now be capable of regenerating a head instead of a tail. This is exactly what happens, according to the masterful experiments carried out by Reed Flickinger of the State University of New York at Buffalo. When worms are embedded in agar blocks to immobilize them, and their anterior regions are then immersed in solutions of certain antimetabolites (e.g., colcemide, β-mercaptoethanol, chloramphenicol) for one or more days, head regeneration can occasionally be induced from posterior wound surfaces that would ordinarily have given rise only to tails. Two-headed flatworms have thus been produced by reversing the normal anterior-posterior metabolic gradient as illustrated in Fig. 26.

More precisely, it has been shown that drugs such as the antibiotic, chloramphenicol (Chloromycetin), inhibit the synthesis of RNA and DNA in regenerating worms (as in other systems). Furthermore, an important difference between blastemas destined to become heads and those developing into tails is that the former express higher rates of RNA and DNA synthesis. Hence, the net effect of chloramphenicol is to suppress the synthesis of these compounds more in the head than in the tail, thereby altering the polarity of a flatworm by acting as an equalizer of nucleic acid production. Since the mitotic inhibitor colcemide can also affect polarity, the deflection of a presumptive tail into an actual head may also be effected by abolishing a differential in mitoitc activity between the two ends.

In some cases it has been possible to promote head formation even in the absence of regeneration. If worms with their heads dipped in chloramphenicol are not amputated and thus do not acquire a posteri-

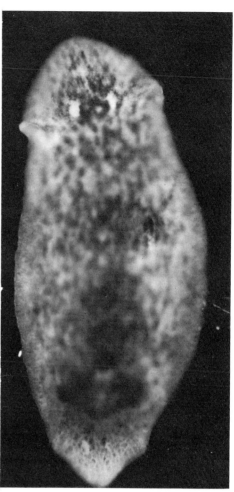

Fig. 26 Left: Experimental technique for reversing flatworm polarity. Embedded in agar, an immobilized worm is immersed head-first in solution of antimetabolite. Right: Bipolar Dugesia dorotocephala produced by exposing intact worm to 0.02 mg of colcemide per milliliter for one day, amputating tail, embedding anterior portion in agar, and submerging head in colcemide solution for another day. Released from agar and allowed to regenerate for six days, the worm grew an extra head (bottom of photograph) where its tail should have been (From Flickinger and Coward, 1962.)

orly directed wound, they may sometimes turn their tails into heads by direct tissue reorganization. By what mechanism this curious phenomenon occurs no one knows. Perhaps it is made possible by the existence of neoblasts throughout the body. Ordinarily their tremendous developmental potentialities are latent, at least until they are released by wounding and ensuing blastema formation. Yet the conversion of an uninjured tail into a head simply by altering the metabolic relationships within the body testifies to the surprisingly labile state of flatworm anatomy. One wonders whether the morphological integrity of the body might not be stabilized by the continuous interplay of various physiological influences upon which structural maintenance may depend. If so, then amputation might call forth regenerative responses not by the physical deletion of body parts *per se*, but by disrupting the balance of physiological control mechanisms operating to maintain body integrity.

The Blastema Neoblasts are undetermined before they become incorporated into a blastema. Once they aggregate at a wound surface, however, they come under the sphere of influence exerted by the neighboring part of the worm. This part of the worm has the job of shaping the destiny of the blastema. Like a teacher confronted with a class of pupils, it must tell them whether to become a head or a tail (presumably in the language of a metabolic gradient). Other important decisions also have to be made. Which side of the head (or tail) shall be on top? How many heads shall form? How big shall they grow? How shall the internal parts be arranged? Lest the resulting product turn out to be abnormal, nothing can be left to chance in this complex task of reconstruction. Our task is to find out how this educational program works.

One way of doing this is to separate the blastema from the stump after various intervals to see whether future development is affected. The results of such experiments, carried out at the Collège de France by Catherine Sengel, show that almost from the time the blastema forms, it has received all the information it needs to complete its mission. If young head or tail blastemas are severed from regenerating worms within only a few days of amputation, they are capable of carrying on by themselves. Miniature heads or tails differentiate from them. They cannot survive indefinitely because such heads are unable to regenerate tails, nor can the tails grow heads of their own. Only by grafting complementary blastemas together can they be made to form a whole worm, complete with pharynx and gut. Nevertheless, it is remarkable that as soon as a blastema becomes big enough to be isolated it can go ahead with the differentiation of eyes, brain and muscle on its own. One suspects that neoblasts may have to be given only very basic information to start with. From such fundamental instructions they may then be able to develop into a morphologically harmonious structure without further outside help. Anterior blastemas, for example, almost always succeed in producing normally formed heads despite even the most ingenious tactics of the experimenter. Worms can be split in two, grafted together, or mutilated in other ingenious ways. No matter what challenges may be hurled at it, the blastema is seldom deceived into making a mistake. The mechanisms of morphogenetic regulation operating in this amazing system deserve our respect as well as our serious attention.

Morphogenetic Fields It is easy to take for granted the fact that a single transversely bisected flatworm regenerates one head. But what if the animal is also bisected longitudinally? Will each half stump now grow half a head or a whole head? These and other problems of morphogenesis have been investigated by a series of brilliant experiments carried out in H. V. Brøndsted's laboratory in the University of Copenhagen. The results of these studies have contributed much to our understanding of morphogenetic fields.

The concept of the morphogenetic field arose by analogy with certain phenomena in the physical sciences. The flame of a match, for example, represents a dynamic equilibrium of burning gases which collectively maintains its shape. If a burning match is split lengthwise, the original flame is divided into two equal and complete flames of somewhat smaller size. Conversely, two matches can be brought together to produce a single flame. A magnetic field exhibits similar properties. In either case, the integrity of the field is not changed by quantitative alterations in the physical substrate from which it emanates. The so-called head field of the regenerating planarian possesses comparable attributes.

By removing the midsection of a decapitated flatworm it is possible to create two separate but diminutive wound surfaces, each of which is capable of regeneration. As long as they are prevented from growing together again, each one will produce its own complete head. Thus, the part of a stump which would normally give rise to only a fraction of the whole head can organize an entire one if isolated from the rest of the system (Fig. 27). This suggests that each part of the wound surface, or of its subtended blastema, is in competition with neighboring regions. All parts are normally capable of regenerating more than they do, presumably because much of what they might have formed is already being made elsewhere. The integrity of the regenerating head is assured by mutual inhibitions between its component parts.

Just as half a planarian can give rise to a whole head, so also can a double planarian. When two worms are joined in parallel parabiosis and their heads cut off, there is produced a single, but extra-wide wound surface. From this there may occasionally regenerate a single

Fig. 27 **The number of heads produced by a decapitated planarian is determined by how many amputation stumps there are. When the wound surface is split into two lateral ones (above), each now regenerates a head independent of the other. Parabiotic worms (below) may sometimes produce a single head from a compound stump.**

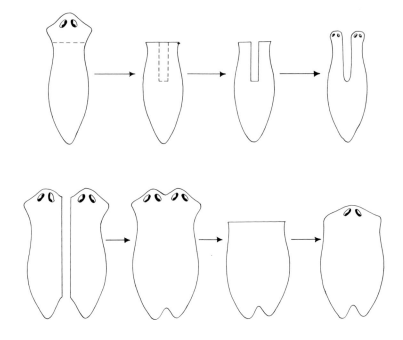

large head (Fig. 27), provided the two worms were fused together intimately enough in the first place. Morphogenesis in the flatworm, therefore, adheres to the definition of a field inasmuch as a unified regenerate tends to be produced irrespective of the completeness or incompleteness of the wound surface from which it grows.

As mentioned earlier, the lateral third of a decapitated planarian can give rise to a whole head if it is isolated from the other two-thirds. Brøndsted reasoned that ordinarily the presence of the rest of the blastema must somehow suppress the expression of the full morphogenetic potential in the lateral regions. Since differentiation in a blastema commences in the center first and later at the sides, the morphogenetic head field is a manifestation of temporal as well as spatial gradients.

When the head of a flatworm is cut off, a blastema begins to form in a day or two, then enlarges for another couple of days, and gives the first indications of eye-spot formation on about the fourth day. The eyes always develop in the middle of the regenerate, but if the lateral third of the worm is isolated, then the eyes form in the middle of *that* blastema. Sometime during the first five days of regeneration the eyes that might have formed in the lateral third of an intact blastema do not do so. By cutting away all but the lateral one-third of a series of planarians at daily intervals after amputation of their heads, it is possible to plot the lateral spread of eye-inhibiting influences propagated from the median part of the regenerate. Such a series of experiments is outlined in Fig. 28.

When the operation is done early in the course of regeneration, eye formation in lateral regenerates is only slightly delayed compared with controls isolated at the time of decapitation. If the operation is put off for a few days, the appearance of eye regenerates in the lateral blastema is postponed considerably. Hence, the longer the original blastema remains intact, the more limited is the expression of eye-forming capacity in the lateral regions. Eventually, of course, the lateral parts of the intact regenerate differentiate into something else, by which time eye-inhibiting influences subside. Evidence along these lines may be taken to indicate, therefore, that during the early days of head regeneration the mid-region of the blastema establishes dominance over the less advanced lateral regions. These mounting inhibitory influences spread laterally at the rate of about 6 μ per hour, affecting the course of neoblast differentiation in the process.

It seems that since the effects exerted on the neoblasts are of an inhibitory nature, the direction of their subsequent differentiation is a matter of progressive restrictions. Originally capable of becoming almost any kind of cell, yet finding it impossible to differentiate in more than one direction at a time, the neoblasts are guided by the

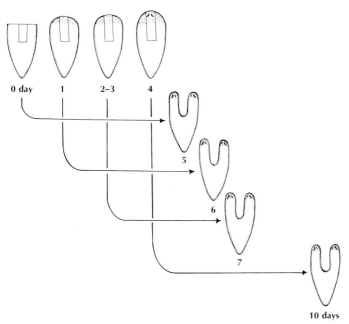

Fig. 28 **Results of Brøndsted's experiments on the course of development in isolated lateral thirds of head blastemas. Ordinarily about five days are required for eyes to develop in the two small regenerates. If subdivision of the blastema is put off for one or more days after decapitation the schedule of development in the isolated portions is set back correspondingly.**

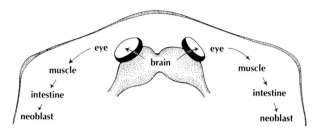

Fig. 29 **Outline of the time-graded re-generation field proposed by Brøndsted. Beginning with the differentiation of centrally located blastema cells into brain tissue, other cells develop into eyes, muscle and intestine in that order, while some remain as undifferentiated neoblasts.**

process of elimination until all but one course of action is eventually closed to each one of them. But since different neoblasts end up in different types of tissues, there must be some mechanism to assure the necessary diversity of differentiation among a population of cells that were all created equal. It is apparently the head start of the centrally located cells which imposes a handicap on those in more lateral positions. This temporal advantage sets up what Brøndsted has called a "time-graded regeneration field." Neoblasts in progressively lateral locations do not differentiate in the same direction because they begin their development at different times. Accordingly, the first ones to differentiate are in the middle of the blastema. They become part of the brain. Next, the eyes are formed, followed by muscle and intestine. The cells left over remain as pluripotent neoblasts.

A scheme of this kind, as illustrated in Fig. 29, is predicated on the assumption that there is a hierarchy among the various possible directions of differentiation a cell is to follow. If all pathways are open, then brain is the preferred course. But as the first neoblasts to differentiate become nerve cells, they inhibit others from doing likewise. The next ones therefore settle for the second choice, which is eye formation. After this niche has been pre-empted, other neoblasts appropriate successive positions in order of decreasing priority. In such a caste system, the status of any given neoblast is determined by its position in the gradients of time and space, but always in relation to its fellow cells.

In the developing head blastema, the most precocious neoblasts in the center become brain or eye, while the retarded ones out to the sides are relegated to the gut. The fortunes of the latter cells can be improved only by removing their more favorably located superiors, in which case a new ranking system is established among whatever cells remain available for differentiation. We must now ask how the neoblasts communicate with each other as their morphogenetic destinies are mutually molded.

As demonstrated above, their communication may be described in the language of inhibition. Once a brain has differentiated, it inhibits the formation of another one. Similarly, it can be shown that one head will inhibit another in its vicinity. Head grafts to the caudal region, for example, will persist, but if an extra head is grafted to a worm next to the host's own head, the graft is resorbed. In the latter case, if the host's head is amputated, then the graft not only survives, but the regeneration of the original head does not occur, its inhibition being in proportion to the size and proximity of the grafted head.

Not all the communication within a blastema is negative, however. The development of certain parts of the body are stimulated by inductive influences emanating from previously formed structures. In a series of classic experiments, Theodore Lender of the University of Paris, demonstrated such a relationship between the brain and the eyes (Fig. 30). For this work he used *Polycelis nigra*, a species of flatworm equipped with as many as seventy eyes arranged in a row around the anterior and lateral edges of the body. If eyes are removed by trimming off some of the lateral margin of the worm, new ones regenerate in about a week to replace them. But if in such a worm the brain is also removed, and is prevented from growing back by repeatedly removing its blastema, then the eyes fail to regenerate. The dependence of the eyes on the brain does not rely upon nervous connections with the brain, for regeneration can occur in grafted tissue placed near the brain but not innervated by it. Nor does the brain promote eye regeneration by supplying neoblasts. X-irradiation of the brain, which kills the neoblasts associated with it, does not

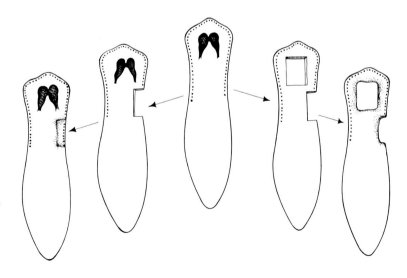

Fig. 30 **The numerous eyes of** *Polycelis nigra* **will regenerate following their excision provided the brain is intact (left), but as Lender has shown, they are not replaced in worms without brains (right).**

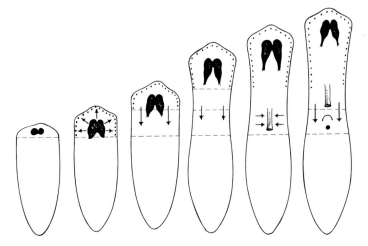

Fig. 31 **Sequence of inductive relationship (arrows) in regenerating flatworm** (*Polycelis nigra*). **From left to right, the brain is the first organ to develop, which is in turn responsible for eye differentiation. The head thus formed then induces a prepharyngeal region behind it, and this brings about the development of the pharyngeal region farther back. The pharyngeal region gives rise to a pharynx medially, and also induces reproductive organs posteriorly.** (*After Wolff, 1962.*)

interfere with the inductive influence. Even necrotic brains exert this effect, as do brains from other species of flatworms. Clearly, there must be a humoral substance released from neural tissues which induces the development of eyes within the territory through which it diffuses.

The existence of such a hormone can be demonstrated by using brainless planarians as assay animals. When eyes are cut off such worms, they will not regenerate of course. But if placed in a medium to which an extract of the head has been added, eyes do regenerate. Tail extracts do not work. Curiously enough, the same head extract which promotes eye formation inhibits head regeneration in decapitated worms. Under the latter conditions, a blastema forms but its neoblasts do not differentiate. Perhaps it is not necessary to postulate separate stimulatory and inhibitory substances. The same factors may simply exert opposite effects on different tissues.

The eye-brain relationship is but one example of a rather widespread phenomenon in flatworm morphogenesis. Etienne Wolff recognized the concatenation of dependent relationships that operates in the regenerating planarian, relationships that have been elucidated by numerous grafting experiments carried out by him and his collaborators at the Collège de France and summarized in Fig. 31. For example, the area between the head and pharynx (prepharyngeal region) depends for its development upon the presence of the head (or brain?). The prepharyngeal region in turn induces the pharyngeal zone proper, which can then stimulate the regeneration of a pharynx and reproductive organs. These and other yet to be discovered inductive relationships assure the orderly development of body parts in the right place at the right time. At the beginning of the sequence is the brain, which is the first structure to regenerate, and to which, directly or indirectly, all other organs owe their inception.

Regeneration and The planarian brain is also important for other reasons, not the least
Learning of which is its allegedly unorthodox method of learning and remembering. Flatworms like the dark, and if a light is suddenly shined on one of them, it immediately stops and contracts. After several such episodes, however, it ignores the light stimulus. A weak electric shock, on the other hand, always elicits a reaction. Now when a worm is given the light treatment followed by the shock treatment, it will later continue to contract when exposed to light alone. This is a classic conditioned reflex learned by a worm expecting to be shocked after each flash of light. The memory of its traumatic experience fortunately lasts long enough for such a worm, if cut in half, to regenerate. Realizing the potentialities of this combination of circumstances, James V. McConnell at the University of Michigan seized upon this unique opportunity to discover whether or not the posterior half of a trained worm would exhibit the same conditioned responses with its newly regenerated brain as does the anterior fragment. As expected, the front half reacted like the unamputated controls because it inherited the conditioned brain. As was not expected, however, the posterior half did likewise. The memory of the pre-amputation experience, therefore, must have been stored throughout the body, not just in the brain.

It is tempting to hazard the educated guess that the ubiquitous neoblasts may have carried forward past memories into the newly regenerated brain. Evidence in favor of this possibility was obtained when untrained planarians were given trained ones to eat. They later showed a significantly higher incidence of conditioned responses than did controls fed upon uneducated worms. This cannibalistic conditioning may have depended upon the ingestion of neoblasts from the consumed worms, a possibility which is not without basis in fact. For example, there is a flatworm known as *Microstomum* which feeds upon *Hydra* whose nematocysts it incorporates intact into its own epidermis. Since digestion in planarians is intracellular, it is conceivable that viable neoblasts might be taken up intact by the host's body and thereby pass on stored information.

Some researchers have carried this story one step beyond. On the theory that learning may be encoded in terms of RNA, it seemed logical to attempt memory transfer by injecting RNA from educated flatworms into naive ones. The rationale for such experiments rested upon the fact that neoblasts themselves are suspiciously well-endowed with RNA. Furthermore, ribonuclease erases the memory of regenerating posterior halves of previously conditioned worms. In the hands of some, but by no means all, investigators, success has been claimed in experiments designed to prove that learning can be achieved by injecting RNA from trained into untrained planarians. Under the impetus of such exciting possibilities in flatworms, others in recent years have been encouraged to try comparable experiments in mammals. Although positive results have been reported, so have negative ones. Where the stakes are as high as they are in this area, a note of caution should be emphasized to protect us from being carried away by our own wishful thinking, but not overemphasized to the extent that exciting possibilities are disregarded. Those of us who follow this game as interested spectators wish the players on our side great success, but we are not betting on the outcome.

REFERENCES

BETCHAKU, T. 1967. Isolation of planarian neoblasts and their behavior *in vitro* with some aspects of the mechanism of the formation of regeneration blastema. *J. Exptl. Zool.* **164:** 407–434.

BRØNDSTED, A. and H. V. BRØNDSTED. 1961. Number of neoblasts in the intact body of *Euplanaria torva* and *Dendrocoelum lacteum. J. Embryol. Exptl. Morphol.* **9:** 167–172.

BRØNDSTED, H. V. 1954. The time-graded regeneration field in planarians and some of its cytophysiological implications. *In* "Recent Developments in Cell Physiology" (J. A. Kitching, ed.), *Proc. 7th Symp. Colston Res. Soc.* **7:** 121–138.

BRØNDSTED, H. V. 1955. Planarian regeneration. *Biol. Rev. Cambridge Phil. Soc.* **30:** 65–126.

BRØNDSTED, H. V. 1968. "Planarian Regeneration." Pergamon Press, London (in press).

DUBOIS, F. 1949. Contribution à l'étude de la migration des cellules de régénération chez les Planaires dulcicoles. *Bull. Biol. France Belg.* **83:** 213–283.

FLICKINGER, R. A. 1964. Isotopic evidence for a local origin of blastema cells in regenerating planaria. *Exptl. Cell Res.* **34:** 403–406.

FLICKINGER, R. A. and S. J. COWARD. 1962. The induction of cephalic differentiation in regenerating *Dugesia dorotocephala* in the presence of the normal head and in unwounded tails. *Develop. Biol.* **5:** 179–204.

HAY, E. D. 1968. Fine structure and origin of regeneration cells in planarians. *Anat. Record* **160:** 363.

JACOBSON, A. L., C. FRIED and S. D. HOROWITZ. 1966. Planarians and memory. *Nature* **209:** 599–601.

KOHL, D. M. and R. A. FLICKINGER. 1966. The role of DNA synthesis in the determination of axial polarity of regenerating planarians. *Biol. Bull.* **131:** 323–330.

LE MOIGNE, A. 1966. Étude du développement embryonnaire et recherches sur les cellules de régénération chez l'embryon de la Planaire *Polycelis nigra* (Turbellarié, Triclade). *J. Embryol. Exptl. Morphol.* **15:** 39–60.

LENDER, T. 1952. Le rôle inducteur du cerveau dans la régénération des yeux d'une Planaire d'eau douce. *Bull. Biol. France Belg.* **86:** 140–215.

LENDER, T. 1956. Recherches expérimentales sur la nature et les propriétés de l'inducteur de la régénération des yeux de la planaire *Polycelis nigra. J. Embryol. Exptl. Morphol.* **4:** 196–216.

LENDER, T. 1960. L'Inhibition spécifique de la différenciation du cerveau des Planaires d'eau douce en régénération. *J. Embryol. Exptl. Morphol.* **8:** 291–301.

LENDER, T. 1962. Factors in morphogenesis of regenerating fresh-water planaria. *In* "Advances in Morphogenesis" (M. Abercrombie and J. Brachet, eds.), Vol. 2, pp. 305–331. Academic Press, New York.

McCONNELL, J. V., A. L. JACOBSON and D. P. KIMBEL. 1959. The effects of regeneration upon retention of a conditioned response in the planarian. *J. Comp. Physiol. Psychol.* **52:** 1–5.

McCONNELL, J. V., R. JACOBSON and M. M. HUMPHRIES. 1961. The effects of ingestion of conditioned planaria on the response level of naive planaria: A pilot study (or: "You are what you eat??"). *Worm Runner's Digest* **3:** 41–47.

PEDERSEN, K. J. 1958. Morphogenetic activities during planarian regeneration as influenced by triethylene melamine. *J. Embryol. Exptl. Morphol.* **6:** 308–334.

PEDERSEN, K. J. 1959. Cytological studies on the planarian neoblast. *Z. Zellforsch.* **50:** 799–817.

SENGEL, C. 1960. Culture *in vitro* de blastèmes de régénération de Planaires. *J. Embryol. Exptl. Morphol.* **8:** 468–476.

WOLFF, E. 1962. Recent researches on the regeneration of planaria. *In* "Regeneration" (D. Rudnick, ed.), pp. 53–84, 20th Growth Symposium. Ronald Press, New York.

WOLFF, E., T. LENDER and C. ZILLER-SENGEL. 1964. Le rôle de facteurs auto-inhibiteurs dans la régénération des Planaires. *Rev. Suisse Zool.* **71:** 75–98.

6   **Segmental Addition in Annelids**

THE scientist, like the cryptographer, faces the task of deciphering messages. To the cryptographer, each different message is a source of new clues to be used in breaking a code. To the student of annelid regeneration, the bewildering profusion of species, no two of which seem to regenerate in exactly the same way, provides a rich source of clues to decode the cryptic mechanisms of growth. Unhappily, nature has embarrassed us with such riches to the extent that we have difficulty distinguishing the variations from the theme. It is useless to try to solve the problem of regeneration in each and every worm individually. The only rational approach is to look for features shared in common by certain representative species. This is a difficult task, for there are few generalizations about annelid regeneration that do not have their exceptions.

In the course of annelid evolution the mode of regeneration has been modified in many ways. Some worms can reproduce by regeneration following spontaneous fragmentation. Others, like the leeches, cannot regenerate at all. Between these two extremes are countless examples that differ from one another in such details as the number of segments replaced, the role of amputation level, and the extent of anterior versus posterior regeneration. Much of what is known of annelid regeneration refers to polychaetes, which are mostly marine worms equipped with segmentally arranged appendages called parapodia; and to oligochaetes, which lack appendages and live in fresh water or terrestrial habitats. Practically all worms in these two classes are capable of rather extensive posterior regeneration. However, the polychaetes in general can replace missing anterior regions more successfully than can oligochaetes, although this potential is more prevalent among those which inhabit tubes than it is in free-living polychaetes. It is tempting to speculate that among the former the anterior segments, which may normally protrude from the tube, are more vulnerable to amputation. If this is the case, then the ability to regenerate would have constituted a greater selective advantage than in other forms. Such an explanation, however, does not reveal the physiological basis for the difference.

To complicate matters further, regeneration is sometimes equivalent to reproduction. There are some polychaetes which reproduce asexually by budding new individuals out to the side on parapodia modified for this purpose. Others subdivide transversely along the length of the body into a chain of offspring in successive stages of completion. The famous marine palolo worm of Samoa, which spontaneously sheds its posterior segments full of gametes each year during the last quarter of the October moon, must subsequently regenerate those segments which have been lost by autotomy. In contrast to such remarkable feats of regeneration as these, the oligochaetes are seldom able to grow back more than only a few cephalic segments, and many forms are unable to regenerate at all in the anterior direction. Sometimes it seems that the mystery deepens with each new case that is investigated.

When a process like regeneration evolves, the least consequential attributes can undergo the greatest changes. The most indispensable aspects of the process, however, must remain immutable if regenerative potentials are to persist. It follows that by comparing a series of cases we should be able to identify the most essential characteristics of regeneration as those which exist in all forms. This is not to say that the variations and exceptions are not important. They reveal to us the latitude that can be tolerated in a regenerative phenomenon without

abolishing the process altogether. But by concentrating on funda-
mentals we may eventually be able to decipher the code and make
some sense out of this regenerative bag of worms.

Source of the Annelids in general do not rely exclusively on pluripotent reserve cells
Regenerate as a source of blastema material. To varying extents, different kinds of
annelids resort to the dedifferentiation of older tissues to supply cells
from which new parts may be formed. Presumably this represents
some sort of phylogenetic concession, perhaps an adaptation to the
greater anatomical specialization of annelid worms over flatworms.
To depend solely upon undifferentiated cells for regenerative potential
necessitates some mechanism for activating them and then getting
them to the amputation site. The communication systems demanded
for these operations probably become increasingly uneconomical
in large and complex animals. Although segmented worms still cling
to these methods, they have augmented them by devising means of
producing blastemas from local sources also. Hence, in most cases the
regenerated portion of a worm owes its origin in part to formerly differentiated tissues in the stump and in part to uncommitted cells.

The latter are of several types, the most conspicuous of which are
the neoblasts found in some oligochaetes, especially the ones capable
of asexual reproduction. Generally located along the ventral nerve
cord, these cells may number as few as one or two per segment. They
are very large cells with basophilic cytoplasm rich in RNA. In addition
to, or instead of, neoblasts, oligochaetes also possess smaller, more
numerous replacement cells. These are the blastocytes. They are situated mainly along the intersegmental septa, but may also be associated
with gut, muscle, or integument. In the event of an injury, they become
activated to increase in size, acquire an abundance of endoplasmic
reticulum, and hence develop into cells similar to, if not identical
with the neoblasts. Polychaetes have unfixed cells in the body cavity
which may play a role comparable to the oligochaete replacement
cell or neoblast. Known as amebocytes, or coelomocytes, these cells
likewise become basophilic after amputation of the worm, and actively migrate to the wound site, where they become mobilized into
the regenerating tissues. Herlant-Meewis, at the University of Brussels,
has made many valuable contributions to our understanding of how
regenerates develop from reserve cells.

The existence of these several kinds of reserve cells raises a number
of important questions, not the least of which concerns their prospec-

tive potencies of differentiation. Are they capable of becoming any and all of the types of cells ultimately represented in the regenerate, or is there perhaps more than one kind of neoblast or blastocyte or amebocyte, each with its own repertoire of possible destinies? What is the nature of the activation mechanism whereby reserve cells are stimulated to migrate toward the region of injury and take part in regeneration, and over how many segments from the level of amputation are they so affected? At least partial answers have been obtained to these questions as the result of irradiation experiments not unlike those previously described in connection with hydroid and planarian regeneration.

As in the latter animals, the reserve cells of annelids are also selectively sensitive to the deleterious effects of X-rays. Total body irradiation either destroys all capacity for regeneration, or permits the initiation of outgrowths that are unable to complete development and eventually degenerate. The appearance of such abortive formations is typical of species in which differentiated stump tissues normally give rise to their counterparts in the regenerate. This sort of morphallaxis can go on only insofar as it does not depend upon cell division. Eventually, however, it must fail.

When only part of a worm is irradiated and then amputated across the exposed region, the occurrence of regeneration is delayed pending the migration of healthy reserve cells through the X-rayed segments. In the oligochaetes *Lumbriculus* and *Enchytraeus,* posterior regeneration begins by outgrowths of irradiated ectoderm and endoderm, to be reinforced later by the arrival of neoblasts from unirradiated segments. Although the latter cells can give rise to mesodermal tissues, they do not become part of the integument or gut, nor are they able to form the nervous system. Such regenerates as these, in which the healthy tissues fail to contribute to the welfare of the unhealthy ones, are destined to die. Comparable experiments on the polychaete *Nereis* have yielded happier results. Here it is possible to obtain posterior regeneration from irradiated segments. At first the regenerated tail is abnormal, but when healthy amebocytes from segments anterior to the irradiated zone eventually reach the new outgrowth, tissues that had been X-rayed are replaced and a normal structure is produced. The amebocytes in this worm, therefore, are truly pluripotent.

Experiments involving localized irradiation demonstrate two things. One is that reserve cells often do take part in annelid regeneration. The other is that they are seldom totipotent. This means that if regeneration is to occur it must usually depend upon dedifferentiation and/or morphallaxis of local stump tissues. The question now arises as to just how versatile these tissues are. Does each give rise to its own kind, or can a cell originally in one germ layer become incorporated into another?

Most investigations of these problems, both descriptive and experimental, indicate that aside from the participation of reserve cells, the integrity of the germ layers tends to be preserved in the course of regeneration. Following amputation of the front part of a worm, the ectoderm and endoderm each heal over their cut ends independently. If cephalic regeneration is possible, then the ectoderm grows inward to form a stomodaeum which fuses with the intestinal cul-de-sac to re-establish the lumen of the gut. A similar process may take place in proctodaeum formation during posterior regeneration, especially when it occurs from the more forward regions of the worm. Alternatively, it is possible for the endoderm to heal directly to the ectoderm at the posterior cut surface of a worm, thus preserving the patency of the gut without interruption. This is the more characteristic procedure when amputations are performed toward the rear of the worm. These differences between head and tail regeneration are diagrammed in Fig. 32. The relatively slower rate of wound healing and regeneration at a worm's hind end has been suggested as a possible reason why the alimentary canal heals to the integument before the latter has a chance

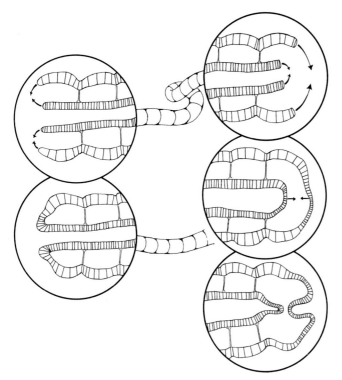

Fig. 32 **Contrasting modes of healing and regeneration at opposite ends of an amputated worm. At the posterior end (left) the intestinal epithelium usually heals directly to the epidermis. Anteriorly, however, each epithelium heals to itself (right). The intestine then grows forward as the stomodaeum grows back from the epidermis to meet it.**

to seal off the entire stump. In any case, it appears that the ectoderm plays a greater role in anterior reconstruction of the gut than in its posterior growth, which may explain why the digestive tract is less essential for cephalic replacement than it is for regeneration in the opposite direction.

These latter conclusions are based on the results of experiments in which a length of the intestine is removed for some distance proximal to the level of amputation. When compelled to regenerate in the absence of the gut, the head segments of annelids usually develop successfully even though the invaginating stomodaeum may find nothing to join. Clearly, head ectoderm can form its own mouth independent of the endodermal region of the gut. In posteriorly directed regeneration, however, the intestine is more important. Worms deprived of the hind gut often fail to regenerate at all, or else they form diminutive outgrowths sometimes consisting of little more than the terminal segment, or pygidium. It may be significant that in most cases the ectoderm alone cannot form an anal opening. Hence, unless one is produced by the remnant of the gut, the entire process of caudal regeneration is arrested or rendered very abnormal.

Here, then, is an example of the utilitarian principle of regeneration. When a structure develops, there exist certain dependent relationships between its component tissues such that one may be responsible for the induction of another, and so on. In the evolution of developmental mechanisms there has been a selective advantage operating in favor of those inductive relationships which are physiologically meaningful. In this way, energy is not expended on the production of useless structures, at least up to a point. A worm's tail is of no use without an anal opening, and we have seen that there are safeguards to make sure that such an improbable regenerate is not produced. On the other hand, the head of a worm is far more than just a mouth. It contains the brain, and often possesses various kinds of sensory appendages as well. From the point of view of evolutionary strategy, there would be less selective advantage in entrusting cephalic regeneration to the presence of the intestine than to other structures of greater physiological importance. Little wonder, therefore, that the presence of the nerve cord is so essential for anterior regeneration in annelids.

The Importance of Nerves

The role of the nervous system has been demonstrated by a variety of extirpation experiments, the simplest of which involves removal of the ventral nerve cord for several segments back from the level of amputation. This often inhibits or retards regeneration, but the results are not always as clear-cut as one would like, presumably because the nerve cord itself regenerates. To obviate this difficulty the nerve cord can be folded back on itself so that any tendency for it to regenerate would carry it in the wrong direction. Under these conditions more conclusive results are obtained, but again regeneration occasionally occurs from the wound surface deprived of its nerve cord. Probably the infrequent persistence of regeneration in the absence of the ventral nerve cord may be attributed to residual nerve fibers inadvertently left intact, or to axon regeneration across several segments to reach the wound site. It does not take very many fibers to promote regeneration, although suboptimal innervation results in the production of imperfect regenerates, which is what is formed after removal or deflection of the nerve cord.

Despite the less than ideal results of such experiments, it cannot be denied that the presence of nerves at the amputation site is important, if not essential, for regeneration to proceed. In fact, the longer the blastema is allowed to remain innervated, the more complete is its subsequent development, as shown by the results of delayed excisions of nerve cords from worms in various stages of regeneration. Yet despite unequivocal proof that nerves do influence regeneration in many cases, there are equally authentic instances in which regeneration can occur without nerves. It is impossible to generalize on this point without inviting contradictions.

In those cases in which nerves are necessary for successful blastema formation and development, what specific tissues in the amputation stump are directly affected by the nerves? The wound epidermis appears to receive the lion's share of the ingrowing nerve fibers, but this does not rule out the possibility that mesodermal innervation might not also be a prerequisite for regeneration. The endoderm, however, is apparently independent of nerve influences as shown so clearly by the experiments of Marcel Avel at the University of Bordeaux (Fig. 33). When the ventral nerve cord has been removed from several segments posterior to the level of decapitation, new head segments fail to develop but the severed digestive tract nevertheless regenerates anteriorly. Having no place to go, its elongating blind end turns back on itself. It never establishes an oral opening because the stomodaeum does not grow in to meet it from the denervated wound epidermis.

The problem of how the nervous system itself regenerates is not well understood. It evidently contains within it the capacity for its own replacement, but its derivation from ectodermal cells cannot be discounted. The ventral nerve cord regenerates by the differentiation into neurons of cells derived from adjacent ganglia. Whether or not this constitutes the only source of new nervous tissue is not known. Con-

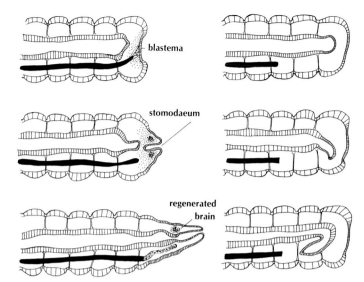

Fig. 33 **Left: Normal stages of head regeneration in** *Eisenia foetida.* **Ectoderm and endoderm maintain their identities. The new brain and ventral nerve cord differentiate from blastema cells. Right: Results of experimental resection of ventral nerve cord several segments back from level of amputation. Stomodaeum fails to develop from the ectoderm, but intestine regenerates anyway.** (*After Avel, 1961.*)

ceivably the cerebral ganglia may develop from undifferentiated blastema cells of uncertain origin, but in this as in other regenerating systems it is not easy to tell where a given kind of cell came from, especially when it is recognizable only by its lack of differentiated features.

We have already seen that the ideal conditions for annelid regeneration include the proximity of the severed end of the ventral nerve cord to the healing wound. Ordinarily occurring only at the place of amputation, this set of conditions can be experimentally simulated by deviating severed nerve cords to lateral wound sites in the total absence of amputation. In this manner it is possible to induce the formation of supernumerary outgrowths, the nature of which, however, is not always discernible. In cases which allow the identification of such accessory regenerates as either heads or tails, it is possible to learn something about how polarity is established in regenerating annelids. According to experiments along these lines, polarity is a function of nerve cord orientation. That is, the posteriorly directed end of an anterior piece of nerve cord induces a tail regenerate. Conversely, a head regenerates where the forward end of the caudal fragment of nerve cord comes into contact with the wounded body wall. Although the same region of an organism may have the capacity to grow either head or tail, what it actually regenerates seems to depend upon the direction of its subjacent nerve cord.

In addition to the local effects of nerves on regeneration, there are also systemic influences mediated by substances of neural origin. Cephalic regeneration in *Eisenia,* for example, is inhibited in the

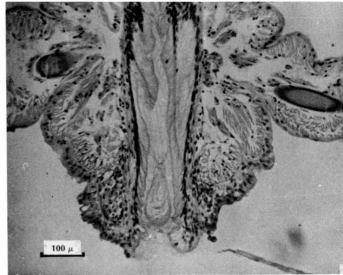

Fig. 34 **Caudal regeneration in** *Nephtys.* **A. Normal tail regenerate as seen in horizontal section 20 days after amputation. B. Nonregenerating worm deprived of its brain. Only wound healing has occurred where tail was cut off 20 days earlier.** (*From Clark, 1965.*)

presence of homogenates of brain and anterior nerve cord. In certain oligochaetes, such as *Allolobophora* and *Eophila,* caudal regeneration is known to occur only during diapause, when the worm is sexually inactive and remains curled up in an underground "cocoon" during the dry season. Active worms, however, which do not normally regenerate, can be induced to do so by removing their brains. This brings on a condition of pseudodiapause which permits regeneration of new tails, as well as new brains. The supraesophageal ganglion is therefore believed to secrete a neurohormone with gonadotropic effects which normally inhibits both diapause and regeneration. Only when neurosecretion is prevented, either by appropriate environmental conditions or by decerebration, does it grow a new tail. Indeed, complete restoration of the tail may also reactivate the brain and thus terminate diapause.

Paradoxically, the converse situation obtains in other kinds of worms in which neurohormones stimulate instead of inhibit regeneration. For example, in the polychaetes *Nephtys* and *Nereis* caudal regeneration cannot occur unless the brain is present. Extirpation of the supraesophageal ganglia totally prevents tail regeneration, or permits only the pygidium, or anal segment to develop. If decerebration is postponed until after amputation, the number of segments produced in the developing tail is proportional to the length of the delay. Implantation of ganglia into brainless worms promotes posterior regeneration (but even this fails to stimulate the replacement of head segments in these species).

These results suggest that the influence of the brain on caudal regeneration is of a humoral nature rather than the direct effect of innervation. Indeed, histochemical evidence has proved the existence of neurosecretory cells in the ganglia of annelids. In the permanent absence of the hormone(s) secreted by these cells, however, many of the amebocytes degenerate and the incipient regenerate is unable to grow by segmentation. Perhaps instead of calling them regeneration hormones, we should refer to the products of neurosecretion as "segmentation hormones." Their importance for development cannot be overemphasized, for it is only by segmentation that the regenerate, as well as the normally growing annelid, is able to develop.

Segmentation

Few annelids have a fixed number of segments. Those that do, either hatch that way, or reach their limit soon after metamorphosis. Subsequent elongation is therefore restricted by the extent to which each segment can enlarge. Most worms, however, continue to add new segments as they grow, and some may eventually become hundreds of segments long. In these forms, segmentation occurs in a growth zone located immediately anterior to the pygidium. It is in this region that extra segments are partitioned off from time to time by the development of new septa. Caudal regeneration recapitulates this normal mode of growth in annelids, which may explain why it is so much more prevalent and extensive than anterior regeneration (Fig. 35). There are innumerable species in which posteriorly facing cut surfaces can regenerate tails from almost any level of amputation except the most anterior ones. There are very few, however, that can do this in the anterior direction. Head regeneration, if it occurs at all, is usually a very limited phenomenon. It is limited both in the number of segments replaced and in how far back along the worm cephalic regeneration is possible.

Since there is no precedent in normal ontogeny for the augmentation of anterior segments, the regenerating head must improvise some

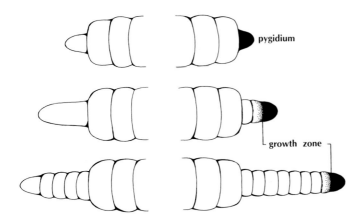

pygidium

growth zone

Fig. 35 **Segmentation in regenerating annelids usually occurs all at once in an anterior outgrowth (left) with no provision for the addition of more segments. In caudal regeneration (right) the pygidium forms first, followed by a series of segments partitioned off sequentially in the growth zone immediately proximal to the pygidium.**

mechanism of segmentation. This it does by developing intersegmental septa more or less simultaneously along its length. Once this is achieved, however, there remains no provision for adding any more. All too frequently the number of segments thus formed is hypomeric, or fewer than normal.

In earthworms, for example, no more than five segments ever regenerate anteriorly. If up to five segments are amputated, then regeneration is equimeric. If more than this number are removed, it is hypomeric. Between the fifteenth and twentieth segments, fewer than the usual five segments are formed, and behind these levels the capacity for regeneration is lost altogether. The polychaete *Chaetopterus* regenerates equimerically up to the loss of eleven anterior segments. If fourteen segments are amputated, it still replaces only eleven. But if fifteen or more segments are removed, nothing regenerates.

Transformation of Segments In cases of hypomeric regeneration, the resulting animal ends up with fewer segments than it had in the beginning, with the result that the normal numerical order of segmentation is interrupted at the junction of the new and the old. In many instances, the worm gets along all right without the missing segments. Some polychaetes, however, have evolved an ingenious means of correcting such discontinuities—a mechanism that involves the transformation of a number of the old segments proximal to the level of amputation into the kinds that were lost but not regenerated. This is what happens in *Sabella pavonina,* a worm consisting of a head segment (from which two rings of branchial tentacles sprout), a short collar segment, several thoracic segments variable in number, and up to a few hundred abdominal segments.

This worm can regenerate anteriorly from practically any level, but when it does so it typically forms only the head, collar, and a single thoracic segment as seen in Fig. 36. If just these three segments are lost there is obviously no problem. But if the worm is cut across its abdomen, then the reconstructed animal will be lacking all but one of its thoracic segments. It resolves this anatomic embarrassment by reorganizing some of its superfluous abdominal segments into thoracic structures, a process which N. J. Berrill described in great detail some years ago. This amazing metamorphosis is externally evidenced by the resorption of setae and other epidermal appendages from their original locations, and the reappearance of new ones elsewhere in an arrangement typical of the thoracic segments. Commencing anteriorly and progressing backward, each original abdominal segment undergoes this transformation in turn, until about half a dozen thoracic segments have been produced.

Fig. 36 **Stages in the regeneration of** *Sabella pavonina* **(dorsal view) amputated at the level of the abdominal segments. Only three new segments, bearing the paired plumes of branchial tentacles, are produced anteriorly. Some of the former abdominal segments, however, transform gradually into thoracic-type segments, as evidenced by the loss of lateral setae and the replacement of dorsally situated uncinigerous grooves with new setigerous appendages.** (*After Berrill and Mees, 1936.*)

It is a curious thing that the conversion of abdominal segments into thoracic ones sometimes takes place farther back on one side of the worm than on the other. This may be taken to indicate that whatever influences transformation acts unilaterally. Experiments have shown that if the branchial tentacles on just one side are cut off, not only do more abdominal segments turn into thoracic ones farther back, but they do so only on the operated side. Moreover, with repeated removal of tentacles, more and more thoracic segments are formed posteriorly with each successive round of amputation. If the reorganization of abdominal segments into thoracic ones were mediated via a hormone of cephalic origin it would be difficult to explain the one-sided effects that have been observed. Alternatively, it is possible that each thoracic segment formed might stimulate the next one behind it in a chain reaction. However, this hypothesis is not consistent with the observation that segments are skipped on occasion, nor does it divulge the nature of such intersegmental communication. Almost by default we are left with the probability of a neural mechanism to account for this interesting phenomenon, a hypothesis, however, which has yet to be put to the experimental test.

The Termination of Regeneration

Perhaps the most intriguing aspect of annelid regeneration relates not so much to how growth is started as to how it is stopped. As we have already seen, it almost seems as though some worms can count. They persistently count off a predetermined number of segments, particularly in anterior regeneration. They may not always count off the correct number, but the fact that they can do so again and again proves the existence of some mechanism to turn off segmentation at a species-specific point. Our problem, therefore, is to figure out how a worm "knows" when it has produced enough segments. Lacking any plausible answers, we can do little more than describe some of the better-known cases and then make a few educated guesses. Yet even theorizing would not be possible today were it not for the incisive experiments of Gairdner Moment of Goucher College near Baltimore, experiments which have attempted to explain how segmentation is quantitatively controlled.

Clymenella torquata is a worm common along the Atlantic coast, where it inhabits tubes of sand. This remarkable polychaete has just twenty-two segments and can not only count, but count correctly forward and backward (Fig. 37). Up to nine segments will regenerate in the anterior direction, replacing exactly the number removed. Amputa-

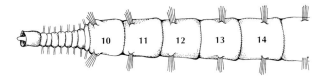

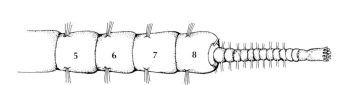

Fig. 37 **There are precisely twenty-two segments in** Clymenella torquata. **Anterior regeneration (above) may restore up to nine of them following amputation. Caudally, however, as many as fourteen may be regenerated (below). Amputation behind the tenth or in front of the eighth segment results in little or no regeneration, and eventual death.**

tion of more segments than this, however, is followed only by the production of short unsegmented outgrowths from those few worms able to survive such drastic bisections. In the posterior direction the number of segments to regenerate also equals the number cut off. In extreme cases, worms amputated behind the eighth segment have been observed to grow back precisely fourteen new caudal ones.

Perhaps it is significant that in this worm there is no zone of segmentation. Once the regenerate (anterior or posterior) has attained an appropriate size, its segments are marked off all at the same time throughout the length of the new part. The lack of a growth zone in worms having determinate numbers of segments is an obvious but interesting correlation, and one could argue that Clymenella does not face the problem of how to stop segmenting, simply because it could not make any more segments if it wanted to.

Quite a different situation obtains in worms which have a persistent growth zone. Earthworms fall into this category, yet in some forms the number of segments is fairly fixed. For this reason, Eisenia foetida, a common inhabitant of manure piles, has been a favorite experimental object in studies of how worms regulate their size. This species typically possesses almost one hundred segments, although the actual number may vary by as many as twenty segments either way. Nevertheless, Eisenia is experimentally useful because posteriorly it regenerates approximately the number of segments that may have been amputated (Fig. 38). If ten segments are cut off, then ten are replaced. If the worm is cut in half, then about fifty caudal segments regenerate. It might appear that this worm is equipped with a negative feedback mechanism that automatically cuts in when the number of segments reaches one hundred. This is not the case, however. If some of the anterior segments are removed, only a few of them are regenerated, as is typical for earthworms. Now, if segments are removed from both

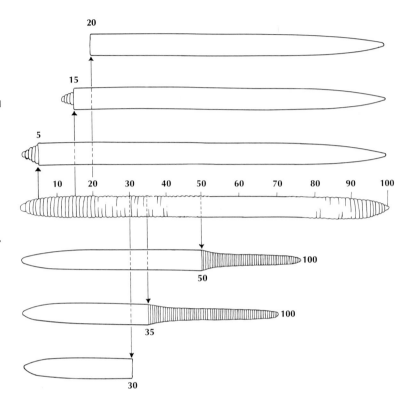

Fig. 38 **Anterior (above) versus posterior (below) regeneration in the earthworm based on analyses by Crowell (1937) and Moment (1946). Up to five anterior segments can be regenerated equimerically, fewer than five back to about the fifteenth segment, and none beyond the twentieth. Assuming a total of one hundred segments, posterior growth usually replaces the number amputated as far forward as the thirty-fifth segment. Ahead of this level, regeneration fails to occur.**

ends of the worm, the middle fragment does not produce any more posterior segments than usual. That is, it does not make up for the missing anterior segments by forming extra posterior ones. Under these conditions, therefore, the worm stops short of the normal limit of one hundred segments. Obviously, there is nothing magic about the number one hundred, but there is something special about the one hundredth segment irrespective of the total length of the worm.

Other experiments have shown that segments are not identical like the links in a chain. Each one of them has a measure of individuality, and occupies a specific position in relation to all the others. Thus, if some segments from the middle of a worm are grafted to the front end, they regenerate according to their original location, not their new position within the organism as a whole. From these and other experiments, we cannot escape the conclusion that completeness in a regenerate is an expression of qualitative factors operating in segment differentiation. Annelids, therefore, do not keep count of how many segments have been formed any more than I am keeping track of how many words there are in this sentence. Rather, they elaborate segments according to a predetermined sequence, and when the end of the message has been read out they put a period to it.

REFERENCES

ABELOOS, M. 1955. Le problème morphogénétique dans la régénération des annélides polychètes. *Bull. Soc. Zool. France* **80:** 228–256.

AVEL, M. 1961. L'influence du système nerveux sur la régénération chez les urodèles et les oligochètes. *Bull. Soc. Zool. France* **86:** 464–483.

BERRILL, N. J. 1931. Regeneration in Sabella pavonina (Sav.) and other sabellid worms. *J. Exptl. Zool.* **58:** 495–523.

BERRILL, N. J. 1952. Regeneration and budding in worms. *Biol. Rev. Cambridge Phil. Soc.* **27:** 401–438.

BERRILL, N. J. and D. MEES. 1936. Reorganization and regeneration in Sabella. II. The influence of temperature. III. The influence of light. *J. Exptl. Zool.* **74:** 61–89.

BOILLY, B. 1968. Étude histologique des premiers stades de l'histogenèse dans la régénération caudale et cephalique chez une Annélide Polychète (*Syllis amica quatrefages*). Considérations sur l'origine des cellules de régénération. *Arch. Anat. Microscop. Morphol. Exptl.* **56:** 167–204.

CHU, J. and S. PAI. 1944. The relations between natural fission and regeneration in Stylaria fossularis (Annelida). *Physiol. Zool.* **17:** 159–166.

CLARK, M. E. 1965. Cellular aspects of regeneration in the polychaete Nephtys. *In* "Regeneration in Animals and Related Problems" (V. Kiortsis and H. A. L. Trampusch, eds.), pp. 240–248. North-Holland Publ. Co., Amsterdam.

CLARK, R. B. and M. E. CLARK. 1959. The role of the supraoesophageal ganglion during the early stages of caudal regeneration in some errant polychaetes. *Nature* **183:** 1834–1835.

CLARK, R. B. and S. M. EVANS. 1961. The effect of delayed brain extirpation and replacement on caudal regeneration in *Nereis diversicolor. J. Embryol. Exptl. Morphol.* **9:** 97–105.

CLARK, R. B. and U. SCULLY. 1964. Hormonal control of growth in *Nereis diversicolor. Gen. Comp. Endocrinol.* **4:** 82–90.

CROWELL, P. S., Jr. 1937. Factors affecting regeneration in the earthworm. *J. Exptl. Zool.* **76:** 1–33.

GOLDING, D. W. 1967a. Regeneration and growth control in *Nereis*. I. Growth and regeneration. II. An axial gradient in growth potentiality. *J. Embryol. Exptl. Morphol.* **18:** 67–77, 79–90.

GOLDING, D. W. 1967b. Neurosecretion and regeneration in *Nereis*. I. Regeneration and the role of the supraesophageal ganglion. *Gen. Comp. Endocrinol.* **8:** 348–355.

GOLDING, D. W. 1967c. Endocrinology, regeneration and maturation in *Nereis*. *Biol. Bull.* **133:** 567–577.

GROSS, F. and J. S. HUXLEY. 1935. Regeneration and reorganization in Sabella. *Arch. Entwicklungsmech. Organ.* **133:** 582–620.

HERLANT-MEEWIS, H. 1964. Regeneration in annelids. *In* "Advances in Morphogenesis" (M. Abercrombie and J. Brachet, eds.), Vol. 4, pp. 155–215. Academic Press, New York.

HYMAN, L. 1940. Aspects of regeneration in annelids. *Am. Naturalist* **7:** 513–527.

KIORTSIS, V. and M. MORAITOU. 1965. Factors of regeneration in *Spirographis spallanzanii*. *In* "Regeneration in Animals and Related Problems" (V. Kiortsis and H. A. L. Trampusch, eds.), pp. 250–261. North-Holland Publ. Co., Amsterdam.

MARCEL, R. 1967. Rôle du système nerveux dans l'inhibition de la régénération antérieure chez *Eisenia foetida* f. *typica* Sav. (Annélide Oligochète). *Compt. Rend. Acad. Sci.* **265:** 693–694.

MOMENT, G. B. 1946. A study of growth limitation in earthworms. *J. Exptl. Zool.* **103:** 487–506.

MOMENT, G. B. 1951. Simultaneous anterior and posterior regeneration and and other growth phenomena in Maldanid polychaetes. *J. Exptl. Zool.* **117:** 1–13.

SAUSSEY, M. 1966. Relations entre la régénération caudale et la diapause chez *Allolobophora icterica* (Savigny) (Oligochète Lombricien). *Compt. Rend. Acad. Sci.* **263:** 1092–1094.

SAYLES, L. P. 1934. Regeneration in the polychaete Clymenella torquata. II. Effect of level of cut on type of new structures in posterior regeneration. *Physiol. Zool.* **7:** 1–16.

SAYLES, L. P. 1936. Regeneration in the polychaete Clymenella torquata. III. Effect of level of cut on type of new structures in anterior regeneration. *Biol. Bull.* **70:** 441–459.

SCULLY, U. 1964. Factors influencing the secretion of regeneration-promoting hormone in *Nereis diversicolor*. *Gen. Comp. Endocrinol.* **4:** 91–98.

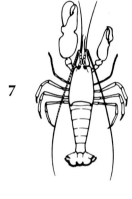

7   Molting, Metamorphosis and Regeneration in Arthropods

EVOLUTION is a two-way street. For each advance there may be an opposite, if not equal, loss. Every time a mutation occurs, the effect of natural selection is to make a decision as to whether or not it shall endure. A decision is a choice, and choices are made by the process of elimination. Phylogenetic advancement can therefore be defined not only in terms of positive adaptations to the challenges of a changing environment, but also by all the alternative specializations that might have evolved, but did not. In playing the game of evolution, a species can seldom have its cake and eat it too.

Arthropods achieved great things when they evolved from their annelid-like ancestors. But in becoming as highly specialized as they did, they abandoned the advantages of simplicity. The very complexities of their bodily organization were incompatible with the regeneration of heads or tails, not to mention long-term survival following decapitation. Although many of them have succeeded in pre-

Fig. 39 **Lobsters regenerate autotomized chelae as direct outgrowths from the stump. These three specimens illustrate regenerates measuring 2, 18 and 27 mm in length. Note the very early signs of segmentation in the smallest one (arrow). Even the largest regenerate is immobile, and will remain so until released from its cuticular sheath at the next molt.** (*Specimens by courtesy of Stanley Cobb, University of Rhode Island.*)

serving the capacity to regenerate their appendages, even this has had to conform to the arthropod way of life.

To grow, an arthropod must molt. This simple fact, made necessary by the presence of an inflexible exoskeleton, dominates all aspects of postembryonic development from mitosis to metamorphosis. It is not surprising, therefore, that the regeneration of a leg should depend upon the ability to molt. It follows that regeneration should also be subject to the same endocrinological controls as molting. Hence, in order to understand how lost parts are replaced in insects and crustaceans, we shall have to take into account the physiological mechanisms by which ecdysis is controlled.

For an arthropod to regenerate an appendage, be it leg or claw or antenna, there are special problems imposed by the existence of an unyielding exoskeleton. In the lobster a chela lost by autotomy is replaced by the straightforward outgrowth of the new appendage. Beginning as a diminutive papilla protruding from the wound site, the regenerating claw gradually acquires its typical shape and segmentation as it elongates. In larval lobsters, such regenerates complete their development in only a couple of weeks. Adults may require several months or more, depending on the season, during which time their new claws grow to lengths of several centimeters (Fig. 39). Enveloped in a thin, flexible cuticle, these regenerates are useless and immobile

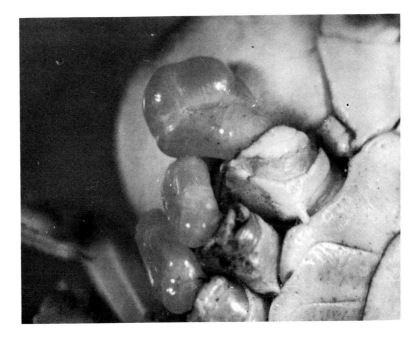

Fig. 40 Regeneration in the crab occurs within a cuticular sheath bulged outward by the new appendage developing inside. The regenerate remains folded upon itself until released from the cuticle at the next molt. (*Courtesy of Dr. Dorothy Bliss.*)

structures until the lobster molts. Only then do they develop a hardened shell and become functional appendages.

In crabs, the regenerating leg commences its growth inside the stump, but as its size increases beyond the dimensions of the old segment it tends to bulge outward (Fig. 40). Nevertheless, it remains ensheathed within a protective layer of cuticle which is not lost until the next molt, whereupon the regenerated leg unfolds and acquires functional competence.

In insects, the usual thing is for the regenerate to remain sequestered in the segment immediately behind the level of amputation. Figure 41 illustrates how this happens in a cockroach. In these protected confines the newly forming appendage can undergo extensive development owing to the pliant condition of its own as yet unhardened cuticle. To do so, the elongating regenerate becomes folded upon itself, not to be fully extended until finally released from its confinement during the next molt. At that time the regenerate unfolds, giving the impression that its development has been a sudden event. As in the emergence of a moth from its cocoon, however, only the final appearance is sudden, made possible by what went on behind the scenes prior to ecdysis.

In view of the impossibility of regeneration in the absence of molting,

Fig. 41 **Insects regenerate appendages inside the next proximal segments. Here a metathoracic leg of an eighth instar nymphal cockroach** (*Periplaneta americana*) **regenerates within the coxa and trochanter. Following autotomy between the trochanter and femur, the young regenerate begins to segment by the fifth day at 26°C. After about a week the slightly flexed leg lies partly within the old coxa, where space is made available for it by muscle degeneration. In two weeks regeneration is essentially complete, by which time the folded limb nestles in the coxal stump ready to be extended at the next molt.** (*After Penzlin, 1963.*)

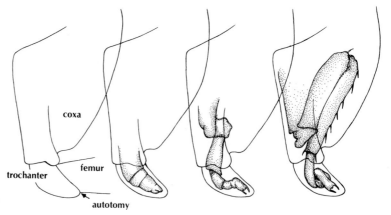

it follows that postmetamorphic insects, which by definition have molted for the last time, cannot regenerate appendages (but see below for exceptions) Crustaceans, in contrast, tend to keep growing and molting long after metamorphosis. As expected, therefore, they are capable of regeneration throughout life. But just because an organism can still molt does not guarantee that it can regenerate, for there are many arthropods that do not replace lost appendages at all, or else do so to very limited degrees.

Most of the research on arthropod regeneration has been carried out perforce on those highly selected species which happen to be most richly endowed with powers of restitution. Among the insects, the Orthoptera have been favored subjects for study, some of the earlier work being done on grasshoppers, walking-sticks and praying mantids, and more recent investigations concentrating on cockroaches. The Hemiptera, to a lesser extent, have also been useful, *Rhodnius prolixus* being the species of choice because of its predictable molting cycles. In addition, caterpillars, silverfish, and other kinds of insects also regenerate well. Crustaceans are in some ways less convenient to study because of their usually longer intermolt periods. Nevertheless, crayfish, shrimp, lobsters and crabs have all contributed generously to our knowledge of regeneration.

Morphogenesis Sometimes that which grows back is not the same structure as the one which was lost. This is called "heteromorphic" regeneration. In the walking-stick, for example, an antenna may be replaced by a leg, especially when amputated proximally. In crustaceans, mandibles have been known to grow in place of antennae, and antennae may sometimes regenerate from amputated eyestalks. Usually, however, the newly developed structure is qualitatively equivalent to the lost part. That is, the type of structure formed is determined by the nature of the stump from which it is produced. In an admirable series of experiments, Dietrich Bodenstein, of the University of Virginia, worked out the factors affecting morphogenesis in regenerating caterpillar legs. He found that if the entire leg is removed, a replacement may still be produced. In fact, it is even possible to excise part of the surrounding body wall along with the leg without abolishing the capacity for regeneration. Hence, the leg territory extends beyond the actual structure itself and tissues not normally included in an appendage may possess the latent capacity for leg development. Such tissues are specified for the kind of limb to be produced, as well as its orientation.

If, for example, the thoracic leg of a caterpillar is transplanted in place of an abdominal leg, subsequent regeneration is in accordance with the graft, not the site of transplantation. Furthermore, the axes of the newly produced appendage are determined by the orientation of the stump.

Fig. 42 **Reversal of asymmetry in the pistol crab. Left: Normal individual showing enlarged right chela. If this large chela is amputated, the smaller one then enlarges at the next molt (right) and takes on the morphology of the lost chela. The latter is replaced by a small chela.** (*Adapted from Wilson, 1903.*)

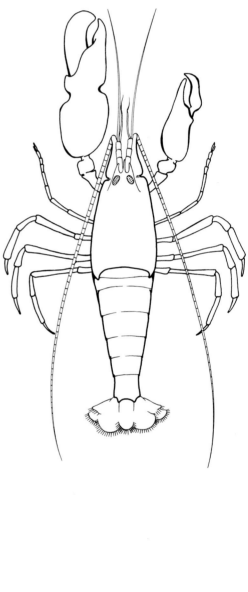

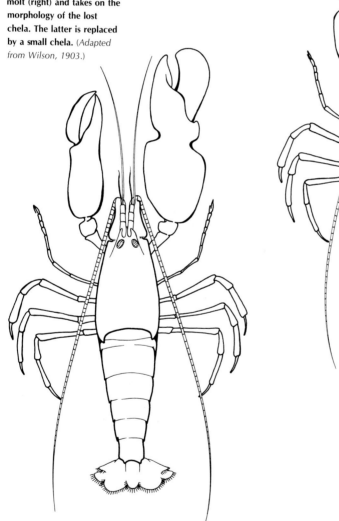

In certain kinds of crabs there is a very curious and poorly understood example of heteromorphic regeneration. The chelae are typically
of two kinds usually referred to as crushers and pincers, which are
distinguishable by characteristic differences in their "dentitions." The
crusher claw is larger than the pincer, a size difference that is especially
conspicuous, for example, in the fiddler crab. This asymmetry may
occur in one or both sexes. In some species the right chela is always
the larger one. In other species the left may dominate. Sometimes the
asymmetry is randomly distributed.

The Florida stone crab, *Menippe mercenaria,* is commercially
valuable because of the meat in its larger chela. Fishermen in Sarasota
Bay are in the custom of removing this claw to sell, and releasing the
rest of the crab. The next year, such animals can be harvested again
because they will have replaced the missing chela. It has been claimed
that now it is the opposite chela which is the larger, while the new
one remains relatively small. The same thing happens in *Crangon*
(*Alpheus*), the pistol crab, which uses its large hammer-type chela to
make loud clicking noises. Here too, what was originally the smaller
chela transforms into the larger type of claw while the large one that
was amputated grows back small (Fig. 42). This reversal works only in
one direction. Removal of the smaller chela does not affect the contralateral larger one during subsequent molts. And if both chelae are
removed, each regenerates according to type. Only a very few kinds of
crustaceans are known to exhibit this curious phenomenon. Lobsters
and most fiddler crabs do not reverse their asymmetry during regeneration.

Clearly there exists some kind of inhibitory communication between
the chelae in several species of crabs such that the potential transformation of the smaller claw into a larger one is normally held in abeyance. Not unless the large chela is removed does the former smaller
one become dominant. In doing so, its shape and size are altered
accordingly at the next molt. Moreover, it now exerts an inhibitory
effect back on the other chela which had once been dominant. This
unilateral, but reversible, influence is probably mediated by way of
nerves since denervation of the smaller chela inhibits its transformation
at the next molt following loss of the opposite large chela.

**Autotomy and Levels
of Amputation** In his studies of the crustaceans of the Antilles, the seventeenth century naturalist, Père Jean Baptiste Du Tertre, was much impressed by
the abilities of these animals to break off their own extremities which
had gotten into trouble. Such a means of self-preservation, he com-

mented, would come in very handy for pickpockets. This useful attribute in arthropods is made possible by a well-developed autotomy reflex. As a result of this, an injury or amputation distal to the predetermined breakage plane often causes the whole limb to detach. Regeneration therefore takes place mainly from the level at which autotomy occurs.

In some forms, however, it is possible to amputate legs at various levels without inducing autotomy. The kissing bug, *Rhodnius prolixus*, is such a case. Martin Lüscher, of the University of Basel, carried out a series of investigations on this insect to learn how leg regeneration is affected by the level of amputation (Fig. 43). He discovered that amputation distally, through the tibia-tarsal joint, permits complete regeneration of the lost parts at the very next molt. Cutting the leg through the tibia may also result in the replacement of all the missing segments, but it usually takes more than one molt to do so. The distal part of the tibia is capable of giving rise to better regenerates than is the proximal region. When the leg is disarticulated between the femur and tibia, regeneration is still possible but it is apt to be incomplete and slow to occur. Amputation at more proximal levels gives poor results. If part of the femur or trochanter is cut off, that which remains is usually discarded and little or no regeneration ensues from the coxa. In the legs of *Rhodnius*, therefore, regenerative ability decreases proximally and is all but absent in the upper half of the limb.

The majority of arthropods avoid the problem of proximo-distal gradients in the capacity to regenerate by concentrating the ability at one level of the limb. The cockroach, for example, regenerates best following amputation between the trochanter and femur. The land crab, *Gecarcinus lateralis*, can replace its terminal segment (the dactyl) by developing a new one within the propus, but amputation at other levels is usually followed by autotomy across a breakage plane in the basi-ischium. It is, of course, at such levels that the capacity for regeneration is greatest.

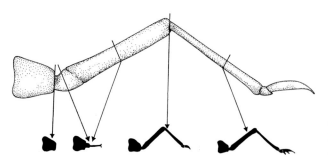

Fig. 43 **Maximum extents of regeneration in** *Rhodnius* **leg amputated at different levels along its length.** (*Modified after Lüscher, 1948.*)

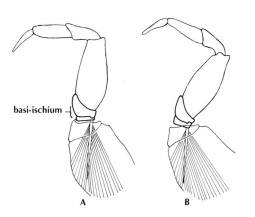

Fig. 44 **Successive stages in the autotomy of the crab leg. A. Normal leg in resting position. B. Contraction of autotomizer muscle forcibly elevates leg, pressing basi-ischium against dorsal margin of coxa. C. The pressure exerted on the basi-ischium splits it in two across the preformed breakage plane.** (After Bliss, 1960.)

basi-ischium

A   B   C

Autotomy occurs as the result of a nervous reflex initiated by injury to the leg. Distal amputation or pinching is often sufficient to set it off. Sometimes it is only necessary to insert a needle into a joint to stimulate the nerves and trigger the reflex. The effect is probably mediated by acetylcholine, high doses of which promote multiple autotomies when injected into crustaceans. Atropine and adrenaline, on the other hand, tend to inhibit autotomy.

The nervous impulse from an injured appendage of a crab, for example, is transmitted along sensory nerves to the ventral ganglion and thence along appropriate motor neurons to an autotomizer muscle which inserts on the basi-ischium. Its contraction pulls the latter segment forcibly against the dorsal margin of the coxa as shown in Fig. 44. This serves to exert pressure on the basi-ischium in such a manner as to break its two components (basis and ischium) apart across the plane of cleavage, neatly separating the leg from the body. There is minimal bleeding when the leg is severed at this level owing to the presence of a septum which partially occludes the circulation. Healing of the wound soon seals off the stump within which a new leg is destined to grow.

Histogenesis of the Regenerate It is characteristic of many arthropods to develop replacements for missing parts of appendages within the next proximal segment. To do this the tissues normally occupying this space must somehow make room for the regenerate that is to be formed. The principal tissue involved, of course, is muscle. In the coxa of the nymphal cockroach leg, Bodenstein has described the regression of muscle during the initial stages of regeneration. By surgically removing varying amounts of this muscle at the time of amputation, he discovered that the size of the resulting regenerate after the next molt was reduced according to the amount of muscle excised. This suggests that the muscle in the coxa is sacrificed for the benefit of the newly developing regenerate. These experiments do not reveal, however, whether the degenerating muscle constitutes a source of dedifferentiated cells out of which the tissues of the new leg will develop, or if the destruction of the muscle is complete and its reutilization a nutritive rather than a cellular phenomenon. In either case, new muscle fibers may eventually be seen to differentiate in the usual way. Uninucleate myoblasts proliferate mitotically, then fuse to form multinucleate myotubes. Once fusion has occurred, proliferation ceases and the differentiation of myofibrils can be detected. Where the undifferentiated myoblasts come from in the first place, however, remains a mystery.

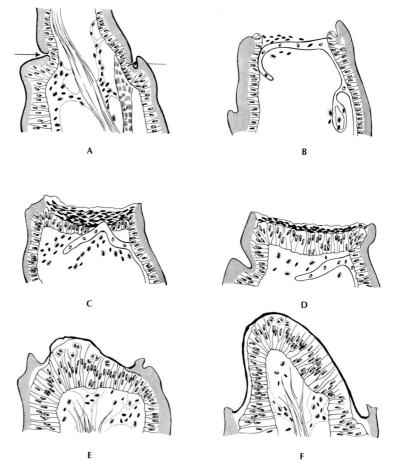

Fig. 45 Histological appearance of regenerating chela in a young fifth instar lobster (length = 1.5 cm). A. The breaking joint (arrows) lies between the basipodite and ischiopodite. B. Following autotomy the stump is sealed off by a valve. C. After one day a blood clot forms, and (D) epidermal cells close the wound by a day and a half. E. The proliferating epidermal cells secrete a thin cuticle on the second day, and at the end of three days (F) a distinct outgrowth is produced. (*After Emmel, 1910.*)

In fact, the whole question of the histological origin of the regenerate is not at all well understood in arthropods. It has been claimed that the new structure is epidermal in origin because of the apparent intimacy of the differentiating muscle fibers with the integument of the regenerate. However, this kind of circumstantial evidence is far from convincing, especially in view of the normal anatomical association between muscle and epidermis. In arthropods the muscles insert on internal extensions of the cuticle, called apodemes. It is easy to be misled, when examining the earlier stages of development, into concluding that these structures share a common origin. Histological examinations of cockroach leg blastemas by Heinz Penzlin at the University of Rostock seem to indicate that the muscles derive from sources other than the wound epidermis. There is good reason to believe that they differentiate from blastema cells formed at least in part from former muscle fibers which have undergone histolysis, and perhaps also from hemocytes. However, until appropriate labeling techniques can be applied to this system, the problem of precisely what tissues in the stump give rise to what ones in the regenerate must be consigned to the future.

The Role of Nerves For many years the possible role of nerves in arthropod appendage regeneration has been a point of contention. The reason is that experiments designed to determine whether or not nerves are required have not yielded clear-cut results. A denervated limb may seldom be entirely prevented from regenerating, but on the other hand it seldom regenerates normally. Therefore, in spite of the difficulty in explaining these equivocal findings, it is the consensus today that nerves do exert a trophic effect on regenerating structures. The lack of an all-or-nothing effect following denervation appears to be the result of technical problems inherent in the system.

Arthur E. Needham, of Oxford University, carried out an interesting series of experiments on a freshwater isopod, *Asellus aquaticus* (Fig. 46). Attempting to learn whether or not the regeneration of legs depended upon their innervation, Needham amputated legs and then isolated the corresponding ventral ganglia from the rest of the central nervous system by severing the intersegmental connectives. Regeneration of these limbs was no different from that observed in sham-operated controls. This indicates that the central nervous system as a whole is not involved in regeneration. Different results were obtained, however, when the nerve fibers were severed at the base of the coxa and the leg

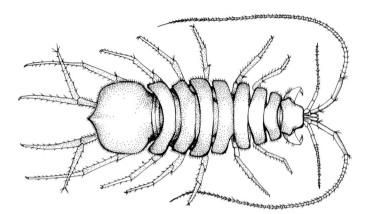

Fig. 46 Asellus aquaticus.

amputated at the autotomy plane. Regeneration almost always occurred from the operated stumps, but such legs were only about two-thirds the length of control limbs. Even unamputated limbs deprived of their nerve supply grew more slowly. At the next molt they measured approximately ten percent less in length than did controls. Obviously the local innervation of a limb is of some importance for its growth and regeneration, but it may not be as decisive as is sometimes believed.

It is entirely possible that supposedly denervated limbs can still regenerate because they may become reinnervated. It is important, therefore, to determine just how successful limb denervation is, and with this object in view Dietrich Bodenstein undertook an exhaustive analysis of the problem in the nymphal cockroach *Periplaneta americana*. First, he merely severed the peripheral fibers at the base of the leg, but this did not prevent the leg from regenerating when amputated between the trochanter and femur. Furthermore, such legs were capable of responding to stimuli, proving that new sensory nerve fibers had grown back into them from the neurons in the corresponding thoracic ganglia. Next he removed half or all of the ganglia from which the leg is normally innervated, but this also failed to work. Nerve fibers persisted in invading the limb stump from either the contralateral half of the partially extirpated ganglion, or from other ganglia in adjacent segments. These frustrating results serve only to emphasize the efficiency with which neurons can regenerate, and they leave the problem of leg regeneration as unsettled as ever.

Indeed, the prospects of ever learning if nerves are truly indispensable for limb regeneration are now more discouraging than ever. Recent investigations on the crayfish have shown that when nerves to the claw are cut, the distal fibers do not necessarily degenerate. These seemingly heretical results are based upon the capacity of such limbs to respond to stimuli at levels distal to the point of nerve interruption, a reaction that can only be explained by the survival of isolated lengths of nerve fibers until such time as they may become reunited with their proximal stumps. In the crayfish, the severed axons may survive for as long as a few months, perhaps by virtue of metabolites supplied to them by their enveloping glial cells. However, this interesting phenomenon is by no means universal among arthropods, for in cockroaches, at least, distal motor nerves degenerate within several days following their separation from the nerve cell bodies. Here it is known that nerve regeneration occurs by the conventional method of sprouting from the proximal stumps.

Despite the foregoing evidence, the possibility that regeneration might still be able to occur in the absence of innervation cannot be abandoned altogether. Denervation of legs by ganglionectomy in caterpillars and mantids has resulted in their regeneration at the next molt, but muscles fail to develop in them. Similarly, if appropriate ganglia are excised from moth pupae, corresponding appendages of the adult develop at metamorphosis, but they are empty shells devoid of musculature. It has been claimed that regeneration recapitulates ontogeny, for blastemas bear a close resemblance to imaginal discs. Structurally the two develop in similar ways. They both react alike to endocrine influences, and neither one can become functional until after molting. Now we can add to this list of comparisons their apparently equal dependence upon a nerve supply, a dependence which may find expression not in external appearance, but in their internal musculature, with which the nerves under normal conditions are most closely associated.

Molting

Thus far I have alluded repeatedly to the nexus between regeneration and molting. Necessitated by the prerequisite that the old cuticle must be shed if new structures are to attain morphological maturity, much less functional competence, this inseparable relationship depends upon the complex interplay of hormones by which the molting cycle is regulated.

Since there can be no regeneration without molting, it follows that the interval between amputation and the next molt should affect how much grows back. In some species, e.g., the walking-stick and the praying mantis, the extent of regeneration is proportional to how much time there is before molting. This is particularly well illustrated in *Rhodnius prolixus*, in which molting is not spontaneous as it is in

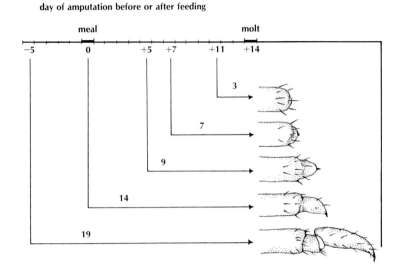

day of amputation before or after feeding

Fig. 47 **Extent of regeneration in the leg of** Rhodnius **following amputation through the tibia at various intervals prior to molting, which takes place fourteen days after a blood meal. Optimal regeneration of tarsal segments follows amputation five days before feeding, or nineteen days before ecdysis. Later amputations yield progressively less well-developed regenerates.** (Modified after Lüscher, 1948.)

most insects. It occurs after a definite lapse of time following a blood meal, and is therefore easily predictable. Martin Lüscher took advantage of the convenience of this postprandial molt to determine the extent of leg regeneration as a function of time prior to the next following episode of ecdysis (Fig. 47).

At 25°C, *Rhodnius* molts about two weeks after feeding. Hence, it is possible to time the amputations with reference to the insect's meal, which may be taken as the fourteenth day before the next scheduled molt. When a leg is amputated through the tibia only a few days prior to molting, that is, ten or twelve days after feeding, only wound healing has time to occur. But following earlier amputations, varying degrees of regeneration take place. With six to eight days available, a tiny claw forms on the stump of the tibia; in nine days a whole new joint develops; in eighteen days two tarsal segments are produced. Maximal regeneration occurs when about twenty days are available, that is, when the insect is not fed until five or six days after amputation. Beyond this interval, less perfect regeneration ensues, which means that if the feeding stimulus is delayed too long after regeneration has started, subsequent development may be interfered with.

Rhodnius, however, is an exception to the general rule. Most other arthropods adhere to an all-or-nothing principle in their regeneration-molting relationship. It is an interesting example of physiological foresight that an amputated appendage will not regenerate at all unless there remains sufficient time to complete the job before the next molt. In this way the production of a partly developed, and therefore useless, structure is avoided.

Scutigera forceps (Fig. 48) is a common household centipede with fifteen pairs of legs. It molts regularly at intervals ranging from sixty days at 20°C to twenty-six days at 45°C. When kept at 30°C it sheds approximately once a month. Under traumatic circumstances this centipede readily autotomizes its legs, which then grow back either completely or not at all by the following molt. When the intermolt period is thirty days, it has been found that regeneration will commence any time up to twenty-four days after the last molt. Six days before the next one is due there cuts in a mechanism to prevent the initiation of an enterprise that cannot be finished in the time remaining. Hence, in the intermolt count-down there is programmed a point of no return beyond which it is too late to start anything new.

The exact timing of this cut-off point varies from animal to animal, but the overall pattern is nearly always the same. In the cockroach *Blattella germanica,* about two-thirds of the intermolt cycle is necessary if leg regeneration is to be initiated. In the shrimp *Palaemon serratus,* a similar relative length of time is needed. In the isopod *Asellus aquaticus,* amputation must be performed not later than half way through the intermolt period. In general, those species with longer intermolt periods require a smaller fraction of that interval in which to grow new legs, for the absolute number of days needed for regeneration to occur is also an important consideration. When amputation occurs too late for regeneration to take place, only a small undifferentiated papilla forms on the end of the stump at ecdysis. Intermediate regenerates do not develop. Not until the next following molt, before which there is ample time for growth, will the papilla have undergone development into the fully differentiated appendage.

Not only does molting affect regeneration, but regeneration affects molting. It may do this in either of two ways. It may accelerate the next molt or delay it. In some crabs, for example, the loss of excessive

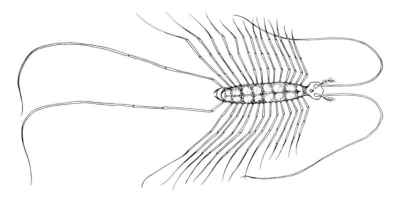

Fig. 48. Scutigera forceps.

numbers of legs may accelerate the onset of the next molt. *Gecarcinus* may autotomize one or two legs without affecting the duration of the intermolt cycle, but if six or more legs are lost, molting occurs earlier than expected. Similarly, in the fiddler crab, *Gelasimus pugilator,* molting occurs sooner when both chelae have been removed than when only one is regenerating. Also in the centipede, *Scutigera forceps,* legless animals molt in half the time it takes others. These reactions are adaptations to the pressing need to repair extreme damage to the body with all deliberate haste.

When only one leg has been lost, the crisis is less acute. Now the important thing is to regenerate a replacement if at all possible during the current intermolt period. Thus, it is not uncommon for the molting cycle to be prolonged when regeneration is under way thus providing a little more time to complete the production of new parts. Eventually, however, subsequent instars are abbreviated and the animal returns to its original routine. But if legs are repeatedly amputated during the life cycle, extra molts may be interposed before adulthood is attained. These and other relationships are especially intriguing in *Blattella germanica,* which has been intensively analyzed by O'Farrell and Stock at the University of New England in New South Wales. Their results are schematically summarized in Fig. 49.

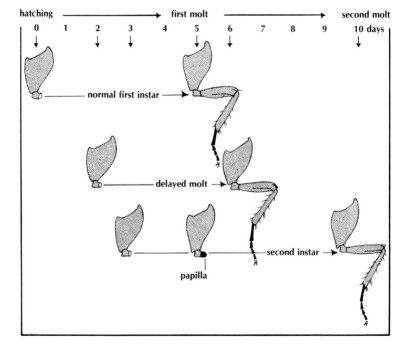

Fig. 49 **Temporal relations between molting and regeneration in legs of the cockroach,** *Blattella germanica,* **as analyzed by O'Farrell and Stock (1953). At 30°C, legs amputated between the trochanter and femur on the day of hatching are fully regenerated by the first molt at five days of age. If amputation is performed on two-day-old nymphs, regeneration is still complete but molting is delayed about one day. Amputation on the third day does not delay the first molt, nor is a regenerate produced until the end of the second instar.**

hatching ⟶ first molt ⟶ second molt

0   1   2   3   4   5   6   7   8   9   10 days

normal first instar ⟶

delayed molt ⟶

papilla

second instar ⟶

In its first instar, this cockroach regularly molts on about the fifth day after hatching from its egg. With such a short time at its disposal, amputation of a leg must be performed not later than four days preceding the next molt if a new leg is to grow. However, if a leg should be cut off on the first or second day after hatching, then the intermolt period is extended for an extra day or so. Thus, by stretching the rules a bit, this nymphal cockroach does itself the favor of providing the extra time required for regeneration. If two legs are amputated, the length of the delay is even greater than in unilateral amputation. Rules may be stretched, however, but not broken. If amputation is carried out on the third day of the instar, then the next molt occurs on schedule. In this case, of course, only an undifferentiated papilla develops. Hence, it is not amputation which delays ecdysis, but regeneration. Whether regeneration occurs or not, the system assures that a new limb shall be produced at the earliest possible time. If amputation is too late to give rise to a replacement in the current cycle, then the next cycle is begun without delay. Only in this way can the papilla that was produced the first time around be converted into a leg in the shortest possible time.

Molting is often, but not always, a regularly periodic event. In some arthropods, such as *Rhodnius*, its timing is controlled by external events (e.g., feeding.). In the land crab, *Gecarcinus*, it takes place only when environmental conditions are propitious. Dorothy Bliss, of the American Museum of Natural History, has made a very careful study of these conditions, especially as they relate to the animal's capacity to regenerate. In general, she has learned that molting most readily takes place when these crabs are given privacy and ample food, and are maintained under conditions of darkness, high humidity, and favorable temperatures. The opposite conditions tend to inhibit growth and ecdysis.

To complicate matters further, the regeneration of legs in the land crab occurs in two, make it three, distinct phases, as graphically illustrated in Fig. 50. The first is that of basal growth which always occurs during the few weeks immediately following autotomy regardless of environmental circumstances. During this period the regenerate develops qualitatively to the extent of becoming segmented and acquiring striated muscle fibers. But if the crab remains under unfavorable conditions, such as illumination, then regeneration soon ceases and the overall growth of the animal levels off. This growth plateau may last for months if the security of a dark and humid burrow is not provided.

If such a crab, having completed its basal growth phase, is returned

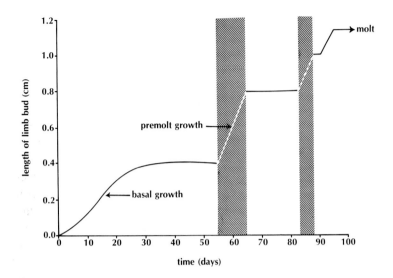

Fig. 50 **Rate of leg regeneration in** *Gecarcinus lateralis* **as affected by alternative light and dark intervals. Basal growth is not inhibited by light. Premolt growth goes on only in darkness (shaded bands). Terminal phase of elongation is again independent of lighting conditions.** (*After Bliss, 1960.*)

to the dark, then its leg resumes regeneration. This second phase differs from the first in that it is inhibited by light. Growth is turned off whenever the lights are turned on. Other things being equal, however, this phase of the regeneration process, lasting about three weeks, is marked by considerable premolt growth, accompanied by the continued differentiation of muscle, nerves and epidermal appendages.

There is a third phase, comprising the last week or so of premolt growth, which goes on in spite of illumination. Hence, leg regeneration eventually reaches a point when continued growth is no longer inhibited by light, and molting cannot be averted no matter how unfavorable the environment may be.

Endocrine Influences It must be abundantly clear by now that the intricacies of regeneration and molting are in need of some clarification. They must somehow be fitted onto the flow sheet of endocrinological factors which are responsible for ordering the events of the molting cycle. In both insects and crustaceans, schematically contrasted in Fig. 51, this sequence of events begins with certain neurosecretory cells associated with the central nervous system. In most forms these cells appear to be intrinsically activated at predetermined intervals coincident with the rhythm of the molting cycle. In some cases they are affected by external factors too, as in the case of *Gecarcinus* cited above. In others, such as *Rhodnius,* they react to nervous stimuli emanating from the gut when it becomes distended with a meal of blood.

The neurosecretory cells of insects are situated in the brain; those of crustaceans are consolidated in the so-called X-organ located in the eyestalks. The products of these cells are transported along axons to the corpora cardiaca in insects and the sinus glands in crustaceans, there to be released, or to promote the release of a second substance, into the hemolymph.

These hormones exert opposite effects in insects and crustaceans. In the former, the brain hormone (prothoracotropin) stimulates secretory activity in the prothoracic gland. In crustaceans it inhibits secretion from the Y-organ, and is therefore referred to as the molt-inhibiting hormone. Why it is that comparable hormones in these two groups have contradictory effects we do not know. One could speculate, however, that in crustaceans, where the neurosecretory cells are located in the eyestalks, their chances of being lost by eyestalk amputation would be greater than in insects, where decapitation would be the only way the brain could be lost. In a decapitated insect, of course, the jig is up. Without the brain there can be no ecdysone secreted from its target organ, the prothoracic gland. Assuming that head regeneration in insects is not possible, a headless insect therefore has nothing to gain by molting.

In crustaceans it is sometimes possible for eyestalks to regenerate. Were their endocrinological set-up like that of insects, eyestalkless crustaceans would be incapable of taking advantage of their regenerative potential because their Y-organs would not be able to secrete the

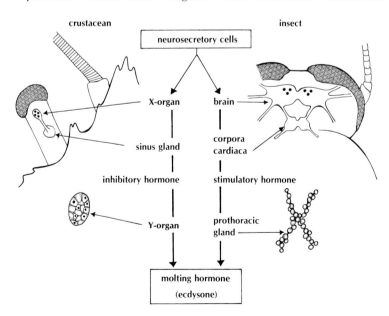

Fig. 51 **Flow sheet of endocrine factors controlling molting in crustaceans (left) and insects (right). In crustaceans, the X-organs and sinus glands release a hormone which inhibits molting. In insects, the brain and corpora cardiaca produce a stimulatory hormone. The molting hormone (ecdysone) is secreted by the crustacean Y-organ only when released from inhibition, while the insect prothoracic gland must be stimulated to secrete it.**

molting hormone in the absence of the X-organs and sinus glands. But as it is, the Y-organs are released from their inhibitions by amputation of the eyestalks. They therefore initiate a new molting cycle, and along with this make it possible for the eyestalks to regenerate if they can. In some species, eyestalks are actually capable of limited regeneration (although they sometimes grow back as antennae when amputated too close to the base). The import of this raises the possibility that even the X-organs and sinus glands may not be without some provision for replacement. If this *could* happen, even if it only took place once upon a time in some long extinct ancestral form, then the inhibitory nature of the neurosecretions in crustaceans would make sense; their endocrinological arrangements may have evolved as a strategy originally intended as a self-correcting feedback.

In both insects and crustaceans, the prothoracic gland and the Y-organ each elaborates a hormone which brings about molting. This molting hormone, or ecdysone, acts on the epidermis to set in motion the physiological processes by which ecdysis is achieved. In insects there is another pair of glands, the corpora allata, which secretes the juvenile hormone. When present in high concentrations, this hormone is responsible for preserving the larval or nymphal characteristics of the immature insect. Lesser amounts of the juvenile hormone promote the formation of a pupa in holometabolous insects. Minimal quantities permit molting to the adult condition by way of metamorphosis.

Given the fact that there can be no regeneration without molting, plus the fact that for a definite period of time before molting regeneration cannot be initiated, how are we to determine which hormone is directly responsible for stimulating the growth of lost appendages? The molting hormone, of course, is a leading contender for this role, except that it may exert opposite effects at different concentrations. Late in the intermolt period, when ecdysone is presumably being secreted in maximal quantities, no new regrowth of lost legs can be undertaken. Earlier in the cycle when regeneration is permissible, the prothoracic gland or Y-organ is probably putting out lesser concentrations of the molting hormone. It is tempting to conclude, therefore, that low titers of ecdysone stimulate regeneration, while high concentrations inhibit.

Alternatively, it could be argued that it is unnecessary to propose anything but an inhibitory action of the molting hormone on regeneration. Should this be the case, then regeneration would be expected always to take place unless precluded by ecdysone. This is not consistent with the facts, however. In adult cockroaches, for example, leg regeneration fails to occur not because there are no more molts, nor because the prothoracic gland normally degenerates after metamorphosis. Were regeneration only inhibited by ecdysone, then it should proceed in the adult even though the new leg would fail to become free of the adult cuticle. This does not happen. Even in the absence of the molting hormone regeneration in adult cockroaches is not even begun. This strongly favors the stimulatory role of ecdysone in insect regeneration.

Further proof of this hypothesis comes from the exciting experiments of Dietrich Bodenstein, who not only has found a way to stimulate supernumerary ecdyses in adult cockroaches, but has gone on to determine that regeneration can occur under these extraordinary conditions. There are several ways to induce molting in adults. If a nymphal cockroach is grafted to an adult by parabiotic union of their thoracic shields, the adult sheds its cuticle when the nymph does. Amputated legs in the adult are now able to regenerate. Similarly, if adult legs are transplanted to nymphs, they also regenerate after amputation when the host molts. Another way to stimulate molting in the adult is by ablation of its corpora allata soon after metamorphosis. This prevents the degeneration of the prothoracic glands which otherwise occurs, with the result that ecdysone can continue to be secreted and molting can still take place. In such animals, leg regeneration also occurs. Finally, it is possible to bring about extra molts in adults by implanting several prothoracic glands (plus the corpora cardiaca) from nymphs into the abdominal cavity of an adult. Here too, the regeneration of legs is restored by reinitiating the molting cycle.

Thus, it is clearly not aging that accounts for the loss of regenerative capacity in insects, nor is it the attainment of adulthood. It is metamorphosis and the cessation of molting cycles. Crustaceans and ametabolous insects preserve the capacity for regeneration into adult stages by continuing to molt throughout life. This they do by retaining actively secreting Y-organs or prothoracic glands which produce ecdysone in fluctuating concentrations so as to promote alternately ecdysis and, if needed, regeneration. But metamorphosis, for all its splendid advantages, is the end of the line for insects because the prothoracic glands degenerate. Metamorphosis is a mechanism of development presumably designed to turn out individuals highly specialized for reproduction. Hemi- and holometabolous insects owe much of their success to the fact that they evolved metamorphosis, but they had to give up regeneration to do it.

REFERENCES

BLISS, D. E. 1960. Autotomy and regeneration. In "The Physiology of Crustacea" (T. H. Waterman, ed.), Vol. I, pp. 561–589. Academic Press, New York.

BODENSTEIN, D. 1953. Regeneration. In "Insect Physiology" (K. D. Roeder, ed.), pp. 866–878. John Wiley, New York.

BODENSTEIN, D. 1953. The role of hormones in molting and metamorphosis. Ibid. pp. 879–931.

BODENSTEIN, D. 1955. Contributions to the problem of regeneration in insects. J. Exptl. Zool. 129: 209–224.

CAMERON, J. A. 1927. Regeneration in Scutigera forceps. J. Exptl. Zool. 46: 169–179.

COWDEN, R. and D. BODENSTEIN. 1961. A cytochemical investigation of striated muscle differentiation in regenerating limbs of the roach, Periplaneta americana. Embryologia 6: 36–50.

EMMEL, V. E. 1907. Regeneration and the question of symmetry in the big claws of the lobster. Science 26: 83–87.

EMMEL, V. E. 1910. A study of the differentiation of tissues in the regenerating crustacean limb. Am. J. Anat. 10: 109–159.

HOY, R. R., G. D. BITTNER and D. KENNEDY. 1967. Regeneration in crustacean motoneurons: Evidence for axonal fusion. Science 156: 251–252.

LÜSCHER, M. 1948. The regeneration of legs in Rhodnius prolixus (Hemiptera). J. Exptl. Biol. 25: 334–343.

NEEDHAM, A. E. 1945. Peripheral nerve and regeneration in crustacea. J. Exptl. Biol. 21: 144–146.

NEEDHAM, A. E. 1953. The central nervous system and regeneration in crustacea. J. Exptl. Biol. 30: 151–159.

O'FARRELL, A. F. and A. STOCK. 1953. Regeneration and the moulting cycle in Blattella germanica L. I. Single regeneration initiated during the first instar. Australian J. Biol. Sci. 6: 485–500.

PASSANO, L. M. 1960. Molting and its control. In "The Physiology of Crustacea" (T. H. Waterman, ed.), Vol. I. pp. 473–536. Academic Press, New York.

PASSANO, L. M. and S. JYSSUM. 1963. The role of the Y-organ in crab proecdysis and limb regeneration. Comp. Biochem. Physiol. 9: 195–213.

PENZLIN, H. 1963. Über die Regeneration bei Schaben (Blattaria). I. Das Regenerationsvermögen und die Genese des Regenerats. Arch. Entwicklungsmech. Organ. 154: 434–465.

WILSON, E. B. 1903. Notes of the renewal of asymmetry in the regeneration of the chelae in Alpheus heterochelis. Biol. Bull. 4: 197–210.

ZELENY, C. 1905. Compensatory regulation. J. Exptl. Zool. 2: 1–102.

8   Regeneration in Fishes

MAN'S interest in regeneration has seldom been purely academic—not, at least, since he first became aware of how unfavorably he compared with lower animals in this respect. How exciting it must have been, two centuries ago, when Spallanzani announced to the world how widespread were the powers of regeneration among animals. And how irresistible it was, even for the great Voltaire, to speculate upon the implications for man of the possibility of head regeneration as supposedly occurred in such animals as the snail. The exciting prospects of those days are not often voiced by today's overly cautious scientists. Yet the excitement of it all is still with us, unspoken except in the ceaseless search for the secrets of regeneration, a search which concentrates not by accident on other vertebrates like ourselves.

Future generations may or may not learn how to stimulate the natural replacement of body parts in themselves. The possibility of such a pragmatic breakthrough is like the apex of an iceberg. It will not become a reality until our basic understanding of growth and regeneration is great enough to bring it to the surface. Today's task, therefore, is to enhance this understanding of vertebrate regeneration, or the lack of same, by studying it in all its expressions. There is no dearth of regenerating vertebrate structures to engage our attention, but no group surpasses the fishes in this regard. And not without good reason. They are by far the most ubiquitous of the cold-blood vertebrates in both numbers and species. No other class of vertebrates exceeds the fishes in diversity of body form. Nor do any others possess such a rich variety of appendages potentially capable of regeneration.

Scales Few objects in nature rival in beauty the exquisite delicacy of fish scales. From the microscopic sculpturing on their surfaces to the precision of their arrangement on the body, the scales of fishes offer many a challenge to the curiosity of the biologist.

Not all fishes have scales, but in those that do they are laid down in the young fry according to an amazingly regular pattern. The first to form is situated at the anterior end of the lateral line, and others appear in an anterior-posterior sequence from there. The scales in this original row become flanked by additional rows that angle off above and below. Hence, the order of scale formation fans out posteriorly, as well as dorsally and ventrally, from the original starting point. The scales that develop in the young fish are all that will ever form unless the organism is called upon to regenerate replacements here and there. This poses a problem for fishes, many of which grow to considerable dimensions in the course of a lifetime.

One of the interesting things about many kinds of fishes is that their growth is without apparent limit—like the stories fishermen tell about them. Since their bodies can continue to increase in size throughout life, while the number of scales remains fixed, it is up to the individual scales to keep pace with the systemic growth by enlarging proportionately. This they do by adding to themselves at the periphery, which accounts for the occurrence of concentric growth rings formed at regular intervals in the course of their existence. These rings have long been used to determine the age of fishes by virtue of their variable widths in different nutritional states. They are wide in the summer and narrow in the winter. The recurring bands of thick and thin rings thus represent annual increments of growth.

Useful as they may be in recording a fish's life history, the rings on scales are not well understood from the developmental point of view.

Little or nothing is known about what physiological rhythms dictate the periodicity of their deposition, not to mention the frequency of such rhythms. Hypophysectomized fishes cease to produce new rings owing to the lack of growth hormone, but this may be only one of many contributing factors. The process by which cells lay down the substance of a scale is equally unknown, as is the mechanism of inscribing on the scale the circular ridges which delineate the rings. For anyone interested in morphogenesis there are many formidable problems here, problems that can be studied either in scales engaged in normal growth or in those undergoing regeneration. The two processes are much the same.

There are many different kinds of scales represented by the various classes of fishes. Some of them, such as the placoid scales of elasmobranchs, are formed jointly by the dermis and the epidermis. Here the homology between scales and teeth is most obvious, partly because the replacement of deciduous teeth has much in common with the regeneration of plucked scales. In teleosts, the scales are strictly dermal in location, if not in origin. The overlying epidermis, however, may also participate in their development since the protein (ichthylepidin) of scales has an amino acid composition more like that of the collagens of epidermal than of mesodermal origins. Formed from aggregates of scleroblasts in the young fish, cycloid scales develop at specific loci on the intersections of lines which may be imagined to form a diagonal grid laid out over the surface of the body. At these sites, a thin layer of acellular bony material is sandwiched over a fibrillary plate of collagen fibers. The cells responsible for the deposition of these structures remain on the surfaces of the scale. This population of scleroblasts may be augmented by proliferation of old and conscription of new cells to keep up with the expanding dimensions of the scale. Although this expansion is most conspicuous in lateral directions, the addition of each new growth ring around the circumference is accompanied by a slight increase in the thickness of the scale. The exact mechanism of scale enlargement at the margins, however, has not been examined at the ultrastructural level, nor has the regular periodicity of ring formation been explained.

As illustrated in Fig. 52, when a scale is plucked there remains an empty pocket in the skin where a new scale will regenerate *in situ*. Enough scleroblasts are left behind in this pocket to reorganize a new papilla within which the intercellular matrix becomes calcified as the new scale begins to form. The original layer of material in this case is much larger than that first produced in the primary scale. As a result, the arrangement of rings in a regenerated scale is easily distinguished

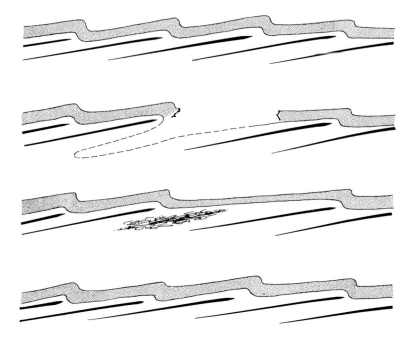

Fig. 52 Arrangement of scales in teleost integument as seen in section. When a scale is plucked, some of the overlying epidermis is also lost. After the wound heals, residual scleroblasts in the dermal scale pocket begin to lay down a new scale which eventually catches up with its neighbors.

from the pattern which was replaced. In the original scale, the rings go all the way to the very center. In the regenerate, there is a large area in the middle of the scale devoid of growth rings (Fig. 53). This ringless area represents the first plate of scale substance to be formed, and it reflects the relatively wide area of the scale pocket where scleroblasts remain after plucking. Once this primary plate has been laid down, subsequent increments are added in the usual manner. Except for its initial short cut, therefore, the regenerated scale grows layer upon layer in the same way its predecessor did.

It is easy to transplant scales. The scale pocket in the skin is a ready-made graft site into which the same or a different scale of appropriate size can be inserted. If care is taken not to disturb the fish unduly after the operation, the graft soon grows in place and may re-establish its vascularity within a day or so. Homografts, which come from other individuals, are rejected by the host, sometimes in only a few days depending on the temperature. If the transplanted scale has pigment cells in its adherent skin the first signs of graft destruction can be detected by the abrupt breakdown of these cells; this does not occur in autografts, which are derived from the same fish.

Transplantation is a useful technique for studying the regeneration and morphogenesis of scales. For example, if a scale of one kind is substituted in place of another, will its morphology be altered according to its new location? The lateral line scales of the goldfish have holes in them through which the lateral line canal passes. When plucked, their replacements are likewise perforated by the regenerating extension of the canal. If an ordinary scale from elsewhere on the body is transplanted in lieu of a lateral line scale, it too develops a hole after a month or two. Apparently the scleroblasts possess morphogenetic potentials specific for their native locations on the body surface. It also seems that any scleroblasts accompanying the transplants are of little or no value in maintaining the morphological integrity of the scale.

The latter conclusion is substantiated by further experiments carried

Fig. 53 **Normal and regenerated cycloid scales from the killifish,** *Fundulus heteroclitus.* **In the normal scale (left) the concentric growth rings extend to the center. In the regenerated scale (right) the central area lacks rings because this part of the scale was deposited concurrently at the beginning of regeneration. Subsequent enlargement occurs by laying down circumferential rings.**

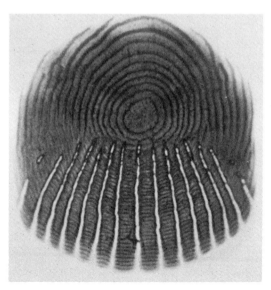

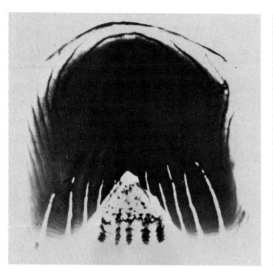

Fig. 54 **Regeneration of parts of scales in** *Fundulus*. **If a notch is cut from the proximal margin (left) and the scale is reinserted into its dermal pocket, the missing portion is replaced** *in situ*. **If only half of a plucked scale is put back (right), the absent half is regenerated.**

out on the killifish (*Fundulus heteroclitus*) in which scales have been transplanted to regions of the body other than the scale pockets. When grafted subcutaneously to the fin, or inserted into the eye beneath the cornea, scales invariably undergo erosion, presumably due to the paucity of scale-forming cells. Scales, therefore, are totally dependent upon the integumentary pockets in which they reside for their maintenance and growth. It might be predicted that scales themselves cannot regenerate but that populations of scleroblasts can.

The ability to repair defects inflicted on scales can be investigated only if they are put back into skin pockets lined with scleroblasts. After a suitable length of time such scales can be removed for examination. When scales are bisected transversely or longitudinally and only one half is replaced in the scale pocket, the missing proximal or lateral halves are replaced adjacent to the residual parts of the scales (Fig. 54). If half of the scale pocket itself is cut away after the scale has been plucked, the remaining half regenerates only half a scale. It does not form a whole scale of miniature proportions. The scleroblasts are therefore arranged in a mosaic pattern which is capable of little or no regulation. Within the scale pocket each cell or group of cells is responsible for producing its own part of the scale and cannot change its job for the sake of the organization.

Fin Regeneration Fishes have evolved various kinds of locomotory appendages which differ from one another in their skeletal support and their capacities for regeneration. The fins of sharks, for example, are supported basally by cartilaginous elements and distally by horny ceratotrichia. They cannot regenerate. In the African lungfish, the fins are slender tapering appendages composed of long chains of cartilaginous articulations. These "fins" do regenerate after amputation, and have been known to produce side branches from lateral lesions. Teleosts possess fins made up of ossified plates in their proximal regions which articulate distally with the rays (lepidotrichia) of dermal bone. These fins regenerate excellently.

The phylogenetic origins of the teleost fin and its rays have long been the subject of speculation among biologists. It has been proposed that the bony rays might be homologous with scales, since scales are lacking on the fins of teleosts (but are present on elasmobranch fins which do not have bony rays). Histologically, the dermal bone of rays and scales is similar, at least to the extent that it is often acellular. But if rays did evolve from scales, is each entire ray equivalent to one scale or to many of them? In the former case, it is conceivable that the ray segments might be homologous with the growth rings of scales, a possibility not without some appeal in view of how fins grow.

Like scales, fin rays grow by addition. They add to themselves terminally because the ray segments already formed cannot elongate. Fins therefore possess a generative zone along the outer margins which provides for their unlimited growth commensurate with the increasing size of the body as a whole. At the very end of each fin ray is a tuft of actinotrichia, which are fine hairlike structures of uncertain composition located in the connective tissue matrix. First produced in the natatory folds of the embryo, the actinotrichia persist throughout life where ray development occurs. Although they precede the bony ray in time and space, their significance is a mystery. One can only surmise that they may serve to support the soft tissues at the end of the fin until the rays become ossified.

Teleost fins are compound organs made up of numerous fin rays. Each ray is segmented throughout its length and branches dichoto-

Fig. 55 **Cross section through
the fin of a catfish. Two fin
rays are visible, each composed of paired bony com-
ponents. Nerves and blood
vessels run interradially and
in the connective tissue
sandwiched between the
two halves of each ray.**

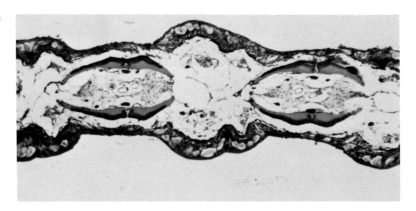

Fig. 55 **Cross section through the fin of a catfish. Two fin rays are visible, each composed of paired bony components. Nerves and blood vessels run interradially and in the connective tissue sandwiched between the two halves of each ray.**

mously as it elongates. The rays are actually double structures, consisting of paired components beneath the skin on either side of the fin (Fig. 55). Between these two halves of the ray are sandwiched nerves and arteries, and between adjacent rays there are veins embedded in the soft tissues of the interradial zones. Amputation proximal to the basal articulations of the rays seldom if ever leads to regeneration. Distal to this level, fins readily replace missing parts by virtue of outgrowths emanating from the stumps of the rays. Fins do not regenerate laterally, but if amputated on the bias the rays tend to grow out at an angle, more or less perpendicular to the cut surface. In general, the fin regenerates as a whole only because each one of its component rays can regenerate as an autonomous unit.

After healing has closed the wound on an amputated fin, a blastema develops by the accumulation of apparently undifferentiated cells derived in part from the loose connective tissue of the radial and interradial regions, and in part from osteoblasts associated with the ray stumps themselves (Fig. 56). The latter cells can be distinguished by their greater cytoplasmic basophila. They aggregate off the ends of the rays and later become intimately associated with the epidermis overlying the blastema. It is at this point of juncture, in the basement membrane between the epidermis and the osteoblasts beneath it, that the earliest signs of new ray formation can be detected (Fig. 57). The new fin rays thus develop initially along the two sides of the elongating regenerate, and only secondarily do they become contiguous with the old ray stumps located proximally at the level of amputation. As regeneration proceeds, the newly forming rays acquire segmentation at regular intervals along their lengths. Actinotrichia are present at the distal ends of the regenerating fin rays, as was the case in the ontogeny of the original fin.

Fig. 56 **Fin regeneration in the catfish** *Ameiurus nebulosus,* **as seen in longitudinal sections. At the left a blastema has developed off the end of a bony fin ray. The overlying epidermis is thickened. On the right, the regenerate has elongated and new bony rays are beginning to differentiate in the epidermal basement membrane on either side of the outgrowth.**

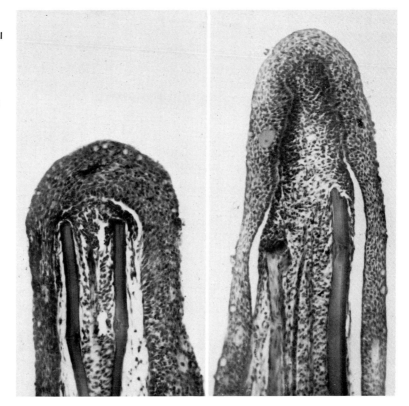

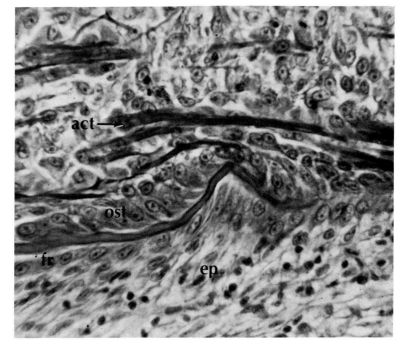

Fig. 57 **High powered view of incipient ray formation in the distal region of a fin regenerate. The ossified matrix of the new fin ray** *(fr)* **is laid down between the epidermis** *(ep)* **and an underlying layer of osteoblasts** *(ost).* **Actinotrichia** *(act)* **may be seen extending distally beyond the differentiating ray.** *(From Fig. 2 (p. 492) of Goss and Stagg, 1957.)*

One of the more conspicuous attributes of the fin blastema is the basophilic staining quality of the cells, particularly those engaged in ray regeneration. Presumably the cytoplasm of these cells is rich in ribosomes, and their future differentiation may well depend upon the RNA they contain. This hypothesis has been elegantly supported by the research of Giovanni Sichel at the University of Catania in Sicily. In the minnow *Gambusia,* he has shown that daily injections of ribonuclease into the abdominal cavity suppress the regeneration of the amputated tail fin. This confirms the prediction that blastema cells should be unable to differentiate in the absence of sufficient RNA to make the required proteins, and that unless cells differentiate organs cannot develop.

In contemplating the course of events in fin regeneration, one wonders to what extent the blastema depends upon the tissues in the stump to determine what it shall become. The bony fin rays, being the dominant formed elements in the appendage, are obviously potential sources of morphogenetic information for the regenerate. This is diagrammatically outlined in Fig. 58. If one of the two halves of a ray is entirely removed from the fin its counterpart in the regenerate does not develop. Such a fin grows out with only the half of the ray corresponding to the one left intact. However, if the ray is not completely excised so that part of its stump remains behind, then regeneration commences at that level and only later does it catch up with the blas-

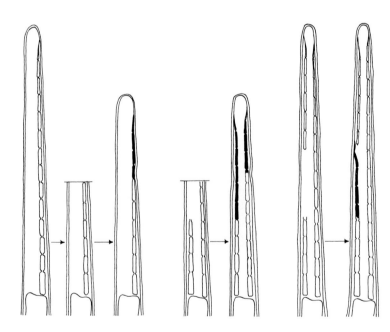

Fig. 58 **Morphogenetic influence of ray stumps on the regeneration of fin rays. If half an entire ray is removed prior to amputation of the fin (left), the latter regenerates minus the missing ray. If several segments of half a ray are extirpated proximal to the level of fin amputation (middle), the operated part of the ray grows out belatedly into the fin regenerate. If several segments of a ray are removed from an unamputated fin (right), they are regenerated in a proximo-distal direction.**

tema that forms farther out where the fin as a whole may have been amputated. It can be concluded, therefore, that ray regeneration cannot proceed unless part of the original ray is present as a source of osteoblasts. If this is true, then the cells of the blastema are not so fully dedifferentiated as their appearances might lead one to believe.

Fin rays also regenerate in the unamputated fin. This can be observed under two conditions. If a hole is cut in the middle of a fin, or if a length of ray is picked out of an otherwise intact fin, the missing parts are also regenerated. In the former case, the type of response depends upon the size of the hole. Large holes, several rays across, regenerate by forming a blastema along the proximal edge which grows out in the usual manner. In rare cases, regeneration may also occur from the distal margin, in which case new fin tissue grows proximally. Therefore, it is possible for a fin to grow new parts in opposite directions at the same time, but despite the reversal of polarity such outgrowths are always morphologically distal with respect to the cut surfaces from which they are produced.

In the case of smaller holes, the healing process usually fills in the aperture before ray regeneration gets underway. When it finally occurs, replacement extends in the distal direction from the proximal stump, eventually to meet the other end of the ray before proximally directed regeneration from the latter begins. Sometimes growth proceeds in both directions, but always sooner and faster from the basal end. The same thing happens when only a few segments of half a ray are removed instead of the full thickness of the fin. Sometimes, however, regenerating rays fail to meet up with their more distal segments. When this happens, they may grow on past into the adjacent interradial region.

Ray regeneration always occurs in the same way, whether in the outgrowths from amputated fins, or within the tissues of the fin following extirpation of parts of rays. New rays invariably develop in the epidermal basement membrane. Aside from blastema formation, the only difference to be found between fin regeneration and ray regeneration, is that actinotrichia are not produced in association with the latter phenomenon. Whatever their role may be, actinotrichia appear not to be necessary for ray regeneration alone, but are somehow involved in the replacement of the fin as a whole.

Fin regeneration can be investigated not only by means of deletion experiments as above, but also by the opposite technique of putting extra rays into the fin. It is possible, with a little care, to insert a length of bony ray into a subcutaneous tunnel made in the interradial region of the fin. When subsequently amputated through such transplants, the fin regenerates correspondingly supernumerary rays. This is compelling evidence that rays induce their own regeneration. Not only that, but they also determine the kind of ray to be produced. For example, in the goldfish tail some rays are long and others are short. If long ones are grafted in between short ones, or vice versa, their regeneration will be true to type. That is, long rays grow faster and farther than short rays, no matter where they may be located in the fin.

The extent of fin regeneration, of course, depends upon how much was cut off in the first place. Fish fins grow back to their original dimensions before they stop regenerating and resume the slower rate of elongation to keep up with normal body growth. However, the rate

Fig. 59 **Rate of regeneration in the long, slender pelvic fins of the gourami,** *Trichogaster,* **following amputation at different levels along their lengths. The more fin cut off, the faster it regenerates. Although all fins eventually grow back to their original lengths, those from more distal levels of amputation complete regeneration earlier.** (*After Tassava and Goss, 1966.*)

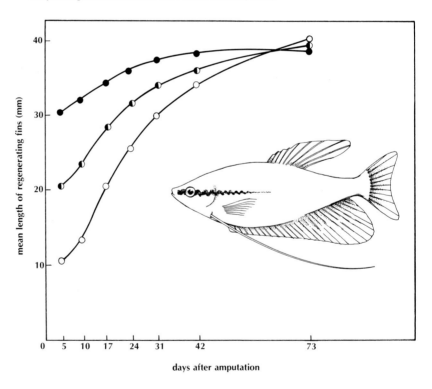

at which fins regenerate is a function of the level of amputation. Early in this century, Thomas Hunt Morgan showed that if a fin is amputated diagonally, the more proximally severed rays grow faster than do those amputated distally. Thus, they all reattain their original lengths at approximately the same time. A fin, however, does not elongate at the same rate throughout the course of its regeneration. After a slow start, when healing and blastema formation are going on, the rate of regeneration soon reaches a maximum and very gradually declines thereafter (Fig. 59). Regardless of how much of the fin has been amputated, the same pattern of regeneration is followed on very much the same time scale. The only factor to vary significantly is the magnitude of the growth rate, which turns out to be greater at the more proximal levels of amputation.

Why it is that proximal levels of a fin grow faster than distal ones we do not know. It is not correlated with the cross-sectional area of the stump, nor with the percentage of the fin amputated. Possibly the decreasing growth rate along the length of a fin may be a function of its innervation or blood supply; or perhaps the explanation resides in some subtle quality inherent in the cells at different positions in the fin. This fascinating problem has thus far eluded all attempts to fathom the mysteries of how growth rates are regulated.

At each level in a fin the tissues seem to be coded for exactly what lies distal to them. Upon amputation this is precisely what they reproduce. Their information content, however, is qualitative as well as quantitative, for they always produce the correct kinds of things in just the right locations. This is most dramatically illustrated in the case of the pigment patterns on fins. If a fin has a black spot on it, for example, which may be completely removed by amputation, the regenerating fin will reconstitute a replica of the original spot. In the zebra fish, *Brachydanio*, fin regeneration occurs in technicolor (Fig. 60). The anal fin of this fish has red, black, and yellow stripes running horizontally across it at nearly right angles to the fin rays. Yet when these stripes are removed by amputation, new ones differentiate as the fin itself regenerates. They do so by virtue of the invasion of the regenerate by undifferentiated pigment cell precursors. When these cells arrive at their proper locations they then become pigmented accordingly. It is a moot question, however, whether the color of pigmentation is determined by the location of the cell in the fin, or whether the distance a cell migrates along the rays is conditioned by the kind of pigment cell precursor it has already been determined to become.

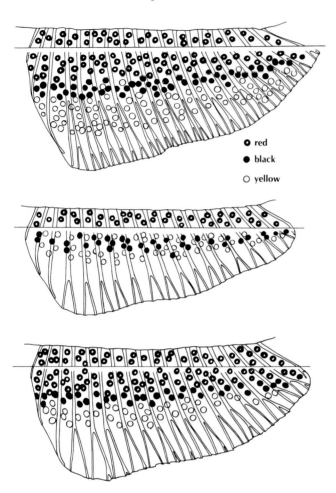

Fig. 60 **Restitution of color pattern in the regenerating anal fin of the zebra fish. Three horizontal stripes are normally present on the fin owing to the existence of red, black and yellow pigment cells. When these are lost by amputation, the new fin becomes repopulated by pigment cells deployed in a stripe pattern that faithfully reproduces the original colors.** (*After Goodrich and Greene, 1959.*)

○ red

● black

○ yellow

Hormonal Effects on Fins   In addition to the interactions of local influences in shaping the morphology of the fin, there are endocrine factors which also control regeneration. As in certain other vertebrate appendages, the pituitary gland plays an important role in the mechanisms of fin replacement. Although hypophysectomy is known to prevent the regeneration of amputated fins, neither the hormone(s) involved nor the mechanisms of action have been elucidated. Antithyroid drugs tend to retard fin regeneration, while thyroxine and thryotropic hormone enhance the rate of regeneration.

Of particular interest is the influence of sex hormones which modulate the development of fins serving as secondary sexual characters in the male *Platypoecilus*, some of the rays of the anal fin metamorphose at maturity into a copulatory organ, the gonopodium. The affected rays are longer and wider than normal and differentiate elaborate serrations near their ends. The anal fins of immature fishes and adult females lack gonopodia, as do those of adult males castrated before sexual maturity. Once a male has differentiated a gonopodium its capacity to regenerate the anal fin is markedly suppressed. Immature fishes and adult females, in contrast, are capable of regeneration. This loss of regenerative capacity is not directly caused by male sex hormones, however, for amputated gonopodia of castrated

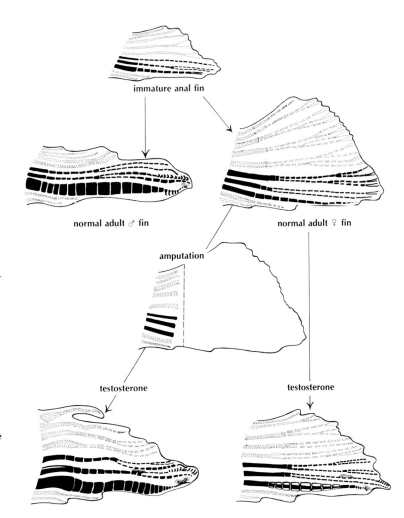

Fig. 61 **Influence of sex hormones on anal fin morphogenesis in** *Platypoecilus.* **In the normally maturing male fish the third, fourth, and fifth anal fin rays develop into a gonopodium (black). Females lack this structure, but can be modified in that direction by treatment with testosterone. Conversion to the male type of fin is even more complete if the female anal fin is first amputated and then allowed to regenerate under the influence of testosterone.** (*After Grobstein, 1940, 1942.*)

immature anal fin

normal adult ♂ fin   normal adult ♀ fin

amputation

testosterone   testosterone

adult males likewise fail to regenerate. Evidently, it is the highly specialized condition of the gonopodium, rather than the sex hormone
originally responsible for its differentiation, which somehow precludes
regeneration. Clifford Grobstein, who did much of the research along
these lines, has emphasized the parallel between this and the case of
the postmetamorphic decline in anuran limb regeneration. Although
different hormones may be acting on different extremities in different
animals, the similarities are inescapable.

Administration of testosterone to adult females or to adult males
castrated before maturity brings about a limited masculinization of the
anal fin in the direction of gonopodial differentiation (Fig. 61). A much
better response is elicited if the anal fins of such fishes are amputated
prior to the injection of testosterone. Hence, the hormone can exert
its influence on fin morphogenesis to a greater extent when the fin is
regenerating than when it is not. In neither case, however, does the
degree of development in the induced gonopodium equal that of the
normal male organ. Nevertheless, subsequent regenerative capacity
is diminished to the extent that these fins are modified by the hormonal
treatment.

Neural Control of There are certain aspects of vertebrate regeneration of such over-
Fin Regeneration whelming importance that they turn up in one appendage after another. One of the most intriguing of these factors is innervation, which
is so frequently found to be indispensable for successful regeneration
in almost all vertebrate extremities. The fin is no exception. Supplied
by branches of the first three spinal nerves, the teleost pectoral fin can
be effectively denervated by interruption of the brachial plexus. Some
of these nerves supply the muscles in the basal regions of the fin;
others run out into the nonmuscular regions in between the two halves
of each fin ray.

The denervated fin is totally incapable of regeneration (Fig. 62).
Wound healing occurs following amputation, but the epidermis does
not become thickened over the stump as in normally innervated fins.
In the absence of blastema formation, the tissues proximal to the level
of amputation become disorganized, a process closely resembling
the dedifferentiation of the cells which normally precedes the onset
of growth. However, in this case the disorganization gives way to
regression, especially in the soft tissues of the interradial regions.
Although evidence for erosion of the fin ray stumps is commonly en-

Fig. 62 **Denervated fins do not regenerate. Here, the two pectoral fins of a catfish were amputated transversely and the nerve supply to the one on the left was cut. After two weeks, the nerveless fin is seen to be regressing in the soft tissues between the rays. The control fin (right) has regenerated normally.** *(From Figs. 3 and 4 (p. 493) of Goss and Stagg, 1957.)*

countered, the more so for the occurrence of osteoclasts, their resistance to destruction seems to be the main factor preventing the complete resorption of the whole fin in the absence of nerves.

Regeneration is a complex phenomenon involving the coordinated development of a number of different tissues, each of which must be reconstituted in harmony if the entire organ is to be replaced. The overall process may be dependent upon nerves, as in the case of the fin, but this does not necessarily mean that the regeneration of each component part is equally impossible under nerveless conditions. To test this in the case of individual bony rays, fins can be denervated and parts of the rays resected. Ray regeneration fails to occur under these conditions. It may be recalled that normally innervated fin rays do regenerate, but usually only from the distally facing surfaces of the proximal stumps. The absent, or at best delayed, regeneration in the opposite direction from the distal stump of the ray may be attributable to the inevitable denervation of that portion caused by the extirpation of more proximal segments. To the extent that reinnervation may occur from the other half of the operated ray, or even from adjacent rays, dilatory regeneration may ensue. A similar explanation may account for the even rarer regeneration, in reverse polarity, from the distal margins of holes cut in fins.

Much more is known about the role of nerves in regeneration from studies on amphibians than on fishes, but the fins of fishes provide certain unique opportunities for investigation not offered in other classes of vertebrates. Fishes of many kinds, as has been previously noted, keep growing indefinitely. Their fins elongate by adding new ray segments onto the ends of those already formed. The mechanisms of normal and regenerative fin growth are therefore remarkably alike. Indeed, as far as we know, they are identical in every detail except rate of growth. It would be surprising if they were not identical processes, inasmuch as regeneration never ceases altogether, but merges imperceptibly with the normal process of fin growth. This is precisely why the fin is so potentially valuable to us, for it could provide an answer to the mystery of why nerves are required for regeneration, but not for the normal ontogeny of extremities (at least in amphibians). The crucial experiment has apparently not been performed, namely, to learn if normal fin growth can continue after the nerves have been severed. If it can, then we must presume that nerves are required only during the earlier phases of regeneration. If the intact fin cannot elongate without nerves, then regeneration in fins can be considered equivalent to normal ontogeny, in which case we would want to know just how early in ontogeny the developing fin becomes dependent upon its innervation. Sometimes what we do not know is more challenging than what we do.

Taste Barbels Nature was kind to us when she provided certain fishes with barbels. These tentacular appendages occur on the jaws of such fishes as the cod and the sturgeon, but reach their greatest dimensions in various species of catfish, where they serve as gustatory and/or tactile organs. The anatomical simplicity of catfish taste barbels, coupled with their wonderful faculty to regenerate, have given us a rare opportunity to analyze the histogenesis and physiology of how new outgrowths are produced. It will be possible to interpret the regeneration of other vertebrate structures, previously discussed or subsequently to be considered, in a more realistic perspective in view of what the taste barbel has to teach us.

In the catfish *Ameiurus nebulosus,* there are eight barbels of various

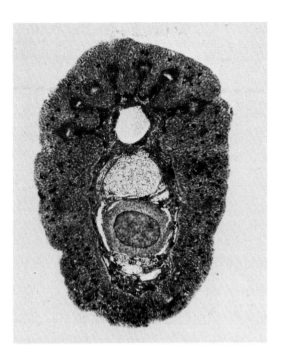

Fig. 63 **Cross section of a catfish taste barbel. Taste buds are arranged in the epidermis around the front of the barbel at the top of the picture. Internally (top to bottom) there is a large artery, a nerve and a rod of supporting cartilage.**

lengths arranged around the mouth. In certain tropical catfish, some of the barbels may be longer than the entire fish. In other species, the barbels may be elaborately branched. Their epidermis is studded with numerous taste buds which are innervated by branches of the seventh cranial nerve. Internally, as revealed in cross section (Fig. 63), the barbel consists of little more than nerves, blood vessels, and a supporting rod of cartilage, the latter being ensheathed in an unusually thick perichondrium.

The amputated barbel promptly regenerates by forming a terminal blastema (Fig. 64), the cells of which differentiate into an extension of the transected cartilaginous rod. The nerves and blood vessels grow out with the regenerate, and new taste buds differentiate in the epidermis. Histologically, it appears that the blastema is derived mostly, if not exclusively, from chondroblasts. The perichondrium next to the level of amputation becomes markedly thinner as its cells migrate distally into the blastema. Except for meager amounts of connective tissue proper, there is little other mesodermal tissue in the barbel to yield potential blastema cells.

The chondrogenic source of blastema cells finds experimental support in barbels from which the cartilaginous rod has been removed. This can be achieved by cutting the rod at its proximal end and pulling

Fig. 64 **Regenerating versus nonregenerating taste barbels.
Left, a barbel which has recently healed over its amputation
surface. Later on (middle) a blastema forms off the end of the
cartilaginous rod. Right, an amputated barbel unable to regenerate after removal of its cartilaginous rod.** (*From Fig. 5
(p. 197) of Goss, 1954.*)

the detached portion out through a small basal incision in the skin.
When such rodless barbels are amputated, no regeneration takes place
because a blastema fails to be produced (Fig. 64). The key roll played
by the cartilaginous rod is further confirmed by experiments designed
to induce lateral outgrowths from barbels which have been incom-
pletely amputated. If only the skin and nerves are cut there develops
nothing more than a very diminutive protuberance consisting of skin
and nerves. But if the rod of cartilage is also cut, the offshoot contains
skin, nerves *and* cartilage, and it regenerates to a length commensurate
with the level of the lateral incision. The presence of a rod stump is
therefore essential to the normal development of a new barbel. In this
appendage, as in the fin, each tissue is necessary for the production of
its counterpart in the regenerate.

Morphogenetically, however, blastema cells are programmed to
give rise to only a single cartilaginous rod irrespective of the composition of the stump. It is possible to remove a rod and then put several
rods back into the barbel. With a little effort, one can insert up to four
rods into one barbel, the extra ones being derived from other barbels
on the same fish. When amputated through the operated region, the
quadruple rods all contribute cells to the blastema, but only one rod

differentiates distal to the level of amputation. The old rod(s) in the stump, therefore, do not exert separate morphogenetic influences on the blastema. In fact, a new rod can differentiate even in the absence of the old one, provided the latter is not removed from the barbel until its chondroblasts have had a chance to form a blastema. Up to about four days after amputation, withdrawal of the rod prevents regeneration of the barbel. Thereafter, the rod can be removed without abolishing regenerative capacities. The catfish taste barbel, therefore, is an appendage which appears to rely on a single source of cells for the histogenesis of mesodermal tissue in its regenerate. Few other vertebrate appendages are so uncomplicated—or so instructive.

Nerves are perhaps even more important in barbels than in any other appendage, for denervation in the absence of amputation causes the otherwise uninjured barbel to regress. Thus, the very integrity of its morphology cannot be maintained unless nerves are present. Regression begins at the distal end where the cartilage undergoes extensive histolysis, as a result of which the length of the barbel gradually decreases. What happens to the cells of the resorbed barbel, whether they become necrotic, are redistributed elsewhere in the body, or are dispensed through the epidermis, is not known.

Although nerves are undeniably necessary for the maintenance and regeneration of the barbel, it remains to be determined which specific tissue(s) respond directly to their trophic influences. In the case of cartilage, this can be tested by virtue of the fact that the cartilaginous rod itself is capable of regenerating in the unamputated barbel as shown in Fig. 65. Following the extirpation of varying lengths of rod, new cartilage is produced with equal facility from either proximal or distal ends to fill in the gap. When such barbels are totally denervated, regeneration of the cartilaginous rod *in situ* occurs just as well as in the normally innervated structure. Clearly, the central rod of cartilage is not dependent upon nerves for its growth, which is hardly surprising in view of the lack of nerves in this tissue.

The contrast between barbel cartilage and bony fin rays in this respect is of some interest. The former can regenerate without nerves, the latter cannot. Perhaps the explanation of the discrepancy lies in the close relation which fin rays bear to the epidermis in their early stages of development. Coupled with the fact that the epidermis of regenerating appendages is heavily invaded by nerve fibers, one is led to suspect that the neural influence might be focused first and foremost on epidermis which might secondarily affect underlying mesodermal tissues in such a way as to promote the accumulation of blastema cells. In the barbel, it is a curious thing that denervation can cause histolysis of

Fig. 65 **Regeneration of the cartilaginous rod in an otherwise intact taste barbel. When a proximal length of rod is extracted from the barbel the remaining distal portion (top) grows back in a proximal direction.** (*From Fig. 4 (p. 47) of Goss, 1956.*)

the terminal part of the cartilaginous rod while at the same time more proximal regions may be regenerating. Again, it is plausible that the tip of the rod might be sustained by a dependent relationship between it and the epidermis, the latter requiring adequate innervation for its own maintenance.

There is a precedent for such neural-epidermal relationships in the well-known case of the taste bud. As in the tongues of mammals, the taste buds of the catfish barbel gradually degenerate if their nerve supply is interrupted. To be more precise, they fail to renew themselves when denervated, for it is in the nature of a taste bud to undergo a constant turnover of its cells. As long as the input equals the output, the organ persists. When this homeostasis is upset by denervation, the taste bud disappears, apparently by default, when it eventually runs out of differentiated sensory cells. Experiments in rats have shown that much the same effect can be obtained if the conscription of new cells is arrested by X-rays or colchicine. Thus, inhibition of epidermal mitosis, which is required to maintain a steady supply of cells for the taste bud, is as effective as denervation in causing the organ to disappear. Whether the trophic influence of nerves stimulates epidermal hyperplasia, or promotes cellular differentiation as well, is one of the next questions to be answered. Reinnervation of the taste buds by sensory nerve fibers reinitiates the recruitment of epidermal cells and restores the morphological integrity of the organ. Although little more is known about how nerves maintain taste buds than how they promote the regeneration of histologically more complex structures, it is a safe bet that what we learn about one will enhance our understanding of the other.

Miscellaneous Structures There is much to be learned by the comparative approach to regeneration. If a sufficiently broad spectrum of appendages could be thoroughly investigated it might be possible to recognize attributes shared in common by those that regenerate which distinguish them from the ones that do not. With this object in mind, let us take a brief inventory of other structures in fishes which might be expected to regenerate (but not all of which do).

In some fishes, such as the salmon and catfish, there is a so-called adipose fin located over the backbone between the dorsal and caudal fins. This structure, unlike other fins, lacks skeletal supports altogether and is incapable of movement. Histologically, it consists of a very thick layer of dermal connective tissue and a core of fatty tissue. When amputated, it gives no signs of regenerating, but the explanation for this shortcoming eludes us.

More closely related to true fins is the lure of the angler fish. This incredible structure is actually a modified ray of the dorsal fin, but it has evolved a fleshy ornament on its end which mimics a small fish when dangled in front of the ready and waiting mouth of the angler fish. In the very nature of things, there is a slight but real probability that the bait, if not part of the fishing rod itself, might occasionally be bitten off by the intended victim. The selective advantage of having retained the ability to regenerate this modified fin ray is therefore obvious. Hopefully someone might be moved eventually to confirm this by experiments in a convenient species such as the Sargassum fish.

The jaws of fishes have yielded conflicting results when tested for regenerative ability. In the hands of some investigators they have failed to grow back, but others have claimed success. It is quite possible that such discrepancies might be attributed to variations in the levels of amputation, and perhaps to species differences. However, the occurrence of jaw regeneration in other vertebrates lends credence to its possible existence in fishes. In urodele amphibians, snouts and mandibles can be replaced following amputation in front of the eyes or anterior to the temporo-mandibular articulations, respectively. The resulting structures are replete with skeletal parts, muscles, and even teeth (but not tongue). It would be interesting to learn how completely the mouthparts of fishes can regenerate, especially in species such as the sea horse, which has a long snout.

In casting about for likely candidates for regeneration, one's attention is inevitably drawn to the gills, and to the operculum which covers them. The latter does not regenerate very well, which makes it a convenient structure to notch in order to identify fishes for future reference. The gills, however, are capable of limited regeneration, depending on how much is amputated. Branching off the gill arches are numerous gill filaments which contain little more than cartilaginous supports (gill rays), blood vessels and the respiratory epithelium. In the goldfish, *Carassius auratus,* these gill filaments will regenerate if not more than two-thirds of their lengths are amputated (Fig. 66). There is no regeneration when they are cut back to the gill arch. The blastema differentiates into a new cartilaginous support, plus extensions of the blood vessels.

The gill arches have not been observed to regenerate when portions of them are resected, perhaps because their anatomy conspires against it. Spinal nerves run ventrally in the gill arches but the blood vessels

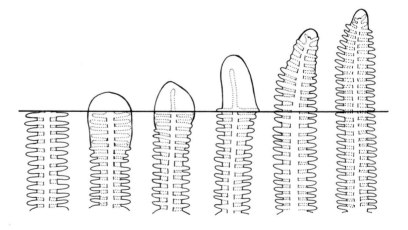

Fig. 66 **Successive stages in the regeneration of a gill filament in the goldfish.** (*After Schäfer, 1936.*)

all flow dorsally. Hence, neither dorsal nor ventral half of a transected gill arch would be expected to possess both the innervation and the vascularity needed for regeneration. Of course, if they did regenerate there would be no way to insure that the dorsal and ventral outgrowths would meet and fuse to re-establish the continuity required for their normal function. Maybe for these reasons there has been no selective advantage in retaining their regenerative potentials.

When the various appendages of fishes are surveyed, it becomes clear that there are certain prerequisites to be met if regeneration is to occur. There must be a mesodermal source of blastema cells, adequate innervation, and an enveloping layer of epithelium. Each one of these features is a *sine qua non* for the successful regeneration of a whole appendage. This is not to say that individual tissues within the appendage cannot repair their own lesions. Regeneration of the entire organ, however, is a different order of developmental process. Yet we are still confronted with the paradox that some structures fulfill all of the foregoing requirements but do not regenerate anyway. Something vital to our understanding still seems to be missing.

REFERENCES

BEIGEL, C. 1912. Regeneration der Barteln bei Siluroiden *Arch. Entwicklungsmech. Organ.* **34:** 363–370.

BIRNIE, J. H. 1934. Regeneration of the tail-fins of Fundulus embryos. *Biol. Bull.* **66:** 316–325.

BLANC, M. 1948. Sur la réparation des nageoires de Poissons Téléostéens après amputation d'un volet median. *Arch. Zool. Exptl. Gen.* **85:** 184–188.

BLANC, M. 1949. Étude histologique de la régénération des nageoires chez quelques Poissons Téléostéens. *Arch. Anat. Microscop. Morphol. Exptl.* **38:** 52–64.

COMFORT, A. and F. DOLJANSKI. 1958. The relation of size and age to rate of tail regeneration in *Lebistes reticulatus. Gerontologia* **2:** 266–283.

FRANÇOIS, Y. and M. BLANC. 1956. Sur la croissance en longueur des rayons de nageoires chez les Poissons Téléostéens. *Bull. Soc. Zool. France* **81:** 26–33.

GOODRICH, H. B. and J. M. GREENE. 1959. An experimental analysis of the development of a color pattern in the fish *Brachydanio albolineatus* Blyth. *J. Exptl. Zool.* **141:** 15–46.

GOSS, R. J. 1954. The role of the central cartilaginous rod in the regeneration of the catfish taste barbel. *J. Exptl. Zool.* **127:** 181–200.

GOSS, R. J. 1956. An experimental analysis of taste barbel regeneration in the catfish. *J. Exptl. Zool.* **131:** 27–50.

GOSS, R. J. and M. W. STAGG. 1957. The regeneration of fins and fin rays in *Fundulus heteroclitus. J. Exptl. Zool.* **136:** 487–508.

GROBSTEIN, C. 1940. Endocrine and developmental studies of gonopod differentiation in certain Poeciliid fishes. I. The structure and development of the gonopod in Platypoecilus maculatus. *Univ. Calif. (Berkeley) Publ. Zool.* **47:** 1–22.

GROBSTEIN, C. 1942. Endocrine and developmental studies of gonopod differentiation in certain Poeciliid fishes. II. Effect of testosterone propionate on the normal and regenerating anal fin of adult *Platypoecilus maculatus* females. *J. Exptl. Zool.* **89:** 305–328.

GROBSTEIN, C. 1947. The role of androgen in declining regenerative capacity during morphogenesis of the Platypoecilus maculatus gonopodium. *J. Exptl. Zool.* **106:** 313–344.

GROBSTEIN, C. 1948. Optimum gonopodial morphogenesis in Platypoecilus maculatus with constant dosage of methyl testosterone. *J. Exptl. Zool.* **109:** 215–238.

KAMRIN, R. P. and M. SINGER. 1955. The influence of the nerve on regeneration and maintenance of the barbel of the catfish, Ameiurus nebulosus. *J. Morphol.* **96:** 173–188.

KEMP, N. E., J. H. PARK, A. K. McWILLIAMS, S. E. AUERBACH and M. J. BOZDECH. 1968. Fine structure of lepidotrichia and actinotrichia in regenerating tailfins of teleosts. *Anat. Record* **160:** 374.

MORGAN, T. H. 1900. Regeneration in teleosts. *Arch. Entwicklungsmech. Organ.* **10:** 120–134.

MORGAN, T. H. 1902. Further experiments on the regeneration of the tail of fishes. *Arch. Entwicklungsmech. Organ.* **14:** 539–561.

NABRIT, S. M. 1929. The role of fin rays in the regeneration in the tail-fins of fishes. *Biol. Bull.* **56:** 235–266.

NABRIT, S. M. 1931. The role of the basal plate in regeneration in the tail-fins of fishes (Fundulus and Carassius). *Biol. Bull.* **60:** 60–63.

NARDI, F. 1935. Das Verhalten der Schuppen erwachsener Fische bei Regenerations- und Transplantationsversuchen. *Arch. Entwicklungsmech. Organ.* **133:** 621–663.

NEAVE, F. 1940. On the histology and regeneration of the teleost scale. *Quart. J. Microscop. Sci.* **81:** 541–568.

OLIVO, O. M. 1928. Rigenerazione di organi sensitivi in "Amiurus nebulosus." *Boll. Soc. Ital. Biol. Sper.* **3:** 1019–1023.

PRENANT, M. 1937. Sur la croissance des lépidotriches articules chez les Téléostéens. *Bull. Soc. Zool. France* **62:** 190–195.

PRENANT, M. 1938. Régénération des rayons osseux articulés après amputation des nageoires chez les Téléostéens. *Compt. Rend. Soc. Biol.* **127:** 980–982.

SAUTER, V. 1934. Regeneration und Transplantation bei erwachsenen Fischen. *Arch. Entwicklungsmech. Organ.* **132:** 1–41.

SCHÄFER, L. W. 1936. Die Regeneration der Kiemen und Flossenstrahlen beim Goldfisch (*Carassius auratus*). *Jena. Z. Naturw.* **70:** 303–358.

SCOTT, G. G. 1909. Regeneration in Fundulus and its relation to the size of the fish. *Biol. Bull.* **17:** 343–353.

SICHEL, G. 1962. Effetto inibente della ribonucleasi sui processi rigenerativi della pinna caudale di *Gambusia holbrooki* Grd. *Boll. Zool.* **29:** 855–877.

TASSAVA, R. and R. J. GOSS. 1966. Regeneration rate and amputation level in fish fins and lizard tails. *Growth* **30:** 9–21.

TURNER, C. L. 1947. The rate of morphogenesis and regeneration of the gonopodium in normal and castrated males of *Gambusia affinis*. *J. Exptl. Zool.* **106:** 125–143.

VAN OOSTEN, J. 1923. A study of the scales of whitefishes of known ages. *Zoologica* **2:** 380–412.

WUNDER, W. and H. SCHIMKE. 1935. Wundheilung und Regeneration beim Karpfen. *Arch. Entwicklungsmech. Organ.* **133:** 245–268.

9   The Amphibian Limb

THOMAS Hunt Morgan was born in Kentucky soon after the Civil War. Named after General John Hunt Morgan of "Morgan's Raiders," and related to the financier J. P. Morgan, this distinguished biologist made many great contributions to regeneration, not the least of which was his book on the subject published in 1901. It still makes excellent reading, if only to appreciate how few of the questions he wondered about then have yet to be answered. Perhaps the most burning question to him was how the morphology of regenerating structures developed. It is said that he abandoned the field of regeneration shortly after the turn of the century because he could not foresee any chance of explaining the problem of morphogenesis in his own lifetime. He was right. But as one of the first to recognize and exploit the now famous potentialities which *Drosophila* had to offer, he went on to become, in 1933, the first of many brilliant geneticists to win the Nobel Prize. Regeneration's loss was genetics' gain.

Fig. 67 **The red-spotted newt,** Triturus (Diemictylus) viridescens.

What Morgan had the wisdom to give up, others have had the courage to pursue. We are still far from solving the riddle of morphogenesis, but much of what has been learned we owe to the regenerating amphibian limb (Fig. 68). We owe as much to the analysis of the problem by Paul Weiss, whose pioneering experiments and theoretical contributions have to this day guided our research into the mysteries of the morphogenetic field.

Histogenesis of the Blastema The origin of limb blastema cells was a major point of controversy for many years. It still is. One school of thought held that they might be derived from precursors distributed throughout the body, with blood cells being the leading contender for the role. This notion, however, was conclusively dispelled in the early 1930's by Elmer Butler's classic experiment carried out at Princeton University. Taking advantage of the growth-inhibiting action of X-rays, he demonstrated that regeneration failed to occur from limb stumps which had been locally irradiated for a distance of only a few millimeters or so back from the level of amputation. This important discovery convincingly proved that the cells of the blastema are of local origin. Thus, the way was cleared for the next question, which was to find out just what tissues in the stump contribute to the blastema.

After many years, and even more experiments, it now seems es-

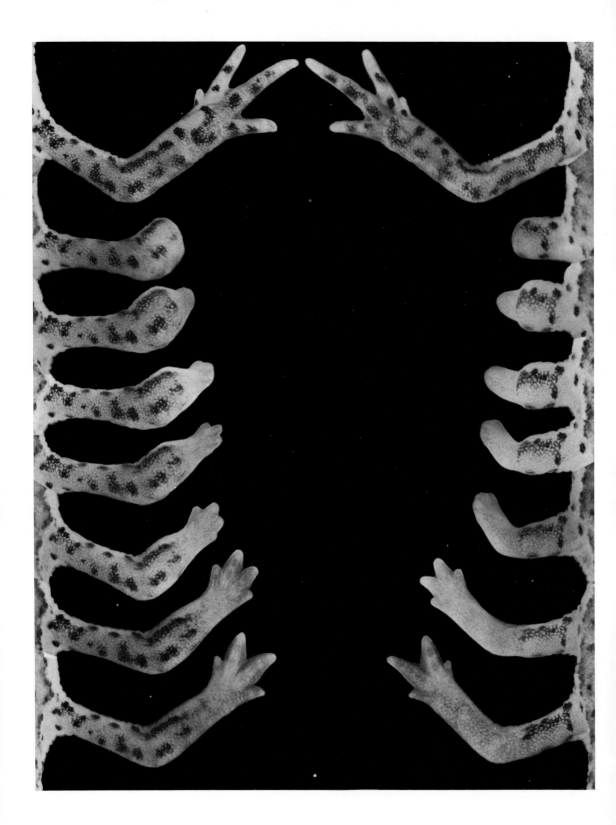

142

tablished that practically all of the mesodermal tissues in the stump are capable of giving rise to blastema cells proper. Yet this answer, like so many solutions to scientific problems, has raised even more provocative questions, questions which strike to the very core of the problem of cellular differentiation.

Do the blastema cells differentiate into the same kinds of tissues from which they came? In the case of the epidermis, the answer is in the affirmative. If tritiated thymidine is administered to an intact newt, the epidermis of the limb becomes selectively labeled because it is the only proliferating tissue there. Following amputation of the limb, the labeled epidermal cells participate in wound healing but are not observed to become incorporated into the aggregation of underlying blastema cells. Results consistent with this have also been obtained in experiments designed to take advantage of naturally labeled cells. In the South African clawed toad, Xenopus laevis, there is a mutant which has only one nucleolus, instead of two, per nucleus. By peeling epidermis off the leg of a larva with single nucleoli in its cells and transplanting the skinned leg to a host with the normal nucleolar complement, the denuded graft soon becomes covered with a layer of the host's epidermal cells containing two nucleoli apiece. When allowed to regenerate, the inner tissues of such grafts all contain cells with single nucleoli. Hence, there can be little doubt that the fate of epidermal cells covering the blastema is dictated by their pasts. Concerning the mesodermal components, however, there is a great deal of doubt.

The uncertainty arises from the fact that the cells of mesodermal tissues dedifferentiate as they leave the old and become part of the new. Morphologically, at least, they completely lose their identities, with the result that blastema cells of multifarious origins are indistinguishable from one another. Histolytic changes affect all tissues in the stump, but are most conspicuous in muscle because this has the most to lose. First described in 1938 by Charles S. Thornton, the validity of muscle fiber dedifferentiation was convincingly confirmed by Elizabeth Hay's elegant electron micrographs of the regenerating limbs of Ambystoma punctatum larvae. What her investigation re-

Fig. 68 Successive stages in the regeneration of opposite limbs in a newt following amputation through lower (left) and upper (right) arms. At the top are the original limbs. Reading down, photographs were taken at 7, 21, 25, 28, 32, 42, and 70 days after amputation. From more proximal stumps (right) the regenerate elongates faster but differentiates more slowly than that growing from more distal level of amputation.

vealed was that the muscle fibers in the healed stump underwent transverse fragmentation, as a result of which many mononucleate units were cut out of the originally multinucleate fiber. It sometimes happens that anucleate fragments may also be produced, but these are probably not destined to survive. Those lucky enough to include nuclei, however, exhibit extensive dissolution of their myofibrils until there is nothing left in their cytoplasm but the usual organelles common to most cells. Thus it is that these once highly specialized cells are reduced to a common denominator, indistinguishable from those derived from other sources. Chondrocytes, released from their disintegrating matrix, likewise become unrecognizable as they join the parade of ex-osteocytes, ex-fibroblasts, ex-Schwann cells, etc., all of which migrate distally to build a blastema.

Cells Incognito No longer is the question whether cells dedifferentiate or not. It is what becomes of them afterward? The blastema is a pot pourri of cells that all look alike despite their varied backgrounds. But are they really alike? Are they fundamentally changed by dedifferentiation, or do they still bear the invisible stamp of what they used to be? Until such questions are answered, the very significance of cellular differentiation will remain in limbo. We now know that differentiation can be a reversible process as far as appearances are concerned. What we need to know is whether or not differentiation involves permanent changes at the level of the gene, changes which lock onto a single unswitchable channel of differentiation from which deviation is impossible.

One likes to think that biological processes are economical—that useless steps in a pathway are eliminated in the course of evolution. If this is true, then it must be asked why dedifferentiation occurs at all in blastema formation. Why doesn't each tissue give rise directly to its counterpart in the regenerate and remain recognizable as it does so? Two explanations suggest themselves. One is to facilitate mitosis, the other to enhance pluripotency.

Cell division can occur in fully differentiated cells of some kinds but not in others. Those which secrete their specialized end products into the extracellular compartment can usually proliferate without giving up their morphological signs of recognition. Although their functional activities seem to be held in abeyance during division, the glandular cells of the body do not have to dedifferentiate in order to multiply. Nonsecretory cells on the other hand, usually cannot proliferate. Their end products are retained within the cytoplasm as integral parts of the cell, a condition which is incompatible with mitotic activity. Since these cells cannot have it both ways, their life histories are characterized by two phases. Immature cells constitute a generative population, the descendants of which forfeit reproductive competence to devote their undivided attention to differentiation. Neurons, Schwann cells and muscle fibers fall into this category, as do such renewing tissues as erythrocytes and epidermis.

Intermediate between these two extremes are those cells which get rid of their products but still do not divide. In cartilage and bone, for example, the nondividing fully differentiated cells do not contain any end products. Their end products contain them. Mitotic activity in these tissues is restricted mostly to the surfaces of the skeletal matrix where there is less end product. The ameloblasts of teeth also cease to divide as soon as they begin to secrete enamel. Again, it may be the close proximity between the cell and its product which precludes proliferation. When the materials secreted by a cell become too concentrated in its microenvironment, the incidence of cell division declines.

In the regenerating limb, therefore, it may be desirable that cells be separated from their specialized end products if they are to multiply. Not only do muscle fibers dispense with their myofibrils, and Schwann cells with their myelin sheaths, but chondrocytes escape from the disintegrating cartilaginous matrix and osteocytes are released from resorbed bone. Almost every kind of cell in the limb, each in its own way, unloads its property and gives up its occupation. Although it cannot be claimed that they become embryonic again, in a sense they revert to a second childhood. The problem is to determine whether these cells in their next incarnation remember what their last existence was.

The blastema is made up of cells with a motley assortment of backgrounds and a rich variety of potentialities. Either their pasts and their futures must be the same, or they may differ. No one would dispute that they may differ. Even in the nonregenerating limb some cells go through changes in form, especially in the connective tissues and skeleton where they need not adhere strictly to a single pathway of differentiation. In the blastema, however, it is important to resolve the degree to which cells are capable of altering their destinies. A rather extreme case would involve the conversion of chondrocytes to muscle fibers, or vice versa. Both of these tissues can be chemically characterized by their specific end products of chondroitin and myosin, and are microscopically distinguishable by their cartilaginous matrix and myofibrils, respectively. Hence, if one should become the other in the course of regeneration, these tissue-specific products would be convenient landmarks for easy recognition. The problem is to trace individual cells through this metaplastic change, if it occurs at all.

This problem has recently been attacked by Ronald C. Eggert at Cornell University. By grafting scapular cartilage to X-rayed newt limbs he found that the resulting blastemas, derived exclusively from the grafts, differentiated only into amorphous masses of cartilage on the ends of the limb stumps. There are two possible explanations as to why these blastemas might have failed to develop into limb regenerates. Either cartilage cells can redifferentiate into nothing except more cartilage, or the scapula lies outside the limb territory and could not give rise to a limb even if its chondrocytes were able to differentiate into other kinds of cells.

These alternatives have been partly resolved by Trygve Steen, who transplanted limb cartilage to the regenerating limbs of the axolotl. Labeled with tritiated thymidine and/or triploid nuclei, such grafted chondrocytes were almost always detected later on in the cartilaginous parts of the regenerate. Although this kind of negative evidence does not categorically exclude the possibility of metaplasia, it suggests that such a phenomenon is by no means common in the regenerating limb.

Cellular and Biochemical Kinetics of Regeneration From the moment a limb is amputated, the tissues of the stump begin to mobilize for the effort to regenerate. Profound physiological changes take place in them, the significance of which we are just beginning to fathom. Wound healing may be achieved in a matter of hours, but subsequent events follow a timetable dictated by the temperature, the size of the limb, and whether the animal is larval or adult. In the adult newt, for example, the blastema appears during the third week at normal temperatures, and recognizable digits are present at the end of a month (Figs. 68 and 69). Larval limbs grow back much faster, but we do not know whether this is attributable to their youthfulness or their smallness. Regeneration is faster to occur from proximal amputations than distal ones, but in the end one can expect one hundred percent replacement of missing parts.

Cellular proliferation is a prominent feature of the regenerating landscape. The normal epidermis of the stump, of course, relies on mitotic activity in its basal layer in order to renew itself. Held in check during wound healing and blastema formation, epidermal hyperplasia does not resume until the regenerate begins to differentiate and grow in length (although the epidermis may have thickened long before these

Fig. 69 **Histological sections of regenerating newt limbs. From top to bottom: Wound healing, blastema formation, early differentiation and completion of morphogenesis.** *(From Fig. 6 (p. 27) of Goss, 1956b.)*

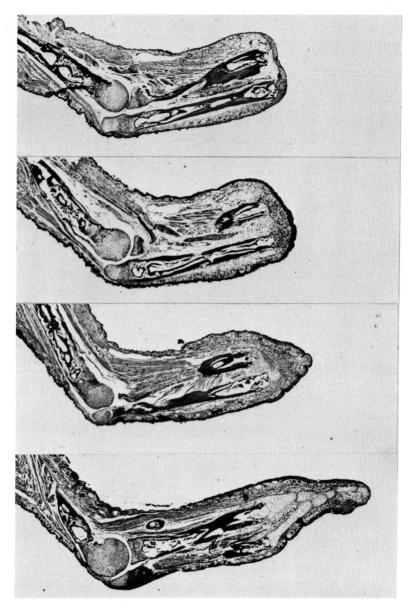

stages). The internal tissues, however, exhibit extensive proliferative activity during the course of dedifferentiation and blastema formation. Once enough cells have accumulated to constitute a conical blastema on the end of the stump, then differentiation commences. This first occurs in the proximal regions. Here the blastema cells develop into new tissues appropriate to the anatomical arrangement of the tissues in the stump, thus insuring the morphological continuity of the old and the new. As differentiation of cells goes on in the regenerate, mitotic activity declines. Since morphogenesis progresses in a proximo-distal direction, the incidence of cell division soon remains high only at the growing tip of the regenerate where new cells continue to be produced as long as there are missing parts still to be formed.

The foregoing events are overt manifestations of more subtle physiological activities which require some sophisticated techniques to visualize. Thanks to autoradiography and histochemistry, however, it has been possible to unravel some of the biochemical antecedents to the imposing array of steps in the pathway leading to the regeneration of a new extremity. Obviously, DNA synthesis occurs in the regenerate in the same pattern as does mitosis, but the synthesis of proteins is of particular importance. This has been traced autoradiographically by Hermann Josef Anton in Cologne and by Charles Bodemer at the University of Washington.

If isotopically labeled amino acids are injected into newts with limbs in varying stages of regeneration, the sites of heightened protein synthesis can be detected by grain counts over the participating tissues. Preparations of this kind have shown that the internal tissues of the amputated limb take up large amounts of label, even during the process of dedifferentiation. Within a week after amputation, many of the tissues are undergoing histolysis, and at the same time are synthesizing proteins. This seemingly paradoxical situation may indicate that proteolytic enzymes are being made by cells to mediate their own degeneration. In muscle fibers, for example, protein synthesis characterizes the distal portions subject to dedifferentiation, but not the intact muscles located more proximally in the stump. Enhanced protein synthesis is likewise typical of cells associated with nerves and periosteum. The blastema itself indulges in conspicuous protein synthesis as revealed autoradiographically by the uptake of labeled amino acids and electron micrographically by the abundance of ribosomes in their cytoplasm. The manufacture of proteins continues as the blastema cells differentiate into new cartilage and muscle, but subsides thereafter as the status quo is approached.

Certainly many of the proteins which are synthesized in the developing regenerate are structural. Actin and myosin are elaborated within muscle fibers, and quantities of collagen are produced in association with the skeletal and dermal components of the new limb. Yet it takes more than structure to make a limb. Anatomy functions. Consequently, metabolic processes must also be built into the regenerate, and this requires the presence of enzymes. At the University of Illinois, Anthony

J. Schmidt has brought his considerable histochemical talents to bear on the problem of enzyme distribution in the amputated stump and growing regenerate. Pioneering investigations such as his will catalyze future research destined to open the way for important discoveries in the years to come. Hopefully the mysteries of morphogenesis will someday be explained not only in the graphic terms of the anatomist but in the molecular language of the physiologist and biochemist as well.

Our inventory of enzymes in regenerating extremities is as yet incomplete, but the data thus far available are beginning to fall into place. Prior to the production of the blastema, enzymes are present in the dedifferentiating tissues of the stump to catalyze the breakdown of proteins. Cathepsins and peptidases are commonly detected during this phase, not only in limbs but in the stumps of amputated tails as well. Collagenase is also present, for slices of regenerating limbs (but not intact ones) incubated on collagen gels bring about solation of the gel in their vicinities. Acid phosphatase, an enzyme often taken as diagnostic of lysosomes, is found to some extent in the muscle fibers of the stump, even more in the blastema cells, and in greatest concentrations in the epidermis throughout the process of regeneration. Possibly the synthesis of proteins in dedifferentiating tissues may reflect the production of these and other enzymes.

The amputation of an appendage is a traumatic experience for the tissues in the stump. Their blood supply is seriously curtailed, and the cells not killed outright must adapt their metabolism to the austerity of the situation. Their respiratory quotient is reduced at this time, and the pH of the stump becomes increasingly acid as autolytic activity proceeds. In skeletal muscle fibers, the normally rich deposits of glycogen disappear in the distal regions beginning to undergo dedifferentiation. Presumably the glycogen is anaerobically metabolized, giving rise to lactic acid which lowers the pH as it accumulates. The high concentrations of lactic dehydrogenase in dedifferentiating tissues accounts for the conversion of pyruvic acid, resulting from glycolysis, into lactic acid. The latter is produced when the Krebs cycle is not operating either because of insufficient oxygen or due to the lack of the necessary enzymes. Probably oxygen is at a premium in the amputated stump as a result of vascular disturbances. But some of the Krebs cycle enzymes are also missing, which testifies to the fact that the metabolism of the early regenerate is anaerobic not only by accident but also by design.

In appendages capable of regeneration, the early regressive phases soon give way to progressive changes. These begin with the formation of the blastema, the metabolism of which is not unlike that of the stump whence it came. Certain of the dehydrogenases normally associated with mitochondria and the Krebs cycle exhibit little or no activity in the blastema. On the other hand, glucose-6-phosphate dehydrogenase can be detected in blastema cells, indicating the operation of the pentose phosphate shunt whereby pentose phosphates otherwise destined for glycolytic degradation are steered into channels of nucleotide and nucleic acid synthesis. It seems that the constructive events of regeneration take precedence over everything else, including energy production.

As soon as differentiation of the blastema cells begins, the metabolic pathways revert to normal. Lactic dehydrogenase activity subsides and the Krebs cycle once again takes over. Respiration becomes aerobic, first in the more proximal regions of the regenerate and later in the distal parts as morphogenesis advances in the elongating limb. One cannot help but be impressed with how morphology and metabolism become modified hand in hand during the course of the developmental process. There is no way of telling whether the morphological changes cause the biochemical alterations, or vice versa. Perhaps such a distinction is inappropriate, since development is itself a physiological process.

The Skin of the Limb It is not enough just to describe what happens in the regenerating limb. We must fit the hard data together so as to arrive at a concatenation of events each step of which is causally related to all others in the process. Unhappily the gaps outnumber the established facts, which inevitably introduces a measure of guesswork into our efforts to understand the *modus operandi* of regeneration. Only by working from both the biochemical and morphological ends can we hope to explain each in terms of the other. Morphologically, few tissues in the limb are as important—or as interesting—as the epidermis. This is the one tissue which all bodily appendages possess by definition, and without which their regeneration is impossible.

If a limb is stripped of its skin, the denuded parts promptly become covered again by epidermis. Healing can be prevented, however, by grafting the skinless portion to an internal location such as the flank musculature or the coelomic cavity. In the latter instance, the cuff of skin remaining on the upper arm heals to the epidermis bordering the hole in the flank through which the skinned limb was inserted. If the intracoelomic part of such a limb is amputated its stump becomes covered with peritoneum but fails to regenerate (Fig. 70). Not until it is exteriorized again, thus permitting the epidermis once more to envelop the distal stump, will regeneration finally be permitted to proceed.

Over and above its undeniably essential role in appendage growth, does the epidermis do any more than just permit regeneration? Does it, for example, have anything to say about what is to be regenerated? This can be tested by causing a limb to be covered with skin from other areas of the body. When this is achieved, either by grafting different

Fig. 70 **Skinless limb stumps grafted into body cavity fail to regenerate. On left, such a limb as it appears after six weeks' residence in coelom. The cuff of body wall is still attached below the elbow. On right, the same limb in section showing only amorphous cartilage on the severed ends of the radius and ulna.** *(From Figs. 1 and 2 (p. 18) of Goss, 1956b.)*

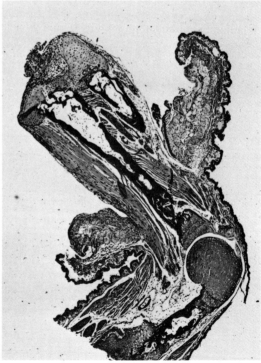

kinds of skin to the limb or by transplanting skinless limbs elsewhere, subsequent regeneration still occurs as a rule. Not all kinds of epidermis have been assayed for their capacity to participate in limb regeneration, but with few exceptions the ones thus far tested do not appear to discriminate. Hence, epidermis from such diverse locations as the abdomen, flank or tail all permit limb regeneration. In the case of tail epidermis there is no tendency for the expression of caudal morphogenesis by the legs with which it may be combined. Except for the occasional duplications of parts or the reversal of axes (which seem to be caused by dermal influences) the epidermis itself has nothing to say about what kind of extremity shall be formed. Therefore, its influence is permissive, not instructive. But it does not always permit.

Regeneration often fails to occur when limbs are covered with head skin, and to a lesser extent, with the skin from the back of the animal. However, there is a species difference in the case of head skin. Charles S. Thornton, at Michigan State University, showed this unequivocally in the case of skin from the heads of two different species of *Ambystoma* larvae. When head skin was substituted for forelimb skin in *A. macrodactylum,* normal regeneration occurred following amputation through the graft region. In *A. talpoideum,* however, regeneration was inhibited under the same conditions. Histological examination of early stages revealed that in the latter case no blastema formed. Nor did the wound epidermis become thickened on the end of the stump to form the apical cap which is invariably associated with the accumulation of blastema cells beneath. Thornton further noted that mucus-secreting cells in the nonregenerating kind of epidermis persisted over the end of the healed stump. Conversely, in successfully regenerating combinations of head epidermis in association with amputated *A. macrodactylum* limbs, cellular specializations disappeared. It is tempting to conclude that this alteration in the epidermal cells has something to do with whether or not they can support the production of outgrowths from underlying tissues. One wonders whether or not other types of even more highly specialized epidermis, e.g., cornea or oral mucosa, might also be able to take part in limb regeneration.

It was shown long ago that regeneration failed to occur if the full thickness of the skin were ligated over the end of an amputated limb or tail. This suggested that the dermis must be excluded from the healing stump in order to allow the wound epidermis to come into intimate contact with the underlying mesodermal tissues. As in the developing limb bud of the embryo there seems to be an interaction between ectoderm and mesoderm, to the mutual benefit of both. We know practically nothing about the chemical basis of this reciprocal induction, but the morphological manifestations of the process leave little room for doubt about its reality. Perhaps the most convincing piece of evidence comes from Thornton's brilliant experiments on the apical epidermal cap, experiments which have conclusively proved that the blastema develops only under the indispensable influence of the wound epidermis.

Soon after healing has sealed off the stump of an amputated limb, the epidermal cells pile up on the end to form a conspicuous mound reminiscent of the apical ectodermal ridge of embryonic limb buds. In both instances there is evidence that the morphogenetic integrity of the growing limb is profoundly affected by this structure. In the chick limb bud, for example, if this ridge is rotated, or if an extra one is added, the resultant limb is correspondingly disoriented or duplicated. In the amphibian limb, the daily removal of the apical epidermal cap delays or inhibits the production of the blastema, depending upon how rapidly a new cap is reconstituted. The site of blastema formation is also determined by the location of the overlying apical epidermal cap. If the cap is experimentally shifted to a lateral position, then the blastema is likewise askew and regeneration occurs at an angle oblique to the longitudinal axis of the limb.

No Regeneration without Innervation

If a limb is meaningless without skin, it is useless without nerves. In keeping with utilitarian principles, it is altogether fitting that the developmental mechanisms by which new limbs are produced should have evolved a dependence upon the nerve supply. Despite the teleological overtones of this relationship, it is sufficient to realize that phylogenetic strategy selects in favor of efficiency. It makes good sense not to invest energy in the production of structure with no payoff in terms of function. Aside from such ultimate interpretations of the phenomenon, however, it is equally important to seek proximate explanations of the role that nerves play in the physiology of regeneration, and no one has contributed more to this endeavor than Marcus Singer of Case Western Reserve University.

It has long been known that denervated limbs cannot regenerate, but all attempts to find out why have thus far met with frustration. Fortunately, however, the frustration has not been complete. Although the final answer still eludes us, much has been learned about how the trophic influence of nerves does, and does not, operate in regenerating limbs. For example, connections with the central nervous system are not required, for if the dorsal roots are interrupted the neurons of the isolated spinal ganglia can still promote normal regeneration of the limb they innervate. All that is needed, apparently, are neurons with intact fibers running to their end organs.

As was true of the epidermis, there seems to be little or no specificity with regard to the source of innervation. Either sensory or motor neurons can provide what is required. Even neurons from other anatomical locations, if combined in association with amputated limbs by appropriate deviations or transplantations, are sufficient to promote regeneration. Apparently the only requirement to be satisfied is that the number of nerve fibers should exceed a certain minimal threshold in relation to the quantity of limb tissue to be innervated. Other things being equal, if this requirement is met then regeneration can proceed.

Parenthetically, it is worth noting that there are two known exceptions in the amphibians to this nearly universal requirement. One is the regeneration of limbs which never became innervated in the first place. Such "aneurogenic" limbs will be discussed later. The other exception is the response of leg regenerates in the South African clawed toad (*Xenopus laevis*). When such a regenerated leg is denervated, and part of the replaced structure is cut off, a new outgrowth may still develop from what remains of the original regenerate. Possibly this anomalous phenomenon may be explained by the fact that regeneration the second time around occurs by the direct outgrowth of cartilage from the stump apparently without passing through a blastema stage.

The arm of a newt receives its innervation from the third, fourth and fifth spinal nerves. In adult *Triturus viridescens,* Singer determined that these three nerves contained about 800, 1285 and 500 fibers, respectively. By selectively cutting one or two of these nerves in various combinations he was able to produce limbs with varying numbers of fibers. When these partially innervated limbs were amputated, those with fewer than one-third to one-half the normal complement of nerve fibers were unable to regenerate. This threshold requirement is an expression of the concentration of fibers in relation to the quantity of limb tissue to be innervated. On this basis, the *absolute* number of nerves needed by the regenerating digits, for example, is much less than in the arm itself, simply because the digits are smaller. However, the number of fibers *per unit of area* at the amputation surface remains approximately the same. Consequently, there is a quantitative aspect to the trophic influence of nerves which may prove to have great significance in explaining why some animals can replace extremities and others cannot.

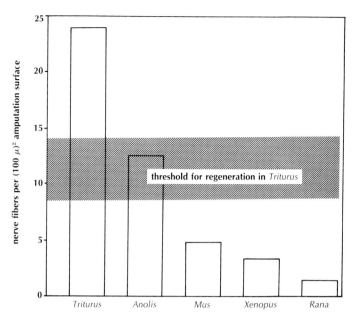

Fig. 71 **Comparative aspects of upper arm innervation in relation to regenerative ability.** *Triturus,* **which regenerates best of all, has the greatest concentration of nerve fibers. By newt standards, the chameleon** (*Anolis*) **has sufficient innervation, but it does not regenerate limbs. The mouse and frog** (*Rana*) **have too few fibers to regenerate limbs.** *Xenopus* **also has relatively few fibers, but its regenerative ability may be attributed to the extra-large axis cylinders in its nerves.** (*After Rzehak and Singer, 1966.*)

This possibility has been explored in a number of different animals by Rzehak and Singer. As graphically summarized in Fig. 71, *Triturus* is in a class by itself. Its high concentration of nerve fibers is more than adequate to support regeneration. Curiously enough, the reptilian limb (*Anolis*) which cannot regenerate has the theoretical threshold number of fibers that suffices for *Triturus*. Mice and frogs, however, fall well below this threshold. Yet *Xenopus* is able to regenerate limbs despite this deficiency, perhaps because its nerve fibers are several times greater in diameter than those of other species.

Therefore it is not sufficient to explain regenerative ability solely in terms of nerve fiber concentration. Nor is there a positive correlation with fiber size. A more consistent relationship is revealed, however, by calculating the product of size and concentration of nerve fibers in the limb. On this basis, Singer has shown that *Xenopus* has as much axoplasm as *Triturus,* but *Rana* does not.

There is also a temporal dimension to the effect of nerves on the complex sequence of events which lead to the reproduction of a complete limb. We know that nerves are not needed for wound healing of the amputated stump. We also know that the qualitative morphological integrity of the fully formed limb does not depend on its innervation. Somewhere in between are the developmental processes for which an adequate nerve supply is indispensable. There is no reason to believe that the process of dedifferentiation is influenced by nerves. Indeed, this goes on without limit in amputated larval urodele limbs deprived of their innervation. It appears that nerves are somehow necessary to check the regressive tendencies of limb stumps, perhaps by initiating the formation of a blastema. In fact, the blastema itself, if transplanted to a denervated larval limb stump, will arrest or deter the process of regression. But without nerves, an amputated limb does not give rise to a blastema. Since this takes about two weeks to develop in adult newts, denervation during the first fortnight following amputation regularly inhibits regeneration. In the larva, this critical period may last only about a week. Once a blastema has been produced, however, the role of the nerves becomes less important. Denervation of limbs which have already formed blastemas does not stop future morphogenetic progress. Cells can differentiate inside the blastema, and the gross morphological aspects of the limb can take shape as usual. The rate of elongation of the regenerate, however, may be impeded by the lack of nerves, with the result that growth in volume does not occur. Hence, nerves are required for quantitative growth during the later phases of regeneration, but their earlier role in promoting blastema formation is of far greater importance.

How is this neural influence mediated? Since either sensory or motor fibers are effective by themselves if present in sufficient numbers, the direction of impulse conduction is apparently not related to the trophic effect of nerves. It is quite possible, however, that one of the neurohumoral substances secreted by nerve endings might stimulate regeneration. In a direct assault on this problem, Singer devised a technique whereby test substances could be injected into the blastemas of adult newt limbs by means of a microinfusion apparatus. By keeping the newts anesthetized for hours at a stretch, it was possible to administer a continuous stream of various drugs directly into the blastema over prolonged periods of time in order to observe their effects on subsequent development.

Inasmuch as sympathectomized limbs are not prevented from regenerating, it is perhaps permissible to rule out adrenaline as a possible neurotrophic factor. This leaves acetylcholine as a leading contender for the role. Indeed, the infusion of atropine, which inhibits the action of acetylcholine, arrests regeneration. This effect can be reversed if sufficient acetylcholine is injected along with the atropine. These results become even more convincing in view of the high concentrations of acetylcholine present in the blastema, in contrast to its gradual decline during differentiation and morphogenesis. And when acetylcholine is maximal, cholinesterase, which normally catalyzes its breakdown, is well below the levels found in normal limbs. Thus, there is an impressive weight of evidence in favor of acetylcholine. Yet it is a credit to the scientific method that Singer impartially sought evidence both pro and con, and in the final analysis found the acetylcholine theory to be lacking.

For example, it has been shown that although the acetylcholine content declines in denervated limb stumps, considerable quantities of it still persist after regenerative capacities have been totally abolished. Furthermore, motor nerve fibers have been found to contain far more acetylcholine than sensory ones, yet the latter fibers support limb regeneration better than the former. But Singer's crucial experiment involved the infusion of acetylcholine into denervated-amputated limbs to see if regeneration could be induced. It could not. Hence, it must be reluctantly concluded that acetylcholine probably does not mediate the trophic influences of nerves in regenerating limbs after all.

What Tissues Do Nerves Affect? In the present state of the art, our techniques do not permit a categorical statement as to what tissue(s) in the limb are directly responsive to the trophic influence of nerves. Muscle and epidermis receive the vast majority of nerve fibers, with most of the motor axons going to muscle and the sensory fibers innervating the epidermis. Yet experiments have shown that exclusive innervation by either motor or sensory nerves can support regeneration. When all sensory nerves are eliminated, and the motor supply is quantitatively adequate, regeneration can occur even in the absence of epidermal innervation. However, this cannot rule out epidermis as an important if not essential target of neural influences since we have no proof that the affected tissue has to be innervated directly. Indeed, there is some evidence that cartilage, which is an altogether nerveless tissue, may grow better in limbs which are innervated than in those which are not. For example, in skinless limbs inserted into the coelomic cavity, regeneration does not take place except for the production of cartilage on the ends of the severed bones (see Fig. 70). When such limbs are denervated, however, there is much less chondrification. A somewhat more dramatic example has been noted in larval *Ambystoma* limbs undergoing skeletal regeneration. If the ulna is extirpated from the arm, a new one usually develops in its place. But if the arm is also denervated, no ulna is regenerated. In fact, many such limbs regress altogether, a phenomenon which may have something to do with the failure of skeletal replacement even in those denervated arms which persist.

Normally when a limb is denervated it atrophies a little but otherwise maintains its shape. In adult newts, denervated limbs persist even after amputation, but in larvae, which possess cartilaginous skeletal parts, amputation stimulates a relentless regression which comes to a halt only when the limb has practically disappeared. If, in the meantime, the nerve stumps regenerate out into the regressing limb, then the process of degeneration may be reversed. There is a balance between destruction and construction which can be maintained only with proper innervation. This is reminiscent of the regression of denervated catfish taste barbels described in the last chapter, except that denervated limbs do not regress unless they are injured. Perhaps by determining which tissues must be wounded in order to stimulate regression of nerveless limbs we might find a clue as to the tissues which specifically depend upon nerves to maintain their morphological integrity, not to mention their regenerative potentials.

Some years ago, Charles Thornton attempted to analyze the nature of the stimulus to regression in denervated larval limbs. By inflicting various kinds of injuries, e.g., crushing or piercing, he was able to traumatize different parts of the limb in a number of ways. Whether pierced or crushed, such limbs regressed. The degeneration was maximal in the area of injury, but in most cases much or all of the limb was eventually caught up in the deterioration. If the nerves were repeatedly resected to prevent the restoration of innervation, the entire limb withered away in a month or so owing to shrinkage of the upper and lower arms and loss of the digits (Fig. 72). The latter process was usually the last to occur, with the result that in advanced stages of regression all that remained of some arms were a few fingers protruding from the shoulder region. Curiously enough, if the digits did not waste away completely, regeneration of the limb could not occur upon

Fig. 72 **Regression of injured denervated fore limb of** Ambystoma punctatum **larva at intervals in days (as indicated by the numbers). Following its reinnervation after six weeks, a blastema is organized which then grows out into a new limb.** (After Thornton and Kraemer, 1951.)

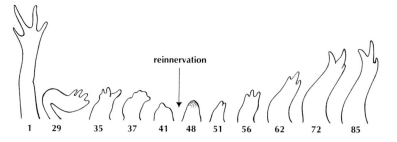

reinnervation. Evidently the persistence of differentiated terminal structures precludes the organization of a new blastema.

Amputation, crushing, and piercing, all of which initiate regression of denervated larval limbs, cause injury to each tissue component of the limb. It is not feasible to injure internal tissues without wounding the skin, but the reverse experiment is possible. When a lesion is inflicted on the epidermis alone, wound healing occurs and no regression of the limb ensues. Thus, it is the internal part of a limb which cannot reverse its regression without nerves, but we still do not know if an epidermal wound is involved in this process in any way.

Regression is the antithesis of regeneration, yet the potential for one does not occur without the other. The dedifferentiation of stump tissues which precedes regeneration may be regarded as a limited form of limb regression which goes on unchecked if nerves are absent. This occurs only in appendages otherwise capable of regeneration, a correlation which is especially evident in the hind legs of metamorphosing tadpoles. Young legs can regenerate from any level, but this capacity is lost in a proximo-distal direction as maturation proceeds. If tadpole legs are denervated and amputated, regression may take place as it does in larval urodele limbs, but it progresses only as far proximally as the ability to regenerate extends. Whatever it is about a limb that determines whether or not it can regenerate also makes regression possible. Both potentials coexist, but nerves are necessary to turn the tide of regression into the constructive channels of regeneration.

Aneurogenic Limbs   It was beginning to look as if the role of nerves in regeneration must be a rule with no exceptions, but then Chester Yntema at the State University of New York in Syracuse discovered that this was not necessarily so. It has long been known that the limbs of embryos do not depend upon nerves for their development. Nerves grow into them secondarily. Yntema succeeded in producing limbs in *Ambystoma punctatum* embryos which were completely nerveless, or nearly so. Limbs such as these, which have never been innervated, are called aneurogenic. They can be produced by removing the part of the embryonic neural tube from which nerves normally grow into the arms. Such a drastic operation, however, seriously incapacitates the animal, to the extent that it cannot feed itself. Only by combining it parabiotically with an intact embryo from which nourishment can be obtained is it able to survive larval life. What is so surprising about aneurogenic limbs is that they can regenerate despite the lack of nerves, as if they never missed what they never had.

Trygve Steen and Charles Thornton followed up this promising lead with a series of ingenious experiments designed to learn which components of the limb are normally dependent upon nerves. This was achieved by replacing the skin of aneurogenic limbs with that from normally innervated ones. When amputated through the region of the graft no regeneration occurred, and in fact most limbs regressed due to insufficient innervation. However, when mesodermal tissues of aneurogenic limbs were removed and comparable tissues from normal limbs were implanted, regeneration proceeded at the expense of the normal tissues. Clearly, it is the skin which seems to become so extraordinarily addicted to the presence of nerves in normally developing limbs. Only when it remains innocent of innervation from the beginning can regeneration occur; once nerves invade a limb it cannot regenerate without them.

The foregoing evidence favors the possibility that nerves might exert their influence directly on the epidermis. Further evidence along these lines derives from studies of the apical cap of cells which characteristically takes shape out of the wound epidermis on the end of the stump. Careful histological examinations have revealed that this cap is richly supplied with nerve fibers. They grow into this part of the epidermis in much greater profusion than anywhere else, which raises the suspicion that the relationship might be a causal one. As S. Meryl Rose has proposed, there may be a stepwise control of regeneration whereby nerves influence the epidermis which in turn promotes blastema formation immediately beneath it. This is an attractive hypothesis, but there is evidence which militates against it. For example, apical epidermal caps still form in aneurogenic limbs. Secondly, limbs totally deprived of their sensory innervation produce apical caps which lack nerves. Thirdly, we have no assurance that the cap forms where nerve fibers are most dense. Maybe the independently developing cap somehow attracts large numbers of nerve fibers to it which play no significant role in subsequent developmental events. Nevertheless, the lion's share of available evidence suggests that the trophic influence of nerves in limb regeneration may be of greater importance in the wound epidermis than elsewhere, a relationship which is especially notable in the production of accessory appendages.

The Definition of Territory As Thornton has demonstrated, a healing wound is necessary for limb regeneration because that is where the apical epidermal cap is formed. This cap is believed to induce the blastema from the dedifferentiating mesodermal tissues with which it is in contact. An amputation stump

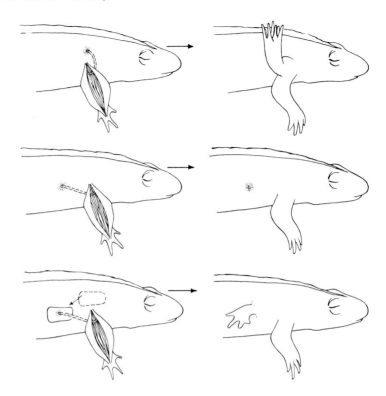

Fig. 73 **Experimental exploration of limb territory in** Triton cristatus. **When a nerve from the arm is diverted to a wound site in the shoulder region (top row), an accessory limb, which is often abnormal, is induced to regenerate there. If the nerve is deviated too far away from the limb (middle row), no regeneration occurs. But if skin from the limb territory is grafted to the formerly nonregenerating area (bottom row), a supernumerary arm can now be induced by the nerve.** (After Guyénot et al., 1948, and Kiortsis, 1953.)

provides the ideal conditions under which nerves, epidermis and mesoderm can all interact in ways which promote the outgrowth of a regenerate. Amputation, however, is not the only way to create these conditions. Traumatization of the unamputated limb may also bring about regeneration provided the neural, epidermal and mesodermal prerequisites are fulfilled. It is even possible to cause supernumerary limbs to grow from the shoulder region by deviating nerves to wound sites (Fig. 73), a technique which enabled Emile Guyénot and his students at the University of Geneva to map out the limb territory. By this method, however, it is not possible to induce the development of extra limbs except within a certain radius of the limb itself, an area which circumscribes the existence of regenerative potentialities. As Vassili Kiortsis has clearly demonstrated, however, the only way to induce extra limbs outside the limb territory is to transplant full thickness skin there from the shoulder region (Fig. 73). Hence, limb specificity resides in the tissues of the territory itself. Yet these tissues yield no histological clues as to whether or not they can participate in regeneration. Under the microscope, nonregenerative regions of the body look the same as those capable of growing appendages. A difference exists, but what it is we cannot tell, except by testing for the development of accessory outgrowths.

This can best be done by diverting a cut nerve to a given region where a wound has been made in the skin. By bringing together regenerating nerve fibers, healing epidermis and injured mesodermal tissues, there develops an apical cap beneath which a blastema may form. The latter event seems to be crucial in defining the territory of an appendage. Nerves and epidermis, as has been shown, are apparently without much morphogenetic specificity. They are necessary if morphogenesis of the region is to be expressed, but the nature of this expression seems to reside in the underlying mesodermal tissues of the area. These tissues are imprinted with latent information concerning the kind of structure to be formed, information which exists in the cells for some distance away from the limb proper. Presumably the limb territory is defined by how widely these "educated" cells are deployed.

For each extremity there is a territory of regeneration. In the hind limb of *Triton*, the European newt, this territory covers much of the pelvic region. Supplemental limbs can be induced to regenerate by deviating the sciatic nerve to various locations around the base of the leg. If the nerve is implanted too far away, no regeneration occurs because the cells outside the territory are not competent to give rise to a leg. In certain directions, however, the nerve may be diverted into adjacent territories of other structures. Posteriorly, for example, the nerve can induce the regeneration of small tail-like outgrowths. If moved to a dorsal location, it may bring about the local production of an extra dorsal crest. Here, therefore, there are three territories of regeneration, one for the dorsal crest, another for the tail, and a third for the hind leg. They can all be induced to express their regenerative potentialities by approximating the same nerve to the wound epidermis in different areas, but it is obvious that the nerve's influence is only permissive, not instructive.

Of course, the best place to induce a supernumerary limb is on the limb itself. The method of nerve deviation works well, but there are other ways of achieving the same results, ways which shed further light on the factors operating in the regenerative process. For example, it was shown long ago that if a limb is ligated, extra limbs may sprout from just behind the ligature. We can only guess at the mechanism of this. More recently, Elmer Butler and Harold Blum at Princeton University found that if larval arms were exposed to ultraviolet light, they would develop side growths from the site of irradiation, presumably owing to the irritation of exposed tissues.

A more popular method of inducing accessory limbs has been to implant various foreign substances subcutaneously into the arm (Fig. 74),

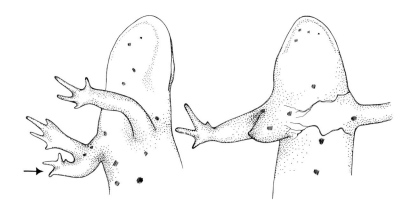

Fig. 74 **On the left, a newt in ventral view bearing an extra arm (arrow) induced to grow by the injection of coal tar containing carcinogens. On the right, a newt which had started to grow an accessory arm induced by carcinogens, but which later developed a sarcoma at the base of the regenerate.** (*After Breedis, 1952.*)

whereupon outgrowths sometimes germinate from the site of implantation. Charles Breedis of the University of Pennsylvania, in seeking a possible link between regeneration and cancer, discovered that if certain carcinogenic substances are put into the limbs of adult newts, tumors sometimes developed but in other cases limbs grew out from the sides of the arms. It almost looked as if what might have become cancerous could occasionally be anatomically organized. However, there is no proof that the carcinogens were acting specifically, for the accessory limbs may well have developed in response to chronic local irritation. Subsequent investigations, notably those of Laurens Ruben at Reed College, not only led support to the chronic irritation hypothesis, but also raise a few other interesting possibilities. He and his colleagues set out to test the capacities of various foreign tissue implants to induce accessory limb regeneration in newts. They found that of a wide variety of organs assayed, frog kidney worked best. Other amphibian organs such as liver, spleen, small intestine, skeletal muscle and heart, all possessed little or no capacity to promote supernumerary limbs. Even renal adenocarcinomas from frogs proved to be poor inducers. One wonders, then, what is so special about frog kidneys, especially since homografts of newt kidneys do not work. It seems reasonable to conclude that something antigenic might be involved, something with both organ and species specificity.

The next task was to find out if living cells are needed in the implant. They are not. At the University of Minnesota, Bruce Carlson confirmed that homogenates of fresh frog kidney are effective in stimulating accessory limbs, as are lyophilized or frozen pieces of tissue. However, if the kidney is first boiled, its efficacy is abolished, which further supports the notion of a possible proteinaceous antigen as the inducing agent. The best educated guess to date as to how such implants induce extra limbs proposes the release of cytolytic factors which affect host tissues so as to set up the local conditions necessary to initiate regeneration. Perhaps the rate of disintegration of implanted organs determines which one(s) shall be effective, for the right concentration of cytolytic agent may have to be present over an appropriate duration of time if success is to be realized. The net result would be a long-term exposure of host cells to irritating agents, an explanation which is consistent with observations on other kinds of implants. Not only can carcinogens induce limb outgrowths, but so can implanted pieces of celloidin, and even bone. Either by mechanical or chemical means, these materials might be expected to traumatize host tissues, which themselves might release cytolytic enzymes instrumental in promoting regeneration. Whatever the answer may be, we still have to figure out how chronic local irritation might be translated into regeneration.

The favored explanation relates to the effects of foreign implants on the overlying dermis. One way or another, they seem to bring about dermal dissolution, thus promoting the juxtaposition of epidermis and nondermal mesoderm. Add to this the fact that foreign grafts elicit an inflammatory reaction on the part of the host, and we have several sources of irritation (mechanical, enzymatic, immunological) which could conspire to arouse reparative responses among host tissues in the vicinity. Indeed, everything necessary for regeneration seems to be at hand except nerves.

In the early stages of accessory limb regeneration there is a piling up of epidermal cells where the blastema is going to form. But this is not excessively innervated as it is in the case of amputated limbs. Since appropriate implants can induce accessory limbs in the absence of intentional interruption and regeneration of nerves, it appears that neurotrophic influences are less important for limb regeneration under these conditions than they are following amputation. However, nerves are not altogether unnecessary because implants fail to stimulate accessory outgrowths in totally denervated limbs. Perhaps, then, there is a considerably reduced threshold for the nerve requirement when regeneration is made to occur by chronic irritation. Why this should be true we do not know, but the relation between nerves and injury is beginning to look very suspicious. Transplanted limbs, for example, can regenerate despite sparse innervation presumably because of the damage they suffer in the process of being grafted and revascularized. One is also reminded of how the regression of denervated limbs is initiated by trauma. Indeed, the trophic influence of nerves cannot be expressed in limbs except when an injury such as amputation has been inflicted. Conversely, the only circumstance under which development can occur in the absence of injury is in the normal ontogeny of the limb bud, and for this nerves are not needed.

When one contemplates the significance of all this, it makes very good sense from the standpoint of phylogenetic strategy. Where there is the ability to regenerate, there must also be safeguards against premature regeneration. Otherwise a limb might sprout offshoots all over the place. Too much of a good thing can be worse than not enough. So it is that the diverse mechanisms leading to the development of a limb regenerate are all linked ultimately to injury as the first cause.

The Genesis of Form

Nothing makes one feel more humble than the unfathomed mysteries of morphogenesis. I have watched countless limbs regenerate, only to deepen my appreciation for T. H. Morgan's attitude toward the problem of how developing regenerates take shape. So formidable is the problem of morphogenesis that we are tempted to attack lesser, but more accessible, targets. We have learned many things about the neural and hormonal factors necessary for regeneration. We can describe in great detail how the cells and tissues of a limb proliferate, migrate, and synthesize enzymes during the course of regeneration. Some of us even think we know why higher vertebrates cannot regenerate their appendages. But these advances, important as they may be, are all beside the point. We must eventually come to grips with the problem of how the structure of a limb is so flawlessly copied when missing parts are replaced.

Morphogenesis occurs at all levels of organization, from the molecule on up. The higher the level, the more difficult the explanation. The gross morphology of the limb is so complicated that it would be presumptuous today for anyone to claim to understand how the development of its structure is controlled. In other vertebrate appendages, such as barbels, fins or tails, the anatomy at one level is essentially the same as at any other. Often there is a segmental arrangement of parts, and growth occurs simply by adding new units at the end of the series. Morphogenesis in such structures is a repetitive phenomenon, whereas in the limb the morphology changes drastically along the length from shoulder to fingertip. The limb is segmented in the sense that there are joints, but each segment of the extremity is anatomically distinct. The uniqueness of each level derives from specific arrangements of its histological components, the morphogenesis of which is best illustrated by the skeletal parts.

Amputation exposes a cross section of tissues to which the anatomy of the regenerate must conform if a useful appendage is to be produced. Each new structure develops as a continuation of its counterpart in the stump, which raises the question of how the blastema cells manage to differentiate into the right tissues in the right places. Of logical necessity, they must react to messages from the stump, messages which convey information as to axes of orientation, at which level along the length of the limb development is to begin, and whether the limb is the right or the left one. One might expect that the tissues of the stump should be responsible for directing the differentiation of those blastema cells situated immediately distal to them. If so, however, this is not a strictly one to one relationship, as indicated by deletion experiments carried out by Paul Weiss and others on the skeletal elements of regenerating limbs.

If the humerus, for example, is removed from the upper arm of an adult newt, the regenerate which develops following amputation through the boneless region will not reflect the deficiency in the stump.

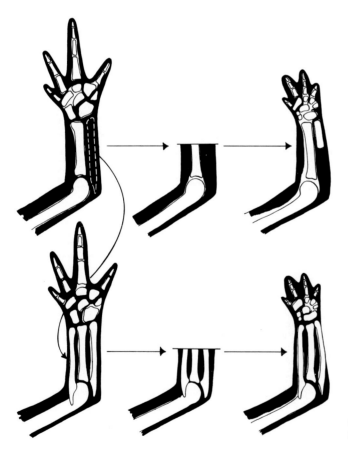

Fig. 75 **The role of bone in limb morphogenesis. Above: Removal of ulna from lower arm does not interfere with the subsequent development of a cartilaginous ulna after amputation through the operated region. Below: Addition of an extra ulna to a lower arm, followed by amputation, brings about the production of a corresponding extra skeletal element in the regenerate.**

Although the missing humerus is not replaced in the stump itself, its distal portion is nevertheless produced in the developing regenerate. This may be taken to indicate that the bone in the stump does not participate in its own distal replacement—that perhaps other tissues in the vicinity foster the differentiation of skeletal structures in the regenerate. Be this as it may, the opposite experiment, as outlined in Fig. 75, contradicts such a simplified explanation. If an extra bone is added to a limb, amputation through the transplant region yields a regenerate containing a cartilaginous extension of the supernumerary bone. Clearly, the stump skeleton is not morphogenetically inert after all. It makes its presence felt, although other tissues can take over in its absence. Thus, the limb is quite capable of compensating for skeletal deficiencies, but it possesses no mechanism to correct for a superabundance of structural subunits. Apparently each tissue of the stump can vote to be represented in the blastema, and some of them can even cast absentee ballots.

Assuming that bones can, when present, take part in skeletal induction, do they communicate with the blastema via cellular or molecular messages? Dead bones do not work, nor do extra bones exposed to X-rays before being grafted to the limb. This evidence argues in favor of an inductive mechanism mediated by bone cells, or by other connective tissue cells when the nearby bone has been removed. It suggests that the skeletal territory, like that of the limb as a whole, extends beyond the overt limits of the primary structure. It also means that chondrocytes can arise in the blastema from precursors not formerly included in skeletal tissues.

The limb is a composite. It is a veritable curiosity shop of overlapping, interacting fields. To the extent that its component parts are architecturally integrated and physiologically coordinated, they must develop interdependently. This is what accounts for the capacity of structurally imperfect limbs to improve themselves in the course of regenerating. As D. R. Newth has emphasized, abnormal extremities tend to grow better parts in lieu of the replaced deficient ones, unless, of course, the abnormality is genetic in nature. So remarkable is the regenerate's capacity to correct mistakes, that even if all possible inner tissues of an arm are removed, minced, and stuffed back in, the appendage that grows from such a "sausage" is far less scrambled than were the parts of the stump from which it originated. Somewhere out of this gemisch there emerges a degree of order which permits a reasonably normal limb to develop with nothing more seriously wrong with it than a few misplaced digits. It seems that normalcy prevails over chaos so long as some part of the stump remains undisturbed.

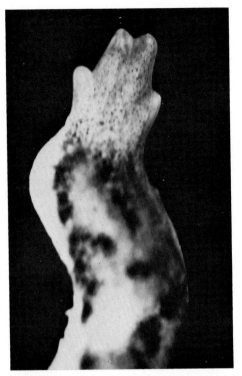

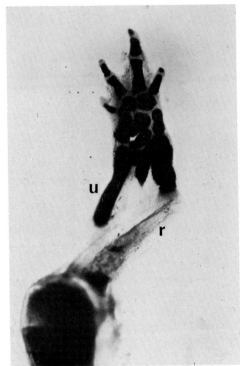

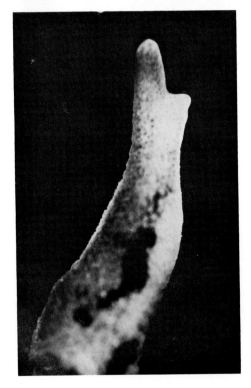

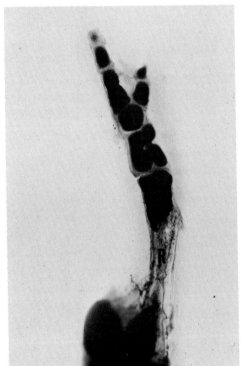

In the search for the source of morphogenetic information it is essential that the stump be tampered with in such a way as to cause a predictable abnormality to be produced. We know that the loss of relatively small fractions of a limb (e.g., bones) does not affect the quality of the regenerate. But how much of a limb can be removed before the effect is reflected morphogenetically? There has to be a limit beyond which regulation cannot occur, but to reach it as much as half the limb must be removed.

When the posterior half of a newt's lower fore limb is cut away from elbow to wrist, subsequent amputation yields a stump that is only half there. From such a bisected limb there grows only half a hand usually containing about two fingers instead of the usual four (Fig. 76). It is interesting that the half-sized blastema that forms does not give rise to a whole hand of diminutive dimensions. Although it develops into a qualitatively incomplete appendage, the sizes of the parts are normal.

On the other hand, if only the internal tissues of the posterior half of the arm are excised, leaving the overlying skin intact, then the resulting regenerate is normal in every respect (Fig. 76). In other words, the presence of the posterior skin is enough to restore completeness to the system, thus implicating the dermis as one source of morphogenetic information.

Another way to study the participation of various parts of the leg stump is by selective X-irradiation. This enables the experimenter to eliminate various portions of the leg from taking part in regeneration without resorting to drastic surgical intervention. In general, if the internal tissues of the posterior half of the leg are X-rayed, with or without irradiation of the posterior skin, only half a foot will be regenerated. Irradiation of the posterior half of the skin alone has no adverse effects of morphogenesis, unless of course the inner tissues have been extirpated.

Experiments along these lines have thus failed to reveal the existence of any one tissue in the limb which exclusively carries the mor-

Fig. 76 **Regeneration of half limbs. Above: When posterior half of lower arm is removed but overlying skin is left intact, a complete limb regenerates at an oblique angle to the longitudinal axis of the limb. The missing ulna (u) is reconstituted as shown in the skeletal preparation (top right). Below: Removal of the entire posterior half of the lower arm, including the skin, results in the regeneration of only half a hand containing skeletal elements corresponding to the radius (r) remaining in the stump.** (*From Figs. 3–6 (page 561) of Goss, 1957a.*)

phogenetic blueprints of what is to regenerate. Rather, this property probably lies in many parts of the limb, any one of which can guide the blastema along normal channels of development when called upon to do so. In terms of the morphogenetic field, a part can express the whole—up to a point. The lower limb (which contains two bones) has at least two fields, one anterior and another posterior. Neither one can make up for the absence of the other, but within each half a remnant of the original can give rise to the new tissues in its domain. This is why the concept of territory is so important, for it defines an anatomical region within which a complete structure can be reorganized from a fraction of the whole. And this, in essence, is what regeneration is all about.

Living systems are very good at replacing missing parts, for in the very nature of things structures are liable to be lost. It is not in the nature of things, however, to acquire extra parts. The accidental grafting of tissues in living systems is so farfetched that for animals to have evolved measures designed to correct for such an improbable event could hardly have been expected. What nature could never do,

Fig. 77 **Unification of regenerates from double limbs. When lower arms of a newt are grafted together in parallel orientation and then amputated below the elbow, a single blastema is formed on the compound stump (left). This may give rise to a single hand formed by the fusion of corresponding skeletal parts (middle). Sometimes unification is incomplete, as shown in the specimen on the right in which the two posterior digits are single but the anterior ones have remained double.** (*From Figs. 3B and 7 (pp. 199, 209) of Goss, 1956c.*)

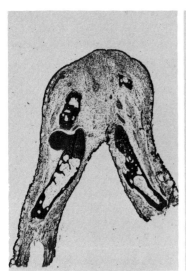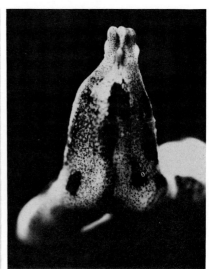

however, experimental zoologists can sometimes achieve, thereby creating a situation without precedent. By confronting a living system with something never before experienced, or for that matter expected, the experimenter attempts to confound it. Such tactics are often very revealing, for living things placed in embarrassing situations tend to betray their true natures.

One way to create an unprecedented situation is to graft two limbs together in parallel. The left and right lower arms of adult newts with their ventral sides together can be thus conjoined as if in prayer. When amputated through the united regions, the limb stump that remains is a double structure. In well-grafted cases, they produce a single large blastema (Fig. 77) which develops into a single regenerated hand. One might at first be led to believe that the compound limb had somehow become unified in the course of regeneration. If this were true, however, the hand would have to be either a left one or a right one, but in fact it could be neither without favoring one component or the other of the double stump. Upon closer inspection, this logical impasse is seen to be solved in the only way possible. The apparently single hand is actually a double structure composed of the fused outside halves of the left and right regenerates (Fig. 77). What would have been the palms, had the arms not been grafted together, were omitted where the two morphogenetic fields overlapped. Sometimes by chance the grafted arms converge distally instead of being parallel. When this happens their respective fields become so superimposed that the two prospective regenerates almost cancel each other out and little or no new growth is produced.

Experiments with half limbs and double limbs show that each region of the stump promotes the development of corresponding structures in the part of the blastema distal to it. Within any given morphogenetic zone, deficiencies can be compensated, but if an entire territory is lacking it cannot be replaced. Conversely, the influence of each component of a limb stump makes itself felt in the blastema. Extra parts in the stump, whether they are transplanted bones or entire grafted limbs, always exert an effect on the regenerate. The blastema does what it is told, even if it means perpetuating an abnormality.

This principle is well illustrated in even more bizarre combinations of grafted tissues, as when parts of different kinds of appendages are combined. For example, if tissues are transplanted from the tail to the limb, and the latter is amputated through the region of the graft, the resultant regenerate will express the characteristics of both appendages. The reciprocal experiment yields comparable results. In either case the regenerate will possess digits or vertebrae or tail fins in proportion to the sources of the cells contributing to it. Such chimeric outgrowths again reflect the fact that stump tissues insist on being represented in the blastema. Their morphogenetic potentialities are not altered by where they are located in the body or by what other tissues surround them.

In a variation of this kind of experiment, tissues from the tail, for example, can be grafted to a limb which has been previously X-rayed. Under these conditions the limb tissues are excluded from participating in regeneration. The transplanted tail tissues therefore have the field to themselves. Accordingly, they give rise to tail-like regenerates; no limb characteristics show up in the new outgrowth. Such regenerates of course are usually incomplete since they arise from pieces of tail muscle, skeleton or skin instead of whole cross sections of tails. Nevertheless, the outcome of this type of experiment emphasizes the fact that regenerating tissues do not completely lose their identities in the process of blastema formation.

Whither the Blastema? The regeneration blastema and the embryonic limb bud have much in common, but they are not identical. The limb bud comes endowed with a full measure of potentialities for becoming an entire limb. The blastema forms only those parts of a limb that normally lie distal to the level of amputation. The embryonic limb bud fulfills its morphogenetic destiny *de novo*. The blastema must conform to the pre-established pattern of the parent stump as its morphogenetic potentialities become anatomic realities.

Is the blastema a predetermined structure? In answering this question we must be careful to distinguish between the blastema cell and the blastema as a whole. The two do not necessarily become determined at the same time. When an architect has finished drawing the plans for a building, its overall design has already been determined. But the fates of individual items of construction material will not be decided until much later. The analogy, however, leaves much to be desired because all bricks may be alike and interchangeable but all cells are not.

The cells in a blastema may look very much the same although their appearances may belie their true identities. Indeed, one cannot distinguish the cells in a tail blastema from those in a limb blastema. They all come from much the same kinds of tissues (muscle, skeleton, connective tissues), and are all capable of giving rise to the same tissues in the regenerate. Yet a tail blastema is not a limb blastema and presumably never can be. If it is transplanted to a limb stump a tail-limb combination may develop, but if the stump has been previously irradiated the tail blastema never becomes anything but a tail. Recalling what happened when differentiated tail tissues were transplanted to X-rayed limbs, one is impressed with the apparent immutable nature of the body's tissues. Cartilage, for example, may occur in all appendages, but is it necessarily true that a chondrocyte is a chondrocyte is a chondrocyte? Could vertebral cartilage develop into a humerus, or femur into mandible, even though their cells are overtly indistinguishable? Similar questions can be asked of muscle fibers, which may not be nonentities either. If the cells of the tail were indelibly imprinted with tailness, and those of the limb territory with limbness, then they could be transplanted to foreign locations, they could be mixed together and never sort themselves out, but always they would remain loyal to their native territories.

Just how discriminating is their histological patriotism? Assuming that a limb cell will always remain a limb cell, how can it remember its address within the limb? Will a cell originally residing in the upper arm become, under the circumstances of regeneration, assimilated into a hand? The answer must be in the affirmative, for hands can obviously regenerate from the tissues of the upper arm. Therefore, the cells in a limb are fortuitously situated. They can exchange one location for another, an aptitude without which regeneration would be impossible.

The versatility of limb cells, however, is not without its limits. What they can or cannot do dictates what is to regenerate. For example, vertebrate appendages, limbs included, can regenerate only in the distal direction. If a limb is grafted onto an animal backwards, regeneration from the former proximal cut surface always gives rise to distal parts even if these duplicate in mirror image the structure of the stump from which they arose (Fig. 78). Clearly, there is a proximo-distal polarity imposed upon appendages which cannot be reversed. To be otherwise would have been very interesting but quite impossible, at least for higher animals.

It will be recalled that worms can and do reverse their polarity under certain special conditions of regeneration. Yet even when a head grows instead of a tail, it is still a distal structure which forms. Thus, when regeneration occurs along an animal's body axis it conforms to a two-way gradient depending upon which direction the cut surface faces. In other words, both directions are distal. Appendage regeneration thus obeys the same rule, for it too can give rise only to distal structures.

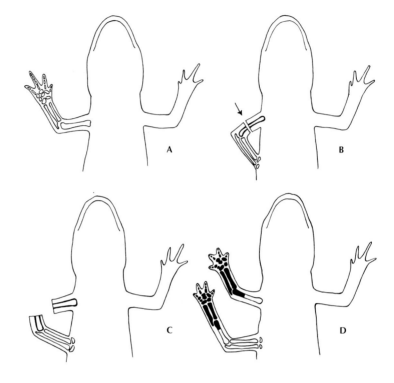

Fig. 78 **Reversal of polarity. The distal end of a limb is grafted to the flank, allowed to establish vascular connections and then severed (arrow) from the rest of the arm; when properly innervated, such a backward limb may regenerate in a proximal direction but will always form distal structures in doing so.**

This means that limb cells are not completely exchangeable. They can only become incorporated into structures normally lying distal to where they originated. Even if the cells in a hand may have been regenerated from the upper arm, they can never go back to what they used to be. Once they become part of a hand their regenerative potential is more limited than before. Now they can only give rise to digits. Regeneration ceases at the fingertips because here the cells can become nothing but what they are already. At the end of the line there is nowhere else to go.

This strict distal polarity likewise makes it impossible for limbs to regenerate laterally. Remove the anterior or posterior half of an arm and the missing parts will never be filled in. If anything at all grows from the wound site it is a hand and digits, that is, distal structures regenerating in a lateral direction.

Regeneration recapitulates ontogeny. An amputated limb grows out not only in space but also in time. As the new limb elongates it also matures. These spatial and temporal dimensions of development cannot be separated. Now from this point of view, what might we expect to happen if regeneration really could proceed in a disto-proximal direction? In the first place, there is no ontogenetic precedent for such an event. Not even the embryonic limb bud can grow backwards. Yet if a limb *could* regenerate proximally it would have to form an extremity with the nerves and blood vessels going in the wrong directions. More important, however, it might be expected to reverse its temporal axis along with its spatial one. Theoretically, such an outgrowth, or rather ingrowth, should become progressively less mature in the course of its development, which I would suppose to be a logical impossibility. The reason for this *reductio ad absurdum* is that development cannot go forward while maturity goes backward. If we want a limb to reverse the polarity of its regeneration we must expect it to become increasingly immature in the process. The nearest thing to this is the regression of larval limbs which occurs following denervation and injury. Here the clock is turned back as the limb is resorbed, until all that is left is a limb bud.

Self-differentiation of the Blastema

It was pointed out earlier that the blastema and the limb bud were alike in some respects but different in others. One of the most important differences relates to their capacities for self-differentiation. The embryonic limb bud can develop autonomously, but the blastema depends upon the limb stump for at least some of its instructions. As the source of blastema cells, the limb stump endows its progeny with information as to what kind of appendage to become, how much of that appendage to form, and in which orientation. We do not know for sure, but the course of tissue differentiation may be left up to the individual cells. What they become may only depend upon where they happen to be in the blastema when differentiation commences. An early blastema can be thoroughly scrambled with a minute needle without seriously disturbing the morphology of the prospective regenerate. Unless the displaced cells sort themselves out afterward, it is difficult to imagine that the destinies of individual cells are rigidly controlled. Yet something must direct their differentiation, and the older tissues of the subjacent stump are in a good position to fulfill this role. But is that all there is to it? Is the blastema totally dependent upon the limb stump or does it have, like the embryonic limb bud, some free will of its own?

To find the answer it is necessary to separate the blastema from the limb and see what, if anything, it becomes. One way to do this would be to culture blastemas *in vitro,* a technique which has finally been achieved by David Stocum at the University of Pennsylvania. This long awaited breakthrough has revealed that blastemas at the cone stage of development or older can continue their growth and differentiation in complete isolation from the stump. Cartilage and muscle tissues differentiate within them, and skeletal elements of the arm and hand are produced. The gross morphology of such regenerates, however, tends to be distorted owing to the lack of a blood supply, among other things, *in vitro*. Consequently, if morphogenesis is to be investigated with any degree of precision, blastemas must be transplanted elsewhere on the body.

When grafted internally (e.g., intramuscularly or into the coelomic cavity) their epidermal covering encysts and the blastema cells seldom differentiate into an organized structure. Hence, the ideal transplantation site is the body surface, preferably to a regeneratively neutral area outside the limb territories. The flank of the body midway between the fore and hind limbs qualifies as such a location. The graft bed is prepared by cutting a small hole of appropriate size in the skin. Then the blastema is carefully freed from all stump tissues, pressed gently into the flank wound, and allowed to heal for several hours in a humid atmosphere before the newt is allowed to regain consciousness and returned to water. Revascularization usually occurs within a few days.

Sometimes no development occurs at all if the transplanted blastema is too small. Whether such failures are due to insufficient numbers of cells or to immaturity of the blastema we do not know. Older (and larger) blastemas, however, usually do develop after grafting. Conical ones, which have not quite begun to differentiate, are particularly interesting. When isolated from stump influences they are nevertheless capable of carrying on, usually forming digits and hands. Progressively older transplants give rise to more and more complete arms.

Jacob Faber, of the Hubrecht Laboratory in Utrecht, has conducted a thorough investigation of this complex problem by analyzing the fates of grafted blastemas in the axolotl. He was particularly impressed with the tendency for such transplants always to form distal limb parts. If any portion of the regenerate was missing it was always the more proximal regions. This "distalization" he considered to be a property of the apical organization center where the blastema cells are least differentiated and most highly proliferative. They are also farthest away from the stump in the normally regenerating limb. Faber discovered that not only can whole undifferentiated blastemas undergo morphogenesis after transplantation, but so can the terminal halves of somewhat older regenerates which are already starting to differentiate proximally. He was thus led to the conclusion that such undeveloped masses of blastema cells are capable of self-organization independent of all stump influences.

According to this hypothesis, there exists a basal morphogenetic field emanating from the stump and upon which the normal proximo-distal course of differentiation depends. In addition, there is an apical morphogenetic field which can presumably organize terminal limb structures autonomously. There is a good deal of truth in this view, for apical blastemas can and do develop in the absence of stump influences. Something makes certain that a regenerate shall always possess distal structures, for if anything goes wrong, a hand without an arm is better than an arm minus its hand. Yet when a hand differentiates from an isolated blastema, it cannot be completely free of stump influences. Something must determine the dorso-ventral and anterior-posterior axes of the hand, and this information could only come from the stump prior to its separation from the blastema. Thus, what appears superficially to be self-differentiation is at least in part the delayed expression of latent instructions for which the blastema is programmed from its earliest inception.

Endocrine Control of Regeneration

In 1926 Oscar Emil Schotté, working in Guyénot's laboratory in Geneva, opened up a new and important approach to regeneration. He discovered that hypophysectomized newts were unable to regenerate amputated limbs. Many men would have been content to make such a valuable contribution as this and leave it at that. Not Schotté. Some years later, at Amherst College, he followed up his original discovery with a series of investigations which have gone a long way toward clarifying the complexities of how the endocrine glands affect regeneration.

For a long time most people believed that the pituitary gland was necessary for regeneration owing to its output of growth hormone. Subsequent investigations have shown that this hormone does promote cellular proliferation in the blastema and does accelerate limb development, but it is not essential to the overall process of regeneration. Schótte and his students showed by replacement therapy that the administration of either cortisone or adrenocorticotropic hormone (ACTH) could restore regenerative capacities in hypophysectomized newts. Thus it appears that the pituitary is required only insofar as it stimulates the secretion of glucocorticoids from the adrenals. It is not possible directly to test the role of the adrenal gland by adrenalectomizing newts because these cells are far too diffusely scattered in small clusters along the dorsal aspect of the coelomic cavity to permit their total extirpation. However, by treating animals with Amphenone, a drug which inhibits cortisone secretion, it is possible to effect a pharmacological adrenalectomy. Under these conditions, limb regeneration is inhibited. It can be restored, however, by giving cortisone, but not ACTH.

Why is limb regeneration dependent upon cortisone? One reason may relate to Selye's general adaptation syndrome whereby glucocorticoids are secreted under conditions of stress, thus enabling an animal to adapt to distressing circumstances. Schotté found that if hypophysectomized newts were subjected to various kinds of trauma they could then regenerate limbs despite the absence of the pituitary. For example, if one limb of a hypophysectomized animal is exposed to hypertonic NaCl solutions, or is repeatedly amputated, the opposite extremity will regenerate. Evidently the chronic stress of injury somehow bypasses the absent pituitary and stimulates the secretion of enough cortisone to enable regeneration to occur.

How does cortisone work? Experiments have shown that if hypophysectomy is performed on newts at various intervals after amputation, regeneration can occur in all cases except those deprived of their pituitaries within a few days of amputation. This may be taken to indicate that the pituitary, via the adrenals, is required only during the earliest stages of regeneration when wound healing is going on. It is not necessary for blastema formation or for the subsequent differentiation of the regenerate. When the nonregenerating limbs of hypophysectomized animals are compared with normal controls, it may be seen that in the former cases a layer of fibrous scar tissue develops beneath the wound epidermis. In controls the apical epidermis remains in intimate contact with the dedifferentiating tissues of the stump. From studies on mammals, it is known that cortisone interferes with wound healing by inhibiting the synthesis of collagen fibers necessary for scar tissue formation. What may happen in the newt limb stump is that cortisone, when present in normal concentrations, retards fibrogenesis enough to prevent precocious scar formation. Only when the interposition of a scar between the epidermis and the stump mesoderm is prevented can these two tissues interact in ways required to set up a blastema. This tempting hypothesis is not necessarily correct, but it has the advantage thus far of being consistent with the known facts.

But the facts are not as clear as the foregoing account might imply. As Schotté originally showed, not all appendages depend upon the pituitary for their regeneration. In many larval newts, for example, hypophysectomy does not interfere with regeneration at all. In adult newts which cannot replace limbs without the pituitary, the tail can still regenerate. Moreover, tadpoles are capable of regenerating both tails and legs in the absence of the pituitary. Thus, there is considerable variation in the effects of the pituitary-adrenal system on regeneration both according to age and to location on the body as well.

Obviously, something must happen at metamorphosis to bring about a dependence upon the pituitary. The change could occur either in the extremities or in the endocrine glands, or both. To test the competence of the larval pituitary to support regeneration, such glands were transplanted to hypophysectomized adult newts. No regeneration of amputated limbs occurred in these newts, although controls bearing grafts of adult pituitaries did regenerate. It must be concluded, therefore, that the larval pituitary is not capable of secreting enough ACTH to stimulate cortisone production in the adult adrenals. Perhaps this is why the pituitary is not missed by the larval limb stump. If so, then how is such a limb able to regenerate in the presumed absence of cortisone? Perhaps the larval adrenals can secrete sufficient cortisone without being stimulated by ACTH at all. Alternatively, the larval limb may not form a precocious scar even in the absence of cortisone.

The significance of local conditions in the limb is most strikingly illustrated by studies of regeneration from reamputated regenerates. On the theory that the immaturity of larval limbs might account for their lack of dependence upon the pituitary-adrenal hormones, regenerates of adult newt limbs at varying stages of development have been tested for their reactions to these hormones. As an adult regenerate matures, it recapitulates in a way what happens to a larval limb during metamorphosis. The chondrified skeleton, for example, becomes ossified, and glands develop in the skin. Thus, when the distal halves of young regenerates of adult newt limbs are severed, regeneration occurs successfully despite the absence of the pituitary. Older regenerates, however, fail to grow back under similar circumstances. The cut-off point falls around forty-five days after the original amputation. Something happens at about that time, mimicking the effects of metamorphosis, which establishes a dependence of limb regeneration on the adrenal hormones.

Another hormone which seems to affect regeneration is thyroxine. This has a dual effect depending upon the stage of development at which it is administered. Early in limb regeneration thyroxine inhibits or retards regeneration, but later on it accelerates development of the new limb. Hypothyroid conditions, brought about by thryoidectomy or treatment with the goitrogen thiourea, has the opposite effect. The adverse influences of thyroxine administered prior to amputation may relate to metamorphic changes induced by the hormone, changes which in anurans, at least, correlate with the loss of regenerative capacities altogether.

Metamorphosis versus Regeneration It is fortunate for the student of regeneration that tadpoles should lose the ability to regenerate at about the time of metamorphosis. This makes it possible to study the extinction of regeneration during the course of ontogeny with a view to finding out what is responsible. Many investigators over the years have been attracted to this fascinating aspect of the problem in the hope that by discovering why the frog cannot regenerate they might also learn why birds and mammals cannot do so either. This approach is based on the precarious assumption that similarities between ontogeny and phylogeny have the same explanation. Perhaps in the case of regeneration they do, but this can be accepted only as an article of faith, not as proven fact.

The hind legs of tadpoles regenerate rather well during their formative stages. As the time for metamorphosis approaches, the legs complete their development and elongate considerably, a process which equips the froglet with a means of terrestrial locomotion after its tail has been resorbed. One wonders if it is significant in the grand design of nature, or merely a coincidence, that the leg loses its regenerative ability just at the time when it becomes most useful to the animal. Urodeles, in contrast, do not depend solely on their legs for movement, and retain the postmetamorphic capacity to replace them.

During the period of transition to the nonregenerative condition, tadpole legs can grow back following amputation at distal levels but not proximal ones. There is an invisible wave propagated in a proximo-distal direction which erases all former regenerative potentialities (Fig. 79). Thereafter, the amputated stump does not form an apical epidermal cap as it would have done before. Perhaps the reconstitution of the dermis over the end of the stump has something to do with this. Or maybe it is the delayed innervation of the wound epidermis. In any event, in the absence of the apical cap the internal tissues of the stump undergo neither dedifferentiation nor blastema formation.

Not all postmetamorphic anurans fail to regenerate legs. There are a few interesting species which can produce outgrowths from amputation stumps, but such structures are little more than tapering extensions

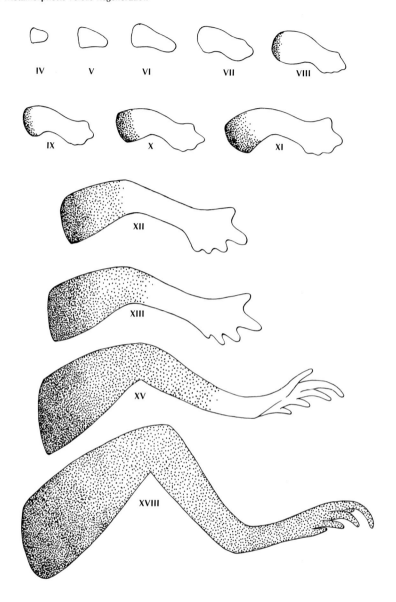

Fig. 79 **Proximo-distal loss of regenerative ability in tadpole legs as delineated by stippled areas. Prior to Taylor and Kollros stage XII, legs can regenerate following amputation through the thigh. By stage XV they lose the capacity to regenerate even at shank levels, and thereafter fail to regenerate at any level.**

of the extremities. The South African clawed toad, *Xenopus laevis,* is a primitive anuran which never quite outgrows its ability to regenerate limbs. As James Norman Dent of the University of Virginia has carefully documented, however, the regenerative ability of its hind legs is markedly reduced during metamorphosis (Fig. 80). As the leg matures, its regenerates turn out to be more and more abnormal until all that forms is an elongated spike.

Fig. 80 **Regeneration of**
Xenopus **legs. Immature legs
regenerate completely, but
the regenerates produced at
progressively older stages of
development are more and
more abnormal. Postmeta-
morphic legs (bottom row)
grow back as unbranched
spikes.** *(After Dent, 1962.)*

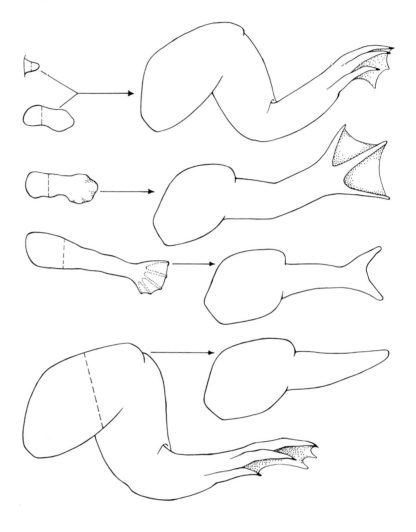

The histogenesis of such unusual regenerates has been studied in the laboratory of Stanislaw Skowron in Krakow. Developing from the cut end of the bone in the stump, these hypomorphic outgrowths consist almost entirely of cartilage and skin. Neither muscles nor joints are formed, but nerves and blood vessels run down the middle of the cartilaginous rod in a peculiar anatomical arrangement unlike anything ever encountered in a normal limb. Although *Xenopus* legs cannot regenerate without a nerve supply, their regenerates, if reamputated, can do so. Possibly the survival of regenerative ability beyond metamorphosis in *Xenopus* is somehow related to this exceptional reduction in the neural threshold.

There is no dearth of explanations for the loss of regeneration in postmetamorphic anurans. For example, it has been claimed that frogs cannot regenerate legs because their tissues are too highly differentiated. Yet how one measures the "degree of differentiation" of muscle or bone is never explained by proponents of this hypothesis. Alternatively, the failure of frogs' legs to regenerate has been attributed to a lack of coordination between the development of its various components. It is true that regeneration is a complicated phenomenon involving the harmonious participation of many processes, but in view of its success in urodeles and larval anurans, sometimes despite drastic experimental interventions, this idea does not inspire as much confidence as do some others.

Theories of a more convincing nature hold that when regenerative ability declines it is because an inhibitor is operating or some essential factor is missing. Such theories often have the advantage that they can be put to the test. Several of them have thus proved tenable, not the least which relates to the dependence of regeneration upon hormones. Metamorphosis, as everyone knows, is triggered by thyroxine, a hormone which has been shown to be antagonistic to the initiation of regeneration. It is doubtful that this hormone directly blocks regeneration, but obviously some change it induces at the local level may preclude regeneration. Possibly the adrenal hormones are of greater importance, for without them the regeneration of limbs is prevented even in adult urodeles. Could the inability of frogs to replace legs be caused by adrenal insufficiency? When Schotté grafted extra adrenal glands to frogs he noted that their limbs could then regenerate to some extent. These results are encouraging but they are not the whole story.

One of the landmarks of regeneration research was Singer's classic experiment in which the nerve supply to the arms of frogs was augmented by sciatic nerves deviated from the hind legs (Fig. 81). The regenerates thus induced were abnormal, but they clearly established the lack of adequate innervation as a major cause of regenerative impotence in frogs, and as later shown, in lizards as well. James Van Stone, at Trinity College in Hartford, sought to confirm this by counting the number of nerve fibers per unit area of tissue in cross sections of the hind limbs of *Rana sylvatica*. He found a correlation between the amount of innervation and the capacity for regeneration at different levels in these legs.

The influences of hormones and nerves in limb regeneration originate elsewhere in the body and are secondarily delivered to the site of amputation. It is at the local level, however, that the ultimate explanation of regeneration must be sought, for here are the tissues which actually do the growing. In nonregenerating limbs there is evidence

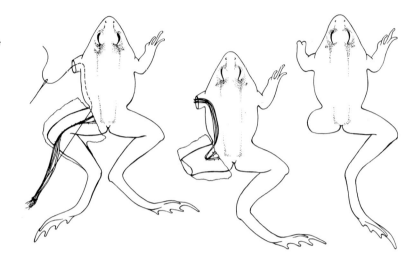

Fig. 81 **Induction of fore limb regeneration in the frog by augmenting its nerve supply. Sciatic nerve from hind leg (left) is threaded under flank skin to the amputated arm (middle). In due course, the latter may grow an abnormal regenerate (right), something which it could not normally do.** (*After Singer, 1951.*)

that amputation stimulates little or no dedifferentiation of stump tissues, without which blastema formation cannot occur. In Moscow, Polezhayev succeeded in stimulating dedifferentiation in anuran legs by various kinds of traumatization. He thereby induced regeneration where it would not otherwise have occurred. In some cases he repeatedly pierced limb stumps with a needle, and in others transplanted legs to the back. Both methods induced dedifferentiation and regeneration. Similar results were obtained by Rose, who exposed limb stumps to strong salt solutions. Apparently any technique which subjects the internal tissues of the stump to prolonged injury will suffice to promote dedifferentiation. If so, then the principal disparity between regenerative and nonregenerative limbs may lie in their divergent capacities for dedifferentiation.

Since these capacities can be aroused experimentally, there is reason to believe that there is nothing intrinsically wrong with the cells in the limbs of frogs. The difficulty may lie at the tissue level, particularly in the tendency for the dermis to close over the amputated stump before the epidermis forms an apical cap. One could speculate that adrenal insufficiency in the adult frog permits precocious fibrogenesis leading to accelerated scar tissue formation. This might do two things. It could hinder the invasion of regenerating nerve fibers into the wound epidermis, which may normally be responsible for apical cap formation, or it could create a barrier between the epidermis and the underlying stump tissues. If the dedifferentiation of the latter depends upon epidermal influences, then the separation of these two components of the limb might be expected to prevent the dissociation of stump tissues from which blastema cells are derived. This scheme may be little more than a working hypothesis, but at least it gives us something to test. It also suggests that regenerative incompetence may have many causes, the correction of any one of which alone would not suffice to restore full regenerative ability. But as long as there are frogs around to challenge the ingenuity of the experimenter, regeneration will remain a vigorously controversial field of research.

REFERENCES

ANTON, H. J. 1965. The origin of blastema cells and protein synthesis during forelimb regeneration in Triturus. In "Regeneration in Animals and Related Problems" (V. Kiortsis and H. A. L. Trampusch, eds.), pp. 377–395. North-Holland Publ. Co., Amsterdam.

BARR, H. J. 1964. The fate of epidermal cells during limb regeneration in larval Xenopus. Anat. Record **148:** 358.

BODEMER, C. W. and N. B. EVERETT. 1959. Localization of newly synthesized proteins in regenerating newt limbs as determined by radioautographic localization of injected methionine-S^{35}. Develop. Biol. **1:** 327–342.

BREEDIS, C. 1952. Induction of accessory limbs and of sarcoma in the newt (Triturus viridescens) with carcinogenic substances. Cancer Res. **12:** 861–866.

BUTLER, E. G. 1933. The effects of X-radiation on the regeneration of the forelimb of Amblystoma larvae. J. Exptl. Zool. **65:** 271–313.

BUTLER, E. G. 1935. Studies on limb regeneration in X-rayed Amblystoma larvae. Anat. Record **62:** 295–307.

BUTLER, E. G. 1955. Regeneration of the urodele forelimb after reversal of its proximo-distal axis. J. Morphol. **96:** 165–282.

BUTLER, E. G. and H. F. BLUM. 1963. Supernumerary limbs of urodele larvae resulting from localized ultraviolet light. Develop. Biol. **7:** 218–233.

BUTLER, E. G. and O. E. SCHOTTÉ. 1949. Effects of delayed denervation on regenerative activity in limbs of urodele larvae. J. Exptl. Zool. **112:** 361–392.

CARLSON, B. M. 1967. The histology of inhibition of limb regeneration in the newt, Triturus, by actinomycin D. J. Morphol. **122:** 249–264.

CARLSON, B. M. and C. F. MORGAN. 1967. Studies on the mechanism of implant-induced supernumerary limb formation in urodeles. II. The effect of heat-treatment, lyophilization and homogenization on the inductive capacity of frog kidney. J. Exptl. Zool. **164:** 243–250.

DECK, J. D. and S. L. SHAPIRO. 1963. Retardation of the newt limb regeneration with semicarbazide, an inhibitor of histamine formation. Anat. Record **146:** 225–234.

DENT, J. N. 1962. Limb regeneration in larvae and metamorphosing individuals of the South African clawed toad. *J. Morphol.* **110:** 61–78.

EGGERT, R. C. 1966. The response of X-irradiated limbs of adult urodeles to autografts of normal cartilage. *J. Exptl. Zool.* **161:** 369–390.

FABER, J. 1965. Autonomous morphogenetic activities of the amphibian regeneration blastema. *In* "Regeneration in Animals and Related Problems" (V. Kiortsis and H. A. L. Trampusch, eds.), pp. 404–418. North-Holland Publ. Co. Amsterdam.

GEBHARDT, D. O. E. and J. FABER. 1966. The influence of aminopterin on limb regeneration in *Ambystoma mexicanum. J. Embryol. Exptl. Morphol.* **16:** 143–158.

GLADE, R. W. 1963. Effects of tail skin, epidermis, and dermis on limb regeneration in *Triturus viridescens* and *Siredon mexicanum. J. Exptl. Zool.* **152:** 169–193.

GOODE, R. P. 1967. The regeneration of limbs in adult anurans. *J. Embryol. Exptl. Morphol.* **18:** 259–267.

GOSS, R. J. 1956a. The relation of bone to the histogenesis of cartilage in regenerating forelimbs and tails of adult Triturus viridescens. *J. Morphol.* **98:** 89–124.

GOSS, R. J. 1956b. Regenerative inhibition following limb amputation and immediate insertion into the body cavity. *Anat. Record* **126:** 15–28.

GOSS, R. J. 1956c. The unification of regenerates from symmetrically duplicated forelimbs. *J. Exptl. Zool.* **133:** 191–210.

GOSS, R. J. 1957a. The relation of skin to defect regulation in regenerating half limbs. *J. Morphol.* **100:** 547–564.

GOSS, R. J. 1957b. The effect of partial irradiation on the morphogenesis of limb regenerates. *J. Morphol.* **101:** 131–148.

GOSS, R. J. 1958. Skeletal regeneration in amphibians. *J. Embryol. Exptl. Morphol.* **6:** 638–644.

GOSS, R. J. 1961. Regeneration of vertebrate appendages. *In* "Advances in Morphogenesis" (M. Abercrombie and J. Brachet, eds.), Vol. 1, pp. 103–152. Academic Press, New York.

GRILLO, H. C., C. M. LAPIÈRE, M. H. DRESDEN and J. GROSS. 1968. Collagenolytic activity in regenerating forelimbs of the adult newt (*Triturus viridescens*). *Develop. Biol.* **17:** 571–583.

GUYÉNOT, E., J. DINICHERT-FAVARGER and M. GALLAND. 1948. L'exploration du territoire de la patte antérieure du Triton (asymétrie, duplicature, orientation des régénérats). *Rev. Suisse Zool.* **55** (Suppl. 2): 1–120.

HAY, E. D. 1956. Effects of thyroxine on limb regeneration in the newt, Triturus viridescens. *Bull. Johns Hopkins Hosp.* **99:** 262–285.

HAY, E. D. 1958. The fine structure of blastema cells and differentiating cartilage cells in regenerating limbs of *Amblystoma* larvae. *J. Biophys. Biochem. Cytol.* **4:** 583–592.

HAY, E. D. 1959. Electron microscopic observations of muscle dedifferentiation in regenerating *Amblystoma* limbs. *Develop. Biol.* **1:** 555–585.

HAY, E. D. and D. A. FISCHMAN. 1961. Origin of the blastema in regenerating limbs of the newt *Triturus viridescens*. *Develop. Biol.* **3:** 26–59.

JOHNSON, E. A. and M. SINGER. 1964. A histochemical study of succinic and lactic dehydrogenases in the regenerating forelimb of the adult newt, *Triturus*. *Proc. Soc. Exptl. Biol. Med.* **117:** 27–31.

KIORTSIS, V. 1953. Potentialités du territoire patte chez le Triton (adultes, larves, embryons). *Rev. Suisse Zool.* **60:** 301–410.

LAGAN, M. 1961. Regeneration from implanted dissociated cells. II. Regenerates produced by dissociated cells derived from different organs. *Folia Biol. (Warsaw)* **9:** 3–26.

LEHMANN, F. E. 1961. Action of morphostatic substances and the role of proteases in regenerating tissues and in tumour cells. *In* "Advances in Morphogenesis" (M. Abercrombie and J. Brachet, eds.), Vol. 1, pp. 153–187. Academic Press, New York.

MORGAN, T. H. 1901. "Regeneration." Macmillan, New York.

NEWTH, D. R. 1958. On regeneration after amputation of abnormal structures. II. Supernumerary induced limbs. *J. Embrol. Exptl. Morphol.* **6:** 384–392.

NEWTH, D. R. 1958. New (and better?) parts for old. *New Biology,* **26:** 47–62.

NORMAN, W. P. and A. J. SCHMIDT. 1967. The fine structure of tissues in the amputated-regenerating limb of the adult newt, *Diemictylus viridescens*. *J. Morphol.* **123:** 271–312.

O'STEEN, W. K. and B. E. WALKER. 1961. Radioautographic studies of regeneration in the common newt. II. Regeneration of the forelimb. *Anat. Record* **139:** 547–555.

POLEZHAYEV, L. W. 1946. The loss and restoration of regenerative capacity in the limbs of tailless amphibia. *Biol. Rev. Cambridge Phil. Soc.* **21:** 141–147.

RIDDIFORD, L. M. 1960. Autoradiographic studies of tritiated thymidine infused into the blastema of the early regenerate in the adult newt, Triturus. *J. Exptl. Zool.* **144:** 25–32.

ROGUSKI, H. 1961. Regeneration from implanted dissociated cells. III. Regenerative capacity of blastemal cells. *Folia Biol. (Warsaw)* **9:** 269–302.

ROSE, S. M. 1945. The effect of NaCl in stimulating regeneration of limbs of frogs. *J. Morphol.* **77:** 119–139.

ROSE, S. M. 1962. Tissue-arc control of regeneration in the amphibian limb.

In "Regeneration" (D. Rudnick, ed.), pp. 153–176, 20th Growth Symposium. Ronald Press, New York.

RUBEN, L. N. and J. M. STEVENS. 1963. Post-embryonic induction in urodele limbs. *J. Morphol.* **112:** 279–302.

RZEHAK, K. and M. SINGER. 1966. Limb regeneration and nerve fiber number in *Rana sylvatica* and *Xenopus laevis. J. Exptl. Zool.* **162:** 15–22.

SCHMIDT, A. J. 1966. "Molecular Basis of Regeneration Enzymes." University of Chicago Press, Chicago.

SCHMIDT, A. J. 1968. "Cellular Biology of Vertebrate Regeneration and Repair." University of Chicago Press, Chicago.

SCHMIDT, A. J. and T. WEIDMAN. 1964. Dehydrogenases and aldolase in the regenerating forelimb of the adult newt, *Diemictylus viridescens. J. Exptl. Zool.* **155:** 303–316.

SCHOTTÉ, O. E. 1961. Systemic factors in initiation of regenerative processes in limbs of larval and adult amphibians. *In* "Synthesis of Molecular and Cellular Structure" (D. Rudnick, ed.), pp. 161–192, 19th Growth Symposium. Ronald Press, New York.

SCHOTTÉ, O. E., E. G. BUTLER and R. T. HOOD. 1941. Effects of transplanted blastemas on amputated nerveless limbs of urodele larvae. *Proc. Soc. Exptl. Biol. Med.* **48:** 500–503.

SCHOTTÉ, O. E. and S. R. HILFER. 1957. Initiation of regeneration in regenerates after hypophysectomy in adult Triturus viridescens. *J. Morphol.* **101:** 25–56.

SCHOTTÉ, O. E. and J. F. WILBER. 1958. Effects of adrenal transplants upon forelimb regeneration in normal and in hypophysectomized adult frogs. *J. Embryol. Exptl. Morphol.* **6:** 247–269.

SIDMAN, R. L. and M. SINGER. 1960. Limb regeneration without innervation of the apical epidermis in the adult newt, *Triturus. J. Exptl. Zool.* **144:** 105–109.

SINGER, M. 1951. Induction of regeneration of forelimb of the frog by augmentation of the nerve supply. *Proc. Soc. Exptl. Biol. Med.* **76:** 413–416.

SINGER, M. 1960. Nervous mechanisms in the regeneration of body parts in vertebrates. *In* "Developing Cell Systems and Their Control" (D. Rudnick, ed.), pp. 115–133, 18th Growth Symposium. Ronald Press, New York.

SINGER, M. and F. R. L. EGLOFF. 1949. The nervous system and regeneration of the forelimb of adult Triturus. VIII. The effect of limited nerve quantities on regeneration. *J. Exptl. Zool.* **111:** 295–314.

SINGER, M. and E. MUTTERPERL. 1963. Nerve fiber requirements for regeneration in forelimb transplants of the newt *Triturus. Develop. Biol.* **7:** 180–191.

SINGER, M., K. RZEHAK and C. S. MAIER. 1967. The relation between the caliber of the axon and the trophic activity of nerves in limb regeneration. *J. Exptl. Zool.* **166:** 89–98.

SKOWRON, S. and Z. KOMALA. 1957. Limb regeneration in postmetamorphic *Xenopus laevis. Folia Biol. (Warsaw)* **5:** 53–72.

SKOWRON, S. and H. ROGUSKI. 1958. Regeneration from implanted dissociated cells. I. Regenerative potentialities of limb and tail cells. *Folia Biol. (Warsaw)* **6:** 163–173.

SMITH, S. D. 1967. Induction of partial limb regeneration in *Rana pipiens* by galvanic stimulation. *Anat. Record* **158:** 89–98.

STEEN, T. P. 1968. Stability of chondrocyte differentiation and contribution of muscle to cartilage during limb regeneration in the axolotl (*Siredon mexicanum*). *J. Exptl. Zool.* **167:** 49–77.

STEEN, T. P. and C. S. THORNTON. 1963. Tissue interaction in amputated aneurogenic limbs of *Amblystoma* larvae. *J. Exptl. Zool.* **154:** 207–221.

STINSON, B. 1964a. The response of X-irradiated limbs of adult urodeles to normal tissue grafts. II. Effects of autografts of anterior or posterior halves of sixty-day forearm regenerates. *J. Exp. Zool.* **155:** 1–24.

STINSON, B. 1964b. The response of X-irradiated limbs of adult urodeles to normal tissue grafts. IV. Comparative effects of autografts and homografts of complete forearm regenerates. *J. Exptl. Zool.* **157:** 159–178.

STOCUM, D. L. 1968. The urodele limb regeneration blastema: a self-organizing system. I. Differentiation *in vitro*. II. Morphogenesis and differentiation of autografted whole and fractional blastemas. *Develop. Biol.* (in press).

THORNTON, C. S. 1938. The histogenesis of the regenerating forelimb of larval *Amblystoma* after exarticulation of the humerus. *J. Morphol.* **62:** 219–241.

THORNTON, C. S. 1956. Epidermal modifications in regenerating and in non-regenerating limbs of anuran larvae. *J. Exptl. Zool.* **131:** 373–394.

THORNTON, C. S. 1957. The effect of apical cap removal on limb regeneration in *Amblystoma* larvae. *J. Exptl. Zool.* **134:** 357–382.

THORNTON, C. S. 1960. Influence of an eccentric epidermal cap on limb regeneration in *Amblystoma* larvae. *Develop. Biol* **2:** 551–569.

THORNTON, C. S. 1962. Influence of head skin on limb regeneration in urodele amphibians. *J. Exptl. Zool.* **150:** 5–16.

THORNTON, C. S. and D. W. KRAEMER. 1951. The effect of injury on denervated unamputated fore limbs of Amblystoma larvae. *J. Exptl. Zool.* **117:** 415–439.

TOTO, P. D. and J. D. ANNONI. 1965. Histogenesis of newt blastema. *J. Dental Res.* **44:** 71–79.

TRAMPUSCH, H. A. L. 1958. The action of X-rays on the morphogenetic field. I. Heterotopic grafts on irradiated limbs. *Proc. Koninkl. Ned. Akad. Wetenschap.* **61:** 417–430.

URBANI, E. 1965. Proteolytic enzymes in regeneration. *In* "Regeneration in Animals and Related Problems" (V. Kiortsis and H. A. L. Trampusch, eds.), pp. 39–55. North-Holland Publ. Co., Amsterdam.

VAN STONE, J. M. 1964. The relation of nerve number to regenerative capacity in the developing hind limb of *Rana sylvatica. J. Exptl Zool.* **155:** 293–302.

WEISS, C. and R. M. ROSENBAUM. 1967. Histochemical studies on cell death and histolysis during regeneration. I. Distribution of acid phosphomonoesterase activity in the normal, the regenerating and the resorbing forelimb of the larval spotted salamander, *Amblystoma maculatum. J. Morphol.* **122:** 203–230.

WEISS, P. 1939. "Principles of Development." Henry Holt, New York.

YNTEMA, C. L. 1959. Regeneration in sparsely innervated and aneurogenic forelimbs of *Amblystoma* larvae. *J. Exptl. Zool.* **140:** 101–124.

10 Heads and Tails

IT goes without saying that structures essential to survival cannot regenerate. Conversely, there is nothing to be gained by regenerating appendages that are relatively useless. To qualify for replacement, a structure must lie between these two extremes. It must be important enough to be missed when it is gone, but not so vital that an animal cannot survive its loss long enough to grow a replacement. The tails of many cold-blooded vertebrates fall into the "useful but nonessential" category. As such, it is not surprising that they should be able to grow back after amputation. The heads of vertebrates, however, are too important to be able to regenerate. Not only that, but decapitation effectively hypophysectomizes an animal. On theoretical grounds, an organ required for regeneration (such as the pituitary) cannot be located in the structure to be replaced. If heads could regenerate (and no one has kept a headless vertebrate alive long enough to find out) it is a safe bet that the process would not require the pituitary. Aside from this, it is difficult to imagine how the regeneration of some hypothetical vertebrate head could recapitulate the complicated mechanisms of its own embryogenesis, for there is no "head bud" in the embryo comparable to limb buds and tail buds.

The fact of the matter is, however, that heads are not altogether lacking in regenerative potential. In some of the lower vertebrates parts of the brain and spinal cord are capable of restitution following their resection. The eyes also have the capacity to recuperate lost lenses, retinae and optic nerves in certain selected forms. Of special interest, however, are the jaws, the regeneration of which was first noted by Spallanzani in 1768.

Jaws and Snouts Amputation of the lower jaw presents special problems for a newt, for in its absence eating and breathing become difficult or impossible. Fortunately, many months are required for these animals to starve to death, by which time a new jaw will have regenerated. But without the floor of the mouth to pump air into the lungs, they must be kept in very shallow water to avoid drowning. When partially submerged the skin can be kept moist enough to facilitate cutaneous respiration and insure survival. Even at that, it takes several months to regenerate a functional replacement of the jaw.

Fig. 82 **Lower jaw of newt in sagittal section.** (*From Fig. 1, p. 292, of Goss and Stagg, 1958a.*)

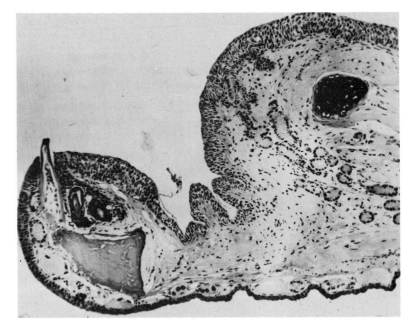

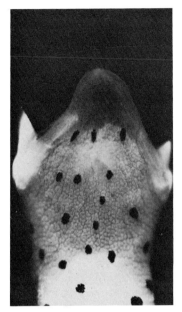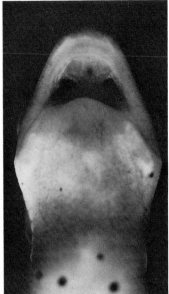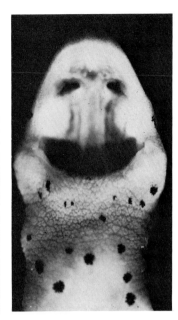

Fig. 83 **The success of regeneration in the newt jaw depends upon how much is amputated. When the distal halves of the mandibles are cut off (left), nearly complete regeneration ensues. Amputation more proximally results in less regeneration (middle), and total removal of the jaw by temporo-mandibular disarticulation precludes regeneration altogether.** (*From Figs. 9–11, p. 300, in Goss and Stagg, 1958a.*)

The mandibles are of special importance in jaw regeneration. Their total removal by exarticulation at the temporo-mandibular joint completely prevents a new jaw from developing (Fig. 83). Regeneration can occur only if mandibular stumps are left intact, but the more distal the amputation the better the outgrowth.

When the blastema begins to differentiate it becomes organized around the remaining portions of the mandibles (Fig. 84). In between, very little morphogenesis is initiated, for neither the tongue nor the hyoid apparatus is replaced. The musculature associated with this part of the jaw, however, appears to be the major source of blastema cells from which the new parts are to be formed. During the first few weeks following amputation the muscles in the floor of the mouth are extensively dismantled to yield quantities of dedifferentiated cells which accumulate in the vicinity of the mandibular stumps. Here one can first detect, after about a month, the earliest signs of differentiation.

Each mandible consists of three skeletal parts, the largest of which is

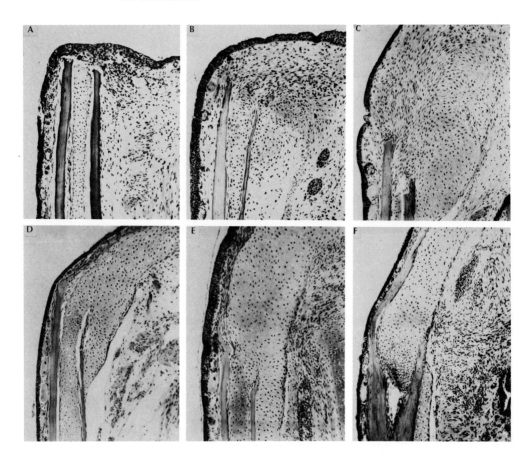

Fig. 84 **Histology of jaw regeneration in the newt. Left mandible sectioned horizontally. A. Two weeks after amputation the stump has healed over. B. After five weeks the blastema has begun to differentiate into cartilage. C. In six weeks the chondrified continuation of the prearticular bone extends into the regenerate. D and E. During the seventh and eighth weeks the cartilaginous regenerate becomes modeled into a mandibular arch. F. By five months the mandible has an ossified dentary bone surrounding a core of cartilage.** (From Figs. 15, 16, 17, and 19, pp. 307 and 309, of Goss and Stagg, 1958a.)

the laterally situated dentary bone. It is in this that the teeth are anchored. Medially there is another bone, the prearticular. Together, these two bones form a tubular structure enclosing a rod of Meckel's cartilage. When the blastema commences its differentiation, it does so by giving rise to cartilage along the distal inside margin of the prearticular bone. As the regenerate elongates, chondrification spreads to the end of the bone and also fuses with Meckel's cartilage.

The dentary bone grows in a different way. It is a dermal bone, and as such does not require chondrogenesis to regenerate. Accordingly, some six or more weeks after amputation, direct ossification of the connective tissue begins to give rise to a distal replacement of the dentary bone. Thus, each of the skeletal components of the mandible preserves its identity. Together they converge from either side of the regenerating jaw to reconstitute a new mandibular symphysis at the apex.

Not only does the regenerating jaw form a reasonably good replica of the missing parts of the mandibles, but it becomes equipped with teeth as well. Even before the dentary bone itself regenerates, epidermal cells grow down into the underlying connective tissue, there to organize into a series of tooth buds. Commencing in continuity with the row of old teeth interrupted by amputation the new dental ridge develops in a proximo-distal direction along the dorsal side of the mandibular regenerate. Ultimately, in keeping with the original anatomical arrangement, teeth become set in bony sockets in the dentary bone. Thus, although the regenerated jaw is an imperfect facsimile of the original, its most important components (mandible with teeth) are replaced, while less necessary parts (tongue and hyoid apparatus) are dispensed with.

Fig. 85 **Intermandibular regeneration in the lower jaw of a newt in ventral view. Soft tissues of the floor of the mouth, including the tongue, were excised. At the end of one week (left) wound healing has occurred around inner margins of the mandibles. At weekly intervals (left to right), centripetal regeneration from the lateral and anterior borders gradually obliterates the aperture by the end of a month.** (*From Figs. 2–5, p. 9, of Goss and Stagg, 1958b.*)

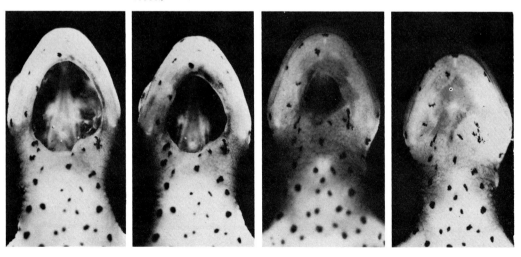

A rather different kind of regeneration occurs in newt jaws when the floor of the mouth is removed, leaving the mandibles intact. This operation eliminates the tongue, salivary glands, hyoid apparatus and associated soft tissues. All that remains of the jaw is the mandible, plus whatever adventitious musculature may remain attached around its inner margins. Yet this gaping hole generally becomes filled in by new tissue within a month after operation, as shown in the sequence of photographs in Fig. 85.

Regeneration is accomplished by growth of blastematous tissue formed around the periphery of the aperture (Fig. 86). This elongated blastema develops only in association with the mandible. Along the posterior border of the hole the tissues contribute to regeneration only by passive contraction rather than active growth. Closure of the aperture occurs by centripetal growth from its lateral and anterior margins.

Fig. 86 **The histology of intermandibular regeneration. In cross section the mandible consists of a dentary bone** (*d*), **Meckel's cartilage** (*m*) **and a prearticular bone** (*p*). **At the end of one week (A) the inner margin of the mandible has healed where the floor of the mouth has been resected. B. After two weeks a blastema** (*b*) **forms. C. By three weeks the regenerate extends inward and nearly meets its counterpart from the other side at the end of four weeks (D). At this time, muscle fibers** (*m*) **have differentiated in the regenerate. E. By five weeks the reconstituted floor of the mouth may form a central mass of cartilage.** (*From Figs. 11–15, p. 11, of Goss and Stagg, 1958b.*)

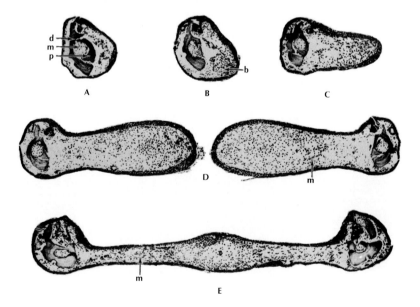

The membranous regenerate converges until the hole is obliterated and continuity is re-established across the intermandibular region. Although some muscle and cartilage may differentiate, neither tongue nor associated skeletal parts are restored. Here again we see an example of how the regenerative process leads to the formation of those parts required for survival, and little more.

The upper jaw can also regenerate—up to a point. If the nose of a newt is cut off, a new snout will grow back (including bones and teeth) provided not too much has been lost in the first place. For successful regeneration to occur, the level of amputation must be far enough in front of the eyes to leave behind part of the nasal capsules. For reasons yet to be explained, these structures play an essential role in the regeneration of the upper jaw, as if no snout at all were better than a noseless one.

An Eye for an Eye It is a curious thing that among all the vertebrates only certain kinds of urodele amphibians possess the unique capacity to regenerate lens, iris and retina in adult life. It could hardly be claimed that their eyes are any more important to them than are those of other animals. Anatomically, they are not obviously different from nonregenerating eyes, nor have significant biochemical dissimilarities been uncovered. Hence, we are at a loss to explain why these few species are favored with such spectacular powers of ocular regeneration—or for that matter, why the rest of us are not.

The case of lens regeneration is one of those rare instances in which new development is initiated solely by the absence of the original structure without the intervention of a wound. The epithelial tissues bordering the dorsal rim of the iris give rise to the new lens following lentectomy, a process which takes only several weeks. Ordinarily, these cells are deterred from becoming a lens by the presence of the old one. There is evidently some form of communication between lens and iris, but experiments thus far have told us only what it is not, not what it is. It is not the physical presence of a lens which inhibits replacement, for the implantation of inert substitutes fails to block regeneration. However, the proximity of lens to iris does matter. Limited lens regeneration may occur following displacement of the original lens away from the pupillary region. Thus, available evidence suggests some kind of chemical inhibition, but attempts to confirm this directly have yielded inconsistent results.

On the other hand, there is convincing evidence that a stimulatory influence on the dorsal iris may be exerted by the neural retina. If a mechanical barrier is inserted between the iris and the retina of a lentectomized eye, lens regeneration is inhibited. Moreover, eyes from which the neural retina has been removed fail to replace missing lenses, at least until the retina itself has begun to regenerate. And if the dorsal iris is grafted to extraocular locations elsewhere in the body it does not produce lens tissue unless some of the retina has been transplanted along with it.

Not only does the retina promote lens regeneration from the dorsal iris, but it also influences the orientation of the new lens. Among the innumerable contributions to the field of ocular regeneration by Leon S. Stone of Yale University, few have surpassed his ingenious demonstration of how the polarity of the lens is determined in the newt eye. By carefully excising a segment of the dorsal iris and replacing it in the eye backwards, he succeeded in showing that the lens which subsequently regenerated was oriented normally with respect to the eye as a whole rather than to the iris from which it developed. Hence, the lens epithelium always faces outward and the lens fibers differentiate on the side toward the retina. In tissue cultures of dorsal irises already in the process of regeneration, incipient lenses can continue to grow in the absence of their retinae. Such lenses, however, lose their lens epithelium and develop as unpolarized masses of lens fibers. Hence,

Fig. 87 **Lens regeneration in the eye of a newt. Lentectomy is followed by the production of a new lens from the cells of the dorsal iris (left). If the dorsal sector of the iris is removed along with the lens (middle), two small lenses may form at each remaining corner of the iris. Transplantation of the dorsal iris to another lentectomized eye (right) results in the regeneration of two lenses, one from the dorsal iris of the host eye, the other from the transplanted one.**

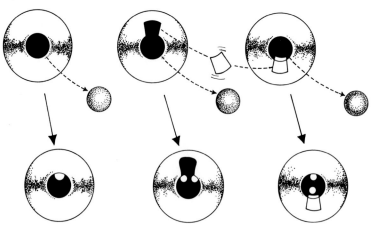

the retina may not induce fiber differentiation directly, but it evidently plays an important role in determining where fibers shall develop in the growing lens. Thus, the exquisite anatomical precision which is essential in a functioning optical instrument is insured by subtle interactions between physiologically related parts during the course of their development. Only by such mechanisms can nothing be left to chance in the formation of an organ in which imperfections cannot be tolerated.

Studies of lens regeneration are properly focused on the tissues of the iris. Here the maximal potential for the differentiation of a lens resides in the most dorsally located epithelium (Fig. 87). It falls off laterally along the margins of the pupil, disappearing altogether near the 9-o'clock and 3-o'clock positions. Yet the iris tissues betray no known morphological differences around their entire circumference, nor do they appear to vary significantly between amphibians which can or cannot regenerate lenses. Randall Reyer, of West Virginia University, has proved that despite the lack of visible distinctions, the capacity for lens regeneration is an intrinsic property of the cells of the dorsal iris themselves, not the intraocular environment in which they exist. He transplanted segments of dorsal iris from the eyes of *Triturus*, which does regenerate, into lentectomized eyes of *Ambystoma*, which does not. Nevertheless, the *Triturus* iris produced lens tissue in the *Ambystoma* eye where not even its own iris can do so. Conversely, *Ambystoma* iris remains incompetent even in the eyes of *Triturus*. There can be no doubt, therefore, that the capacity for lens regeneration is the exclusive property of the dorsal iris epithelium and that the essential retinal influence exists even in eyes unable to grow new lenses.

The dorsal iris cells are capable of a remarkable kind of metaplasia in which they become transformed from fully differentiated pigment epithelial cells into equally specialized lens cells. How this change comes about has been meticulously documented by Goro Eguchi at Nagoya University. By electron microscopic examination, he has solved the mystery of how the iris epithelial cells dispense with their pigment granules preliminary to lens development. They do so by a combination of extrusion and phagocytosis during the first week or so after lentectomy (Fig. 88). Their melanin granules are transferred from the cells of the iris epithelium to ameboid cells of uncertain origin which invade the area of the iris where regeneration is destined to occur. The pigment-laden amebocytes eventually disappear, leaving the iris cells unencumbered by their former products of differentiation and free to reorganize into a lens.

While this is going on, some interesting events are occurring at the

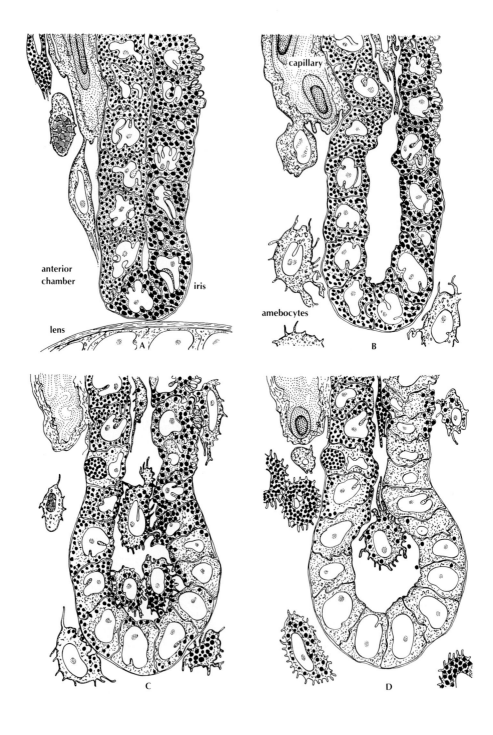

molecular level of organization. These events have been explored by Eguchi in Japan and by Tuneo Yamada and his colleagues at Oak Ridge National Laboratory in Tennessee. One of the earliest indications that the absence of the lens has been detected and reacted to by the dorsal iris cells is the increased synthesis of RNA by their nuclei. As early as one day after lentectomy, the dorsal iris incorporates significantly more tritiated cytidine and uridine than does either the ventral iris, or the dorsal iris of the opposite intact control eye, a difference which becomes increasingly pronounced during the next week (Fig. 89). Following this, there are similar increases in alkaline phosphatase activity and the uptake of P^{32} by the tissues of the dorsal iris (Fig. 90). These metabolic changes reflect the rising rate of protein synthesis by the dorsal iris as measured by tritiated leucine incorporation. During the first week, when no lens vesicle has as yet formed, protein synthesis is only slightly elevated. After the second week, however, when the new lens is growing rapidly, the rate of protein synthesis climbs steeply. This signals the onset of crystallin protein synthesis by the newly differentiated lens fibers.

In the transformation of iris into lens, proliferation and differentiation both contribute to the finished product. Yet there is a mutual exclusion between these two important processes which has been elucidated by Yamada's skillful application of immunofluorescent techniques to newt eyes in various stages of lens regeneration. Antibodies against lens crystallin proteins were first conjugated with fluorescein isothiocyanate. Sections of iris at different intervals after lentectomy were then exposed to the fluorescent antibody which selectively combined with appropriate antigenic proteins wherever they had been produced in the developing regenerates. The earliest stages of lens fiber differentiation could thus be pinpointed by the telltale fluorescence of such preparations when viewed under ultraviolet light. Studies along these lines have shown that any given cell either divides mitotically or synthesizes lens proteins, not both. These results may be taken to indicate

Fig. 88 Electron microscopy of early stages in the conversion of the iris epithelium into a lens in the newt as viewed in sagittal sections of the eye. A. Intact dorsal iris composed of double layer of pigmented epithelium. B. Three days after lentectomy ameboid phagocytes appear on the scene. C. After eight days the amebocytes have phagocytized numerous pigment granules expelled by iris epithelial cells. D. On the twelfth day most of the pigment granules have been transferred to the departing phagocytes. The colorless epithelium is now beginning to reorganize into a new lens. (After Eguchi, 1963.)

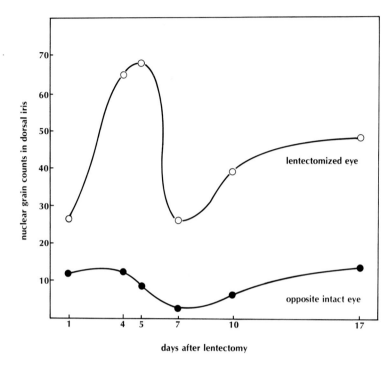

Fig. 89 **RNA synthesis in the
dorsal iris of** *Triturus
viridescens* **following unilateral lentectomy, as
measured autoradiograph-
ically by nuclear grain
counts after injection of
uridine-H³. Loss of the lens
triggers a sharp but transient
rise in the rate of RNA
synthesis in the dorsal iris
of the experimental eye (○)
but not in that of the control
eye (●) nor in the ventral
iris of either eye.** (*Plotted
from data of Yamada and
Karasaki, 1963.*)

days after lentectomy

that when the genes for the synthesis of lens fiber proteins are activated, those required to initiate mitosis (and DNA synthesis?) are turned
off.

Much the same rule applies to the retina, which is capable of equally
amazing regeneration. The neural component of the urodele retina
consists of cells unable to proliferate once they have begun to differentiate, but which can be replaced by virtue of a layer of pigmented
epithelial cells capable of dedifferentiation and multiplication. Retinal
regeneration enjoys a wider distribution among amphibians than does
lens regeneration. It occurs not only in *Triturus,* which can replace
lenses too, but also in *Ambystoma,* which cannot regenerate lenses.
It has been reported to be possible in a number of larval anurans, and
can take place to some extent even in fishes and chick embryos.

When the neural retina of urodele amphibians is extirpated, or is
permanently detached from its adjacent pigmented epithelium, the
latter undergoes many of the same changes already noted in the cells
of the iris preparing for lens regeneration. Ameboid phagocytes appear
on the scene to dispose of the melanin granules, whereupon proliferation of the former pigment cells gives rise to a population of
undifferentiated cells which pile up into a multilayered tissue destined

to become the new neural retina. The outermost cells of this layer differentiate into rods and cones, those situated toward the inside of the eyeball give rise to the two layers of neurons. The newly formed ganglion cells send out axons which regenerate through the remnants of the original optic nerve to the brain. Here they find their way to the appropriate neurons in the optic tectum to re-establish orderly synaptic connections and thereby promote visual recovery. Needless to say, the mechanism by which these ingrowing axons from the retina navigate through the labyrinth of neurons in the brain to seek out the correct ones needed to restore the original visual integration is a mystery of great importance and even greater perplexity.

Few vertebrates are endowed with the capacity to regenerate the retina at the histological level of organization. Even in mammals, however, cellular and molecular regeneration is not impossible. If a rat, for example, is deprived of vitamin A for a long enough time, the rods of its retina lose their differentiated characteristics. At Johns

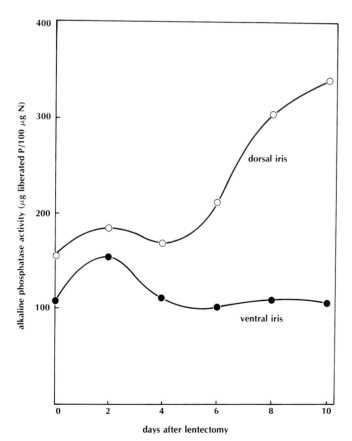

Fig. 90 **Comparison of alkaline phosphatase activities in dorsal (○) and ventral (●) iris epithelia following removal of lenses from the eyes of** Triturus pyrrhogaster. **The rise in phosphatase activity in the dorsal iris during the second week is accompanied by a similar increase in the rate of P^{32} uptake. It is during this period that crystallin proteins are first synthesized in the young lens regenerate.** (After Eguchi and Ishikawa, 1963.)

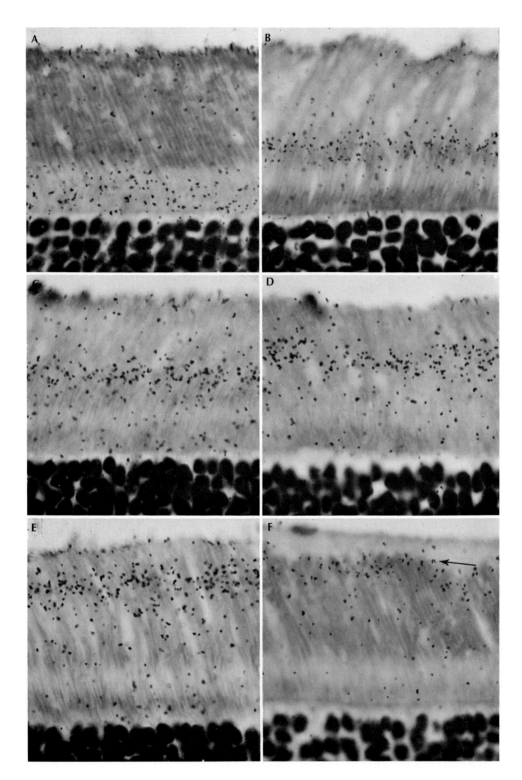

204

Hopkins University, John E. Dowling has demonstrated that when the rat's reserves of vitamin A are finally depleted retinene can no longer be replenished nor can rhodopsin be made. Deprived of molecules essential to their normal function, the rods of the retina cannot maintain their structural integrity. The outer rod segments become disrupted and in due course the cell is reduced to a functionless unspecialized entity. If the vitamin deficiency persists for many months these effete cells disappear completely; but if vitamin A is restored before the night blindness becomes permanent, they can once again recover their original state of differentiation and physiological activity, a feat they achieve in less than two weeks. The photoreceptors of the retina are therefore competent to regenerate their specialized parts, including the outer rod segments, a phenomenon which may be merely an exaggerated version of what goes on at all times in such cells at the molecular level of organization.

Richard W. Young, at the University of California at Los Angeles, has made some noteworthy observations on protein turnover in retinal rods. Unable to renew themselves at the cellular level, the outer rod segments have now been found to undergo a constant regeneration of their proteins and perhaps some of their organelles as well (Fig. 91). When rats were injected with tritiated methionine and their rods were examined autoradiographically at intervals thereafter, it was discovered that some of the label gradually shifted its position in the cell. During the first few hours the label was located in the inner rod segment. By the end of the first day, however, it was in the proximal region of the outer rod segment, and in the course of the next week was propagated distally until it finally disappeared at the far end. There is no way of knowing just what proteins had incorporated the labeled methionine, but there is reason to suspect that the opsins might have been involved. Perhaps only the proteins move through the cells, but it is equally possible that the entire membranous architecture of the outer rod segments might be in a state of continued escalation. In either case, this illustrates the point that regeneration is

Fig. 91 **Autoradiography of protein turnover in the retinal rods of the rat after injection of methionine-H³. A. Half an hour after injection the label appears in the inner segments of the photoreceptors. B. After two days it has shifted to the basal regions of the outer rod segments. C–F. Three, four, seven and nine days after injection. Reaction band migrates to the ends of the outer segments, where it disappears.** *(From Young, 1967.)*

an essential and ubiquitous attribute of living systems. The only thing that varies from one animal to another is the level of organization at which it occurs.

The Central Nervous System

Perhaps the most unlikely place to look for regeneration is in the brain. Yet in certain fishes and amphibians, those parts of the brain which can be lost without lethal consequences are sometimes replaced in remarkably good order. This property is best represented in the case of the forebrain, or telencephalon, where removal of the cerebral hemispheres is tolerated by lower vertebrates without serious untoward effects. Accordingly, the forebrain is capable of practically complete regeneration in fishes and urodele amphibians (Fig. 92). Anurans, however, cannot replace their forebrains, except in *Xenopus,* which does so in both larval and adult forms. In general, regeneration is slower to occur in older animals. For example, forebrains may be completely replaced in only three weeks in the tadpoles of *Xenopus.* The same process requires about eight weeks in postmetamorphic *Xenopus,* which is about how long it takes in the adult rainbow fish, *Lebistes reticulatus.*

Experiments on amphibian embryos have shown that the cerebral hemispheres do not grow as much as normal after the nasal placodes have been removed. The ingrowth of olfactory nerve fibers is needed to stimulate proliferation of cells in the telencephalon, a part of the brain which originally evolved as a center specialized for the sense of smell. The regeneration of cerebral hemispheres is likewise dependent upon olfactory innervation. Removal of the nasal organ, from which the olfactory nerves originate, either prevents or seriously

Fig. 92 **Forebrain regeneration in the amphibian. Removal of the cerebral hemisphere is followed first by the regeneration of new olfactory nerves. When these reach the diencephalon, its ependymal epithelium proliferates and develops into a new forebrain.**

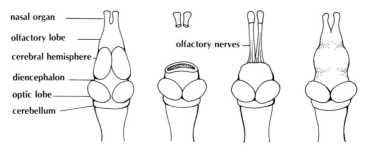

nasal organ

olfactory lobe

cerebral hemisphere

diencephalon

optic lobe

cerebellum

olfactory nerves

retards the development of a new forebrain following its ablation. It seems that the central nervous system responds to the trophic influence of nerves as do regenerating appendages.

All indications point to ependymal cells as a source of the regenerating forebrain. The ependymal epithelium lines the ventricles of the brain, and when the cerebral hemispheres have been removed it is the ependyma which first seals off the wound at the level of the diencephalon. At this site there are numerous mitotic divisions as the new outgrowth gradually takes shape, having first been invaded by regenerating olfactory nerve fibers. Once a sufficient population of cells has accumulated, the differentiation of new neurons occurs and the regenerating hemispheres take on the histological organization of the ones they have replaced.

When both cerebral hemispheres are removed, they are replaced by the ependyma of the diencephalon. If only one hemisphere is removed, the ependyma of the opposite side may also participate in its renewal. But if the olfactory organ is removed unilaterally along with its cerebral hemisphere, the latter cannot regenerate but the contralateral hemisphere may undergo some compensatory hypertrophy. Much the same is true of the optic lobes, which receive exogenous innervation from the retina. Removal of the eyes retards their development. Unilateral excision of an optic lobe, however, leads to its regeneration in embryonic and larval urodeles and in early frog embryos. This is achieved by proliferation and migration of cells from the opposite lobe and their subsequent differentiation into specialized neurons.

It is probably no coincidence that the two parts of the brain which regenerate best—cerebral hemispheres and optic lobes—are those innervated by axons from neurons located in sense organs. In both cases, growth is influenced by the incoming olfactory or optic nerve fibers.

As for the distribution of brain regeneration among lower vertebrates, it is clear that it occurs more readily in younger animals, but may even persist into adult stages in some fishes and amphibians. As a rule, it would seem that whenever regeneration can occur in the brain, the animal is still capable of growing in body size (although the reverse is not necessarily true). Since differentiated neurons cannot multiply, even in lower vertebrates, brain regeneration depends upon the presence of reserve cells (e.g., glia, ependyma) from which new neuroblasts can be formed. Many fishes and amphibians keep growing throughout much of their lives, and if their brains are to keep pace with the rest of the body there would have to be some provision for augmenting the number of neurons to supplement the collateral branching of their fibers long after embryonic stages. Although such a notion lacks documentation it would seem plausible that the prolongation of neurogenesis in normal development and the postembryonic potential to regenerate parts of the central nervous system might both be attributable to the persistence of cells competent to differentiate into neurons.

If this is true in the brain, it is even more true in the spinal cord. When simply transected, restitution of the spinal cord is achieved by the regeneration of nerve fibers across the gap. This occurs quite readily in some fishes, urodele amphibians and larval anurans. Adult frogs, however, recover from such injuries very poorly, if at all. When a segment of the spinal cord is resected instead of merely severed, reconstitution must involve more than just fiber regeneration. New cells need to be produced if the missing segment is to be fully restored. This takes place in certain species of fishes, urodele amphibians and to a lesser extent in tadpoles. The ependymal cells first close over both cut ends of the central canal, each of which then swells into a small vesicle. Meanwhile, nerve fibers from either side grow across the gap and proliferating ependymal cells extend the neural canals until they meet in the middle (Fig. 93). The new gray matter of the regenerated

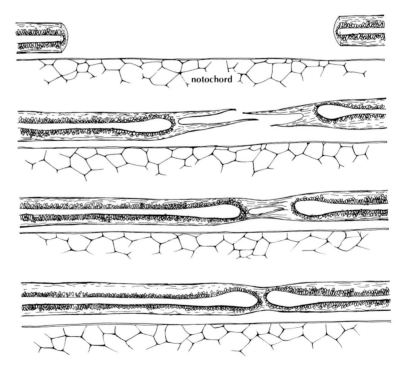

Fig. 93 Stages in the regeneration of a 2-mm length of spinal cord in the larval salamander. Neural tube grows faster from the anterior than the posterior end. Regenerating nerve fibers grow out from either end and establish first contact. Outgrowing neural canals, swollen into terminal vesicles, later meet and fuse. (After Butler and Ward, 1965.)

notochord

portion of the spinal cord is derived from ependymal cells, as well as from neurons which migrate from the severed ends of the transected cord. In urodeles, at least, the replaced segment of the spinal cord approaches normal, both functionally and anatomically. The chief difference seems to be in the failure of Mauthner's fibers to regenerate across severed spinal cords in all urodeles above embryonic stages of development. Why these fibers do not regenerate following spinal transection, but do grow back in regenerating tails of urodele larvae, is a curious inconsistency. It may mean that spinal cord regeneration following tail amputation does not obey the same rules as regrowth across a gap.

Tail Regeneration Tails must be very important, for practically all vertebrates have them except men and frogs. They come in many forms, but from the point of view of regeneration what matters is whether or not they contain a spinal cord. Unless they do, regeneration is usually impossible. When spinal cords are removed surgically from the tails of most animals (tadpoles excepted), axial regeneration of such tails almost never occurs. Indeed so necessary is it for tail regeneration that the main reason the tail regenerates at all seems to be to encase the spinal cord.

It is around the spinal cord that the anatomy of the tail is organized in all lower vertebrates (Fig. 94). In the immediate vicinity are the supporting tissues—a notochord in young or primitive animals, and the vertebral skeleton in older or more advanced ones. Outside these there are segmentally arranged muscle masses, and above and below the myotomes are the tail fins. The spinal cord induces the differentiation of the cartilaginous vertebrae in larval urodele tails, and probably also is necessary for muscle formation. The notochord, when it regenerates at all, is capable of promoting its own replacement.

In larval lampreys, the tail consists of spinal cord, notochord, muscles and cartilaginous fin rays. When amputated, such tails regenerate replicas of the original by redifferentiation of blastema cells. The spinal cord, from which paired spinal ganglia eventually regenerate, grows out directly from its own remnant, and has been found to be necessary for tail regeneration as a whole. In the absence of the notochord, however, the tail can be replaced with all its normal tissue components except the notochord. These chordless regenerates are unable to grow to normal lengths presumably because they lack sufficient supporting tissues. Nevertheless they prove that the notochord is essential for its own regeneration, although the new one does not

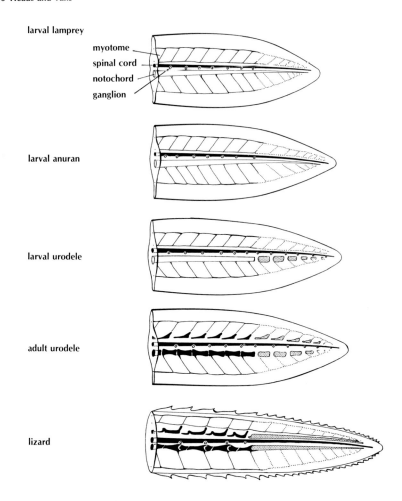

Fig. 94 **Comparative anatomy of tail regeneration. The regenerates of larval lamprey and tadpole tails are morphologically similar, but the latter are incomplete in that new spinal ganglia are not produced. Urodele tails regenerate completely, including ganglia. Those of larval urodeles, however, form cartilaginous vertebrae in place of the notochord. Lizard tails regenerate an unsegmented cartilaginous tube instead of vertebrae, but also give rise to segmentally arranged myotomes.**

appear to grow out directly from the old stump. Rather, the cells of the blastema organize into a notochord independently, and only secondarily do they establish continuity with the original one.

Tadpole tails have much in common structurally with those of lampreys (Fig. 94). Without its notochord, the tadpole tail regenerates very poorly. Although muscle and spinal cord may grow out of the stump, their orientations are distorted in the absence of the axial guidance normally provided by the notochord. Even when transplanted elsewhere in the fin, notochords can regenerate by themselves. On the other hand, as Morgan discovered many years ago and others have since confirmed, the spinal cord is not required for tadpole tail regeneration. When several segments of its length are removed proximal to the level of tail amputation, regeneration can still occur in its absence. These spineless tails have not been studied in histological detail, but appear to consist of myotomes and a notochord as in normal tail regenerates. They are also innervated by nerves from spinal ganglia back in the stump.

It is a very curious thing, especially in view of the absolute necessity of the spinal cord for the regeneration of all other kinds of tails, that tadpole tails should exhibit such anomalous developmental behavior as not to depend on its spinal cord to regenerate. But this is not the only unusual attribute of the tadpole tail. First and foremost, when the spinal cord itself regenerates, it consists of little more than an ependymal tube, devoid of neurons and accompanied by few nerve fibers. This contrasts with the practically complete replacement of urodele spinal cords in regenerating tails. Another difference between anuran and urodele tail regenerates is that tadpoles do not form new spinal ganglia beyond the level of amputation, while urodeles do. Tadpole tails are transient structures programmed for resorption at metamor-

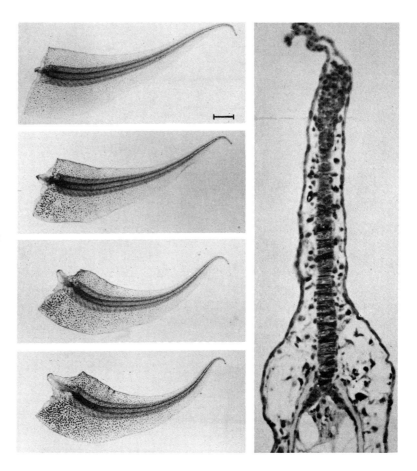

Fig. 95 **Regeneration in reversed direction of a larval** Xenopus **tail isolated** in vitro. **Left: A distal regenerate grows from the anterior cut surface of the tail as seen (top to bottom) after 6, 8, 10 and 12 days. Scale = 1 mm.** (From Weber, 1967.) **Right: Frontal section through a week-old regenerate of an isolated tail. The notochordal outgrowth in reverse polarity extends down the middle of the regenerate.** (Courtesy of Dr. Rudolf Hauser, University of Bern.)

phosis. It could be argued teleologically that unnecessary construction is wasted in an organ marked for demolition.

Finally, the tadpole tail happens to be one of the few structures which has been observed to regenerate *in vitro. Xenopus* tails, cultured aseptically in Holtfreter's solution, grow small regenerates of reversed polarity from their proximal cut surfaces (Fig. 95). This exciting achievement has been investigated at the University of Bern by Rudolf Hauser and Fritz E. Lehmann. The regenerates from such isolated tail tips are produced in the total absence of hormones or of a blood supply, and contain extensions of the spinal cord and notochord but have not been observed to develop muscles beyond the myoblast stage. They seldom exceed a length of one millimeter, which is less than one-quarter of the length attained by normal tail regenerates. Recent experiments, however, have indicated that the stunted condition of the regenerates of isolated tail tips may be attributed to the absence of certain trophic factors normally emanating from the midbrain of the tadpole.

The several unique aspects of anuran tails—their dependence on the notochord instead of the spinal cord, their failure to regenerate spinal ganglia, and their resorption during metamorphosis—may have nothing at all to do with each other. Yet these exceptions in anurans to the so-called rules of tail growth warn us against the pitfalls of extrapolating too freely from one kind of tail to another in an effort to seek generalizations about how they grow (Table 2).

The spinal cord is definitely necessary for the regeneration of urodele tails. In its absence there is no regeneration of axial structures of the tail, although the tail fin may grow around the end of the stump. Thus, there appear to be two distinct regeneration territories in the tail —the axial, which depends on the spinal cord, and the tail fin, which does not.

Table 2 *Comparative aspects of tail regeneration*

	Spinal cord necessary?	Spinal ganglia regenerated?	Notochord necessary?	Can notochord regenerate independently?
Larval Lamprey	Yes	Yes	No	No
Larval Anuran	No	No	Partly	Yes
Larval Urodele	Yes	Yes	No	No
Adult Urodele	Yes	Yes		
Lizard	Yes	No		

What is the nature of this spinal influence on tail regeneration? As usual, we know more about what it is not than what it is. The spinal ganglia alone are not adequate to support tail regeneration, for when the urodele spinal cord is removed the ganglia and associated spinal nerves remain intact. Yet tail regeneration still fails to occur. Vassili Kiortsis tested the possibility that sciatic nerves deviated from the hind legs to the tail might make up for the loss of the spinal cord. They do not. Nor do pieces of forebrain transplanted in place of the spinal cord permit the regeneration of anything but fin tissue. Only if the grafted pieces were derived from the medulla or any part of the spinal cord behind it does tail regeneration occur. It is quite possible, therefore, that the influence of the spinal cord on tail regeneration depends not upon nerves but on the ependymal lining of the neural canal, a tissue which can itself regenerate.

It takes more than just spinal cord to produce a tail in urodeles, however. The neural elements cannot induce anything unless there are receptive tissues present to respond to their influences. These tissues are confined to the axial part of the tail, for the fin lacks the capacity to give rise to other parts of the tail. If spinal cords are transplanted or deviated into fin tissue, subsequent amputation through the grafts does not lead to the regeneration of extra tails. But if spinal cords are similarly implanted into tail myotomes, an accessory set of axial tissues is organized around the graft. These and other experiments carried out by the Holtzers at the University of Pennsylvania have yielded some interesting and surprising information about how morphogenesis is controlled in regenerating urodele tails.

The most unexpected aspect of tail regeneration in urodeles relates to the notochord. This structure is present in young larval tails but is eventually replaced in older larvae by cartilaginous vertebrae, which in turn become ossified during metamorphosis. The urodele notochord behaves differently from those of larval lampreys and anurans (Fig. 94). It will be recalled that in tadpoles the notochord is not only capable of regeneration, but is required for its own replacement. In larval urodeles, the notochord can be removed from tail stumps without affecting the course of tail regeneration. If transplanted elsewhere in the tail, it shows no tendency to produce an outgrowth. All indications point toward the total inability of the larval urodele notochord to regenerate, which makes no difference anyway because their tail regenerates lack a notochord altogether. When the tails of young urodele larvae are amputated, they develop cartilaginous vertebrae where the notochord would have been whether the notochord is still there or not. This short cut to maturity reflects the latent capacity of the tail tissues to differentiate into skeletal parts when stimulated to do so during the process of regeneration. And as in embryonic development, it is the inductive influence of the spinal cord which is responsible for organizing the axial musculature and cartilage of the tail regenerate.

The interrupted spinal cord of urodeles can replace missing segments. In tail regeneration, however, it must also give rise to completely new ganglia from which many of the nerves supplying the regenerated myotomes originate. The spinal cord itself is replaced by an ependymal outgrowth from the neural canal in the stump. This elongating tube penetrates the blastema and is responsible for inducing cellular differentiation, if not the formation of the blastema in the first place. In due course, new neurons differentiate from the ependymal cells and contribute nerve fibers to the developing white matter. Nerve fibers also regenerate from those severed in the original spinal cord by tail amputation. (Mauthner's fibers are an exception: they do not grow into the spinal cords of regenerating tails of tadpoles or adult urodeles. Only in larval urodeles do they regenerate, and here only after tail amputation, not transection of the spinal cord.) The new ganglia in regenerated salamander tails are produced by cells which migrate out from the spinal cord during the neural tube stage of development. These segmentally arranged clusters of cells at first become isolated from the cord, but later re-establish both central and peripheral connections.

The lizard tail is in a class by itself. Anyone who has ever tried to catch a lizard soon learns how proficient they can be at sacrificing their tails to escape predators. It is a general rule in biology that whenever a structure can be lost by autotomy there are usually provisions for its replacement. The lizard tail is rarely an exception. Not only does it possess an efficient autotomy reflex, but it also is endowed with an equally efficient means of regeneration. This is all the more remarkable in lizards since no other reptilian appendage can regenerate, with the possible exception of limb stumps, which on rare occasions may produce abortive outgrowths.

Autotomy of the tail can occur by virtue of the existence of preformed breakage planes across the caudal vertebrae (Fig. 94). Cleavage septa also extend across the fat bodies and between the myotomes. Externally, the autotomy planes may be seen between the rings of scales in the skin, being particularly evident in the tails of the lizard *Anolis carolinensis*. When there is sufficient local nervous stimulation, the flexor muscles arranged segmentally around a vertebra contract violently enough to break the vertebra apart transversely. The subsequent separation of the soft tissues surrounding the skeletal axis efectively detaches the distal part of the tail, which may keep wiggling for a few minutes afterward. Meanwhile, sphincters constrict around the blood vessels in the tail stump, thus reducing the loss of blood to a minimum. Not all lizards come equipped with mechanisms for caudal autotomy. Most of those which do, however, can grow new tails. Those without this adaptation are not known to regenerate. Yet it is not the existence of an autotomy plane per se which accounts for the capacity to regenerate, for when a tail is cut off *between* two successive fracture planes a new tail can still grow back. When amputated in front of the most anterior plane, however, regeneration does not occur. Hence, the tail territory coincides with the capacity for autotomy, but this is not what really makes the difference between the ability to regenerate or not.

Lizard tails are one of nature's best examples of heteromorphic regeneration, for what grows back is only a mock imitation of what was lost. A few weeks after amputation, the scab on the tail stump, together with part of the terminal vertebra, drops off as the blastema pushes out from beneath. This blastema consists of many undifferentiated cells derived from various sources in the underlying older tissues, including dedifferentiated muscles if these have been injured by amputation. In its center is the spinal cord regenerate which is little more than an elongating ependymal tube with a terminal vesicle where most of the cellular proliferation seems to be concentrated. The epidermis covering the blastema is smooth and shiny in these early stages of growth before new scales are formed. As in other regenerating structures, however, the tail epidermis gives evidence of forming the equivalent of an apical cap during incipient blastema development. This takes the form of a papilla of epidermal cells which extends inward toward the terminal vesicle of the ependymal tube. Although the two structures do not make contact morphologically, their proximity suggests the possibility of a meaningful relationship between them.

Differentiation in the blastema proceeds in a proximo-distal direction as its cells organize into myotomes, adipose tissue and cartilage. The original segmentation of the tail is not repeated except in the musculature of the regenerate. The scales in the integument, which are smaller than the ones they replaced, are homogeneously arranged without externally visible signs of segmentation. Vertebrae are not regenerated. Instead, there develops a tapering cartilaginous tube around the extension of the spinal cord. This tube is attached basally to the last vertebra that remains in the tail stump. It is perforated by blood vessels while the regenerate is still growing, but these openings are eventually abolished. The proximal portions of the cartilage may become calcified in older regenerates. Terminally, the tube opens into the growing tip of the regenerate. Here the ependymal canal maintains direct contact with the proliferating mesodermal cells at the apex of the regenerate. Here also the descending nerve fibers find access to the overlying epidermis.

The spinal cord regenerates no more of itself than is necessary. As its ependymal cells multiply to extend the neural canal into the new tail, some of the nerve fibers originating from neurons in the stump grow out along with it. Only glial cells, but no new neurons, are produced in the cord regenerate. Gray matter is therefore absent.

Since nerve fibers from the spinal cord do not penetrate the cartilaginous tube, the myotomes must receive their innervation from the spinal nerves in the stump. These are all derived from the last three pairs of spinal ganglia immediately proximal to the level of amputation. Interrupted by the loss of the tail, motor nerves regenerate into the new myotomes and sensory fibers innervate the skin. Schwann cells of uncertain origin take up positions along the regenerating nerves. Although the new tail is an imperfect replica of the original, it is available to be sacrificed again, and then to regenerate duplicates of itself as many times as may be necessary.

The lizard tail offers another example, like those in cyclostomes and urodeles (but not tadpoles), of the dependence of regeneration upon the spinal cord. Its removal for several segments back from the level of amputation completely precludes regeneration of the tail. Evidently its influence is not mediated via nerve fibers, for there are plenty of them left in the spinal nerves of cordless tails, yet regeneration still fails to occur. Sidney Simpson of Case Western Reserve University, working on the brown skink, *Lygosoma laterale,* has carried out some crucial experiments, outlined in Fig. 96, which convincingly show that it is the ependymal tube alone which is responsible for tail regeneration.

His problem was to separate the ependyma of the spinal cord from the surrounding nerve fibers, but this was impossible so long as there were neurons present to sprout new fibers even if the old ones could have been destroyed. Having shown that the spinal cord in the tail regenerate is devoid of neurons, he took advantage of this situation to obtain pure ependymal tubes. Cartilaginous tubes together with their contained spinal cords from the regenerated portions of tails were transplanted to their respective tail stumps. Here the severed lengths of nerve fibers degenerated, not to be replaced for lack of cell bodies. All that remained were the ependymal linings of the neural canals encased within the cartilaginous tubes. When such grafts were implanted

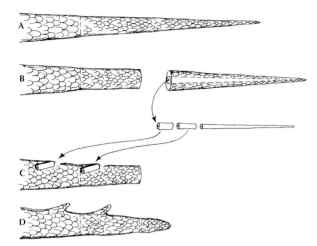

Fig. 96 Experimental demonstration of role of ependymal tube in lizard tail regeneration. A. Tail is first allowed to regenerate. B. Then the cartilaginous tube is dissected free with its ependymal canal inside. C. Segments of this are then transplanted obliquely beneath the skin of the remaining portion of the tail and its regenerate. D. From such graft sites there regenerate extra tails induced by the ependymal tubes. (Adapted from Simpson, 1964.)

obliquely into the muscle along the dorsal side of the tail, they induced accessory tail outgrowths. When grafted to the muscle of a tail stump, they induced extra cartilaginous tubes in the regenerating tail. If only the cartilaginous tube, without its ependyma, was similarly transplanted, nothing grew from it. Ependymal epithelium, therefore, directly induces the cartilaginous tube, and may be indirectly responsible for the differentiation of the surrounding musculature. These experiments do not prove that nerve fibers are not needed for regeneration in lizard tails, but suggest that if nerves do play a role, it is a minor one. The production of branched tails following incomplete autotomy, or the infliction of lateral wounds, is also explained. Such side growths seldom if ever develop unless the original lesion includes the spinal cord (Fig. 97).

Still another interesting aspect of regeneration in lizard tails relates to the development of regeneration itself. Angus D'A. Bellairs and his colleagues at St. Mary's Hospital Medical School in London have investigated the unexpected possibility that the tails of embryonic lizards apparently do not regenerate. The common European lizard, *Lacerta vivipara*, is ovoviviparous. By removing eggs from gravid females and maintaining them under warm, moist, sterile conditions, it was possible to operate on the embryos *in ovo*, often without interrupting the course of subsequent development and hatching. During the last week of embryonic life, tail regeneration frequently took place, as it does of course in postnatal lizards. When the tails were amputated two or more weeks prior to hatching, however, wound healing occurred but not regeneration. Sometimes small outgrowths resembling blastemas would form, but these eventually regressed. Even when such

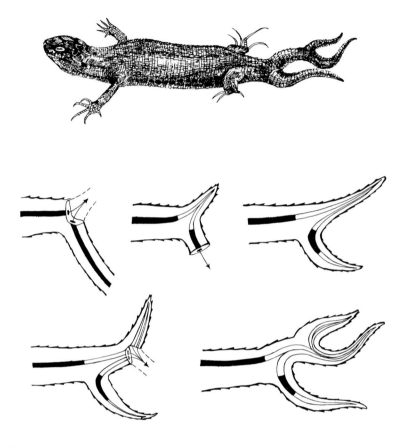

lizards were kept alive for several weeks after hatching, their missing tails were not replaced unless reamputated. It is apparently the maturity of the tissues at the time the tail is cut off which determines whether or not regeneration shall occur. Perhaps it has something to do with the development of the autotomy plane.

The tails of embryonic fishes and amphibians, like those of lizards, are also incapable of regenerating. Following amputation, or the removal of various portions of the presumptive fin regions, the defects inflicted on tail buds usually persist even after the capacity for regeneration has developed. Not unless a new wound is inflicted will the missing parts be replaced, and even then the resulting regenerate may be incomplete if the stump from which it grows is imperfect.

The failure of embryonic appendages to regenerate signifies a lack of regulative capacities. But is embryonic regulation the same as regeneration? The former reflects the operation of embryogenic mechanisms. The latter is a postembryonic manifestation. Regeneration, to be sure, utilizes many of the same developmental processes that embryos do, but superimposed upon this is the physiological and morphological substrate of the adult. Neural influences come into play, and hormones not present in the embryo must be reckoned with in adult organisms. Equally important is the state of tissue differentiation. It seems paradoxical that the renewal of development as it occurs in regeneration should depend more upon maturity than immaturity. This disquieting revelation can mean only one thing: that regeneration is a highly specialized process not entirely equivalent to embryonic development. It is not just left over after embryogenesis is complete, but is a capacity acquired as a consequence of development. Exactly what it is that must be acquired will be the point at issue in the years to come.

REFERENCES

BUTLER, E. G. and M. B. WARD. 1965. Reconstitution of the spinal cord following ablation in urodele larvae. *J. Exptl. Zool.* **160:** 47–66.

BUTLER, E. G. and M. B. WARD. 1967. Reconstitution of the spinal cord after ablation in adult *Triturus. Develop. Biol.* **15:** 464–486.

CAMPBELL, J. C. and K. W. JONES. 1968. The *in vitro* development of lens from cornea of larval *Xenopus laevis. Develop. Biol.* **17:** 1–15.

DEUCHAR, E. M., R. WEBER and F. E. LEHMANN. 1957. Differential changes of catheptic activity in regenerating tails of *Xenopus* larvae, related to protein breakdown and total nitrogen. *Helv. Physiol. Pharmacol. Acta* **15:** 212–229.

DOWLING, J. E. 1966. Night blindness. *Sci. Am.* **215** (4): 78–84.

EGUCHI, G. 1963. Electron microscopic studies on lens regeneration. I. Mechanism of depigmentation of the iris. *Embryologia* **8:** 45–62.

EGUCHI, G. 1967. *In vitro* analysis of Wolffian lens regeneration: Differentiation of the regenerating lens rudiment of the newt, *Triturus pyrrhogaster. Embryologia* **9:** 246–266.

EGUCHI, G. and M. ISHIKAWA. 1963. Alkaline phosphatase in the dorsal and the ventral halves of the iris during early stages of lens-regeneration in the newt. *Embryologia* **7:** 295–305.

EISENBERG, S. and T. YAMADA. 1966. A study of DNA synthesis during the transformation of the iris into lens in the lentectomized newt. *J. Exptl. Zool.* **162:** 353–368.

GOSS, R. J. and M. W. STAGG. 1958a. Regeneration of lower jaws in adult newts. *J. Morphol.* **102:** 289–309.

GOSS, R. J. and M. W. STAGG. 1958b. Regeneration in lower jaws of newts after excision of the intermandibular regions. *J. Exptl. Zool.* **137:** 1–12.

GRÄPER, L. 1909. Über eine dreischwänzige Eidechse mit sieben Schwanz-skeleten. *Arch. Entwicklungsmech. Organ.* **27:** 640–652.

HAUSER, R. 1965. Autonome Regenerationsleistungen des larvalen Schwanzes von *Xenopus laevis* und ihre Abhängigkeit vom Zentralnervensystem. *Arch. Entwicklungsmech. Organ.* **156:** 404–448.

HAUSER, R. and F. E. LEHMANN. 1962. Regeneration in isolated tails of *Xenopus* larvae. *Experientia* **18:** 83–84.

HAUSER, R. and F. E. LEHMANN. 1966. Abhängigkeit der normogenetischen Regeneration der Schwanzspitze bei *Xenopus laevis* Daud. von einem neurogenen Faktor im Liquor cerebrospinalis. *Rev. Suisse Zool.* **73:** 503–511.

HAY, E. D. 1963. The fine structure of differentiating muscle in the salamander tail. *Z. Zellforsch. Mikroskop. Anat.* **59:** 6–34.

HOLTZER, H., S. HOLTZER and G. AVERY. 1955. An experimental analysis of the development of the spinal column. IV. Morphogenesis of tail verte-brae during regeneration. *J. Morphol.* **96:** 145–172.

HOLTZER, S. 1956. The inductive activity of the spinal cord in urodele tail regeneration. *J. Morphol.* **99:** 1–40.

HUGHES, A. and D. NEW. 1959. Tail regeneration in the Geckonid lizard, *Sphaerodactylus.* *J. Embryol. Exptl. Morphol.* **7:** 281–302.

JENSEN, P. K., F. E. LEHMANN and R. WEBER. 1956. Catheptic activity in the regenerating tail of Xenopus larvae and its reaction to histostatic sub-stances. *Helv. Physiol. Pharmacol. Acta* **14:** 188–201.

JORDAN, M. 1958. Regeneration of the endbrain in postmetamorphic *Xeno-pus laevis.* *Folia Biol.* (*Warsaw*) **6:** 103–116.

KIORTSIS, V. and A. DROIN. 1961. La régénération caudale des Urodèles (Induction et réactivité du territoire). *J. Embryol. Exptl. Morphol.* **9:** 77–96.

KOSCIUSZKO, H. 1958. The influence of the olfactory nerves on the regen-eration of the endbrain in *Xenopus laevis* tadpoles. *Folia Biol.* (*Warsaw*) **6:** 117–130.

MARON, K. 1963a. Endbrain regeneration in Lebistes reticulatus. *Folia Biol.* (*Warsaw*) **11:** 1–10.

MARON, K. 1963b. Regeneration of the spinal cord in shark embryos (*Scyliorhinus canicula*). *Folia Biol.* (*Warsaw*) **11:** 269–275.

MOFFAT, L. A. and A. D'A. BELLAIRS. 1964. The regenerative capacity of the tail in embryonic and post-natal lizards (*Lacerta vivipara* Jacquin). *J. Em-bryol. Exptl. Morphol.* **12:** 769–786.

MORGAN, T. H. and S. E. DAVIS. 1902. The internal factors in the regenera-tion of the tail of the tadpole. *Arch. Entwicklungsmech. Organ.* **15:** 314–318.

NIAZI, I. A. 1963. The histology of tail regeneration in the ammocoetes. *Can. J. Zool.* **41:** 125–146.

NIAZI, I. A. 1964. Effect of destruction of the notochord in the stump on tail regeneration in the ammocoetes. *Can. J. Zool.* **42:** 707–714.

NIAZI, I. A. 1966. Role of the notochord in regeneration of the tail in frog tadpoles. *Acta Anat.* **64:** 341–350.

NIAZI, I. A. 1967. A contribution to the study of lens regeneration capacity in chick embryos. *Experientia* **23:** 970–972.

PIATT, J. 1955. Regeneration of the spinal cord in the salamander. *J. Exptl. Zool.* **129:** 177–207.

PRATT, C. W. M. 1946. The plane of fracture of the caudal vertebrae of certain lacertilians. *J. Anat.* **80:** 184–188.

REYER, R. W. 1962. Regeneration in the amphibian eye. *In* "Regeneration" (D. Rudnick, ed.), pp. 211–265. 20th Growth Symposium. Ronald Press, New York.

ROGUSKI, H. 1957. Influence of the spinal cord on the regeneration of the tail in urodele and anuran larvae. *Folia Biol.* (Warsaw) **5:** 249–266.

ROGUSKI, H. 1959. On the regeneration of the spinal cord in post-metamorphic *Xenopus laevis. Folia Biol.* (Warsaw) **7:** 129–133.

SIMPSON, S. B., Jr. 1964. Analysis of tail regeneration in the lizard *Lygosoma laterale.* I. Initiation of regeneration and cartilage differentiation: the role of ependyma. *J. Morphol.* **114:** 425–436.

SREBRO, Z. 1959. Investigations on the regenerative capacity of the between-brain and the influence of its removal upon development of *Xenopus laevis* tadpoles. *Folio Biol.* (Warsaw) **7:** 191–202.

STONE, L. S. 1959. Regeneration of the retina, iris, and lens. *In* "Regeneration in Vertebrates" (C. S. Thornton, ed.), pp. 3–14. University of Chicago Press, Chicago.

TERRY, R. J. 1956. Studies on midbrain regeneration in embryos and larvae of Rana pipiens. *J. Exptl. Zool.* **133:** 389–408.

VALLETTE, M. 1929. Régénération du museau et territoires de régénération chez les Urodèles. *Bull. Biol. France Belg.* **63:** 95–148.

WEBER, R. 1967. Biochemistry of amphibian metamorphosis. *In* "The Biochemistry of Animal Development" (R. Weber, ed.), Vol. 2, pp. 227–301. Academic Press, New York.

WERNER, Y. L. 1967. Regeneration of the caudal axial skeleton in a Gekkonid lizard (*Hemidactylus*) with particular reference to the 'latent' period. *Acta Zoologica* **48:** 103–125.

WINDLE, W. F. (editor). 1955. "Regeneration in the Central Nervous System." Thomas, Springfield, Illinois.

YAMADA, T. and S. KARASAKI. 1963. Nuclear RNA synthesis in newt iris cells engaged in regenerative transformation into lens cells. *Develop. Biol.* **7:** 595–604.

YAMADA, T. and C. TAKATA. 1963. An autoradiographic study of protein synthesis in regenerative tissue transformation of iris into lens in the newt. *Develop. Biol.* **8:** 358–369.

YOUNG, R. W. 1967. The renewal of photoreceptor cell outer segments. *J. Cell Biol.* **33:** 61–72.

ZALIK, S. E. and I. MEZA. 1968. *In vitro* culture of the regenerating lens. *Nature* **217:** 179–180.

11   **Horns and Antlers**

ABOUT twenty-five million years ago, the ancestors of today's ungulates evolved some very curious structures on their heads. All we have to go by is the fossil record, but skulls have been unearthed with bony outgrowths of strange and interesting conformations, outgrowths believed to represent the antecedents of horns and antlers. There is no way to tell exactly what kind of skin enveloped these early protuberances. Probably the first ones were covered permanently with hair, not unlike the horns of the giraffe. From such precursors there evolved two alternative specializations designed to protect and strengthen these cephalic appendages. Some acquired a tough sheath of horn on the outside of a viable core of porous bone. Others retained a hairy integument destined to be peeled off when the bone inside became solid and dead. In either case, these remarkable headpieces evolved into unique status symbols used as offensive weapons by males during the rutting season.

223

Fig. 98 Cranioceras, a three-horned deer from the late Tertiary period. Such primitive deer typically had relatively short antlers on the ends of very long pedicles.

Horns differ from antlers both structurally and developmentally (Fig. 99). First and foremost, horns are cornified, antlers ossified. Except for their keratinized portions, horns are continuously living structures. Antlers, however, are dead once they shed the velvet. Horns are

Fig. 99 Diagrammatic comparisons between horns and antlers. In the giraffe and okapi there are simple bony protuberances permanently covered with skin and hair. In the pronghorn antelope the horn sheath is branched, but the bony core is not. Here the cornified portion is shed and replaced annually. The horns of cattle and most other ungulates have a bony core covered with thick layers of cornified epidermis. Deer antlers are viable while growing in velvet. When growth is complete, the velvet is shed as the underlying bone becomes compact and dead.

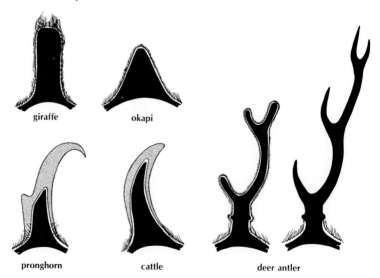

giraffe   okapi

pronghorn   cattle   deer antler

never branched, although those of the pronghorn antelope are bifurcate in the outer sheath (but not in the bony core). Antlers in contrast usually become branched once they reach certain proportions. These configurational differences reflect their modes of growth. Horns grow from the base, like blades of grass. Since the older portions are pushed ahead of the younger ones, there can be no provision for branching. Antlers, on the other hand, elongate on their ends. Like the apical meristems of plants, their growing tips are able to branch dichotomously. The most striking difference between the two, however, is that horns do not regenerate whereas antlers do, which is correlated with the fact that horns are permanent structures and antlers deciduous ones.

Patterns of Horn Growth

For obvious reasons, horns cannot begin their development prenatally like other parts of the body. However, they make up for the handicap by commencing to grow within days after birth in some cases. Moreover, their rate of elongation is out of all proportion to the rest of the head. In Dorset rams, for example, the horns may grow more than five centimeters a month, decelerating gradually as they mature. Such growth is partly due to the accretion of successive increments of keratinized epidermis and partly the result of bone growth inside this horny sheath. From its very inception, horn development is a cooperative effort between the epidermal and skeletal components.

In the newborn animal, the integument where the horn is destined to form is covered only by hair. Underneath, the rudiment of the future bony core exists either as an ossicle, the os cornu, lying free in the dermal connective tissue, or as a small excrescence on the frontal bone. Normally, cornification and ossification go on hand in hand in the course of subsequent development. The epidermis, which formerly produced fur, now begins to lay down the stratum corneum. The os cornu, if present, fuses with the skull, and the frontal exostosis elongates at a rate commensurate with that of the keratinizing skin above it. In view of this apparently inseparable relationship between bone and skin, one might ask just how important each component really is in the genesis of horns.

Some years ago, W. Franklin Dove, at the University of Maine, attempted to answer this question by means of various extirpation and transplantation experiments on kids and calves. He found that if the os cornu were removed, a horn grew anyway and new bone was induced in association with it. If the skin of the prospective horn region were excised, however, horn growth did not occur. When the os cornu was transplanted beneath the skin elsewhere on the head, no horn developed. But grafts of skin from the horn region, with or without the underlying bone, could give rise to horns in ectopic locations. Thus, the skin provides the primary impetus for horn formation, while the skeletal components become secondarily involved.

Usually only two horns develop. In some kinds of sheep and antelope, however, four horns may normally be produced (Fig. 100). Indeed small supernumerary horns, or "scurs," are not uncommonly encountered in the vicinity of the primary horns of sheep and cattle. It is also possible to produce extra horns by surgically subdividing horn buds and grafting the parts to separate regions of the head. Conversely, one can create artificial "unicorns" by fusing the two horn buds together in the middle of the frontal bone, as Dove succeeded in doing to an Ayrshire bull soon after its birth in 1933. When it grew up, this magnificent beast was equipped with a single large horn growing out of his forehead (Fig. 101). For the first time in modern history, man had created a unicorn simulating the legendary ones whose horns were believed to be a universal antidote against all the poisons with which ancient rulers were afraid of being assassinated. Little wonder they were willing to pay royal prices for such fabulous horns, for even the most lethal of poisons could be safely consumed from drinking vessels carved out of them. Many a king must have been duped by

Fig. 100 **Four-horned sheep.**
(*Specimen by courtesy of Franklin Park Zoo, Boston.*)

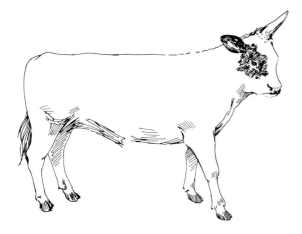

Fig. 101 **Artificially created unicorn. Horn buds of a newborn Ayrshire calf were grafted together in the middle of the head and grew out as a single structure.** *(After Dove, 1936.)*

ancient confidence men who had learned the secret of fusing horn buds together, a trick they probably resorted to when suspicious monarchs, wise to rhinoceros horns and narwhal tusks, began to demand their unicorns on the hoof!

The way horns grow is deceptively simple. Most of them continue to elongate throughout life, although the rate of growth falls off with age. Over the years, they may reach impressive dimensions, as in the sweeping horns of the Indian water buffalo which have been known to grow to almost two meters in length. Equally remarkable for different reasons are the trophies grown by bighorn sheep. Their horns elongate faster in front than in back, as a result of which they curl around in a graceful backward arc with the oldest material at the tip and the most recently produced horn at the base. It is possible to determine the age of these sheep by counting the number of annual rings in their horns, rings demarcated each fall and winter when the horns stop growing during the breeding season. Thus, from the geometry of their stratification, one can read the record of cornification as it occurred from birth to death.

Such lifetime records are the result of sustained epidermal growth in the absence of shedding (Fig. 102). This combination of circumstances is responsible for the deposition of layer upon layer of horn substance. As each new increment is laid down, all the ones produced before it are pushed upward. It is the progressive accumulation of this cornified material which gives rise to the durable, but dead parts of the horn. The living portion of a horn is on the inside. The germinative zone of the epidermis is not only located around the base of the horn but also lines the inner surface of the cornified sheath. Growth occurs from the inside at the interface between the keratogenous tissues of the epider-

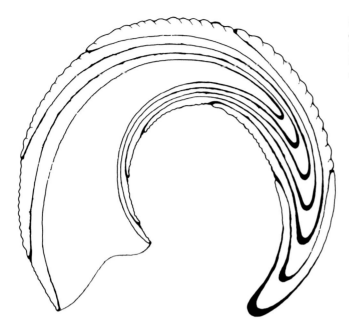

Fig. 102 Diagram of how horn growth occurs in the bighorn sheep. Each year's increment is laid down as a cone of keratinized tissue fitted inside those already produced in previous years.

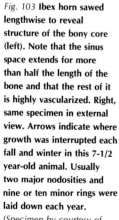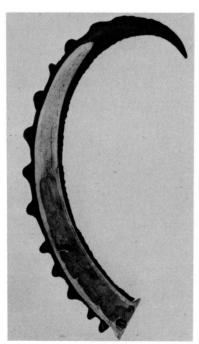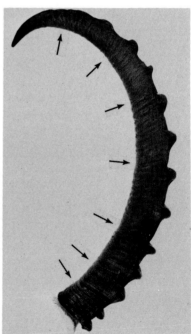

Fig. 103 Ibex horn sawed lengthwise to reveal structure of the bony core (left). Note that the sinus space extends for more than half the length of the bone and that the rest of it is highly vascularized. Right, same specimen in external view. Arrows indicate where growth was interrupted each fall and winter in this 7-1/2 year-old animal. Usually two major nodosities and nine or ten minor rings were laid down each year. *(Specimen by courtesy of the Museum of Comparative Zoology, Harvard University.)*

mis and the underlying connective tissue surrounding the bony core. The conical configuration of the horn bone is basically responsible for the general contours of the outer sheath, to which new material is added in the fashion of a cone within a cone.

The bony core itself also grows. In larger specimens, this bone tends to be hollow or porous, its cavities often being continuous with the sinus spaces in the skull. This adaptation, so pronounced in the ibex (Fig. 103), probably serves to reduce the weight of what would otherwise be an inconveniently ponderous headpiece. The vascularity of the horn bone contributes to its cancellous nature, especially near the apex where the increased blood supply keeps the temperature high enough to avert freezing in the winter, and supplies nutrients to the region where growth is most active. Thus, the overall development of a horn results from the coordinated growth of its epidermal and skeletal components. Both parts continue to become longer and thicker throughout life, but the accumulation of solid horn off the end of the bone produces an additive effect causing the horn as a whole to grow at a rate equal to the sum of its two parts.

The outside of a horn tells as interesting a story as the inside. Some horns are smooth on the surface, but those of sheep, goats and antelopes are often thrown into corrugations of unexplained but intriguing significance. These rugosities are not to be confused with the annual rings of bighorn sheep, which mark off each year's increment of horn production by the cessation of growth from about October to March. Other species of sheep and goats also show where horn growth slows down or stops during the mating season, but none is so conspicuous about it as the bighorn and some leave hardly a trace of where growth was interrupted each year.

This annual arrest of horn growth occurs mainly in animals native to temperate zones. The fact that it happens during the colder times of the year, however, does not mean that it can be attributed to lowered temperatures or poor nutrition. It occurs even in well-fed zoo animals. The more likely explanation of this phenomenon relates to the period of rut, for the horns of many animals stop growing while the males are fertile and the females are undergoing estrous cycles. Spermatogenesis and ovulation cease in the spring when the horns resume growth. Perhaps, then, the sex hormones exert antagonistic effects on the process of cornification, but this possibility has never been tested experimentally. Even if the administration of sex hormones did stop horn growth, say during the summer months, this would not be the whole explanation. Some domestic sheep, for example, are fertile all year round and their horns grow continuously throughout the year.

Fig. 104 **Male ibex about to produce a new pair of nodosities on its horns. Adjacent forehead (arrow) is very swollen just below the horn base where the cornified thickening is to be produced.** (*Specimen by courtesy of Catskill Game Farm, New York. Photo by Charlotte Corkran.*)

Neither castration nor injection of sex hormones stops their horns from elongating. And in the African and Asian tropics, where antelopes may reproduce at all seasons, horn growth is a continuous process. Hence, the existence of annual variations in the rate of horn growth seems to be correlated with seasonal changes in reproductive abilities, which in turn probably relate to annual fluctuations in day length at different latitudes.

The corrugations on horns come in various shapes and sizes. Probably the most conspicuous ones are the large thickenings, or nodosities, on the leading edges of male ibex horns (Fig. 104). The Alpine ibex has been extensively studied by Marcel Couturier of Grenoble, France, who has described in great detail the horns of these proud and beautiful animals. Growing to almost a meter in length, these spectacular horns usually produce two ridges each year. With advancing age, however, only single ridges may be formed per season and their dimensions tend to become smaller. The growing season in these horns lasts from March to November, but we cannot even guess what physiological factors cause the horn to become outfitted with these bumps with such recurrent regularity.

In addition to the major ridges, the ibex horn is adorned with more numerous transverse rings of lesser dimensions. These are comparable to the corrugations on the horns of most other ungulates although the number formed per year varies with the species. In the ibex, eight to ten growth rings develop each year. The bighorn sheep produces about thirteen of them during the course of its seven-month growing season (Fig. 105). The aoudad, or Barbary sheep, has horns with clearly defined rings. Although an annual break is not visible, their rate of growth can be determined by filing a scratch near the base and measuring how many rings are formed during the growing season from spring to fall. As shown in Fig. 106, there are approximately nine growth rings produced in this time, or about one every three weeks. Other animals, such as the numerous species of African antelopes, have not come under study from this point of view. Yet the waterbuck and springbok, the oryx and impala, all have splendid horns with rings or ridges often spaced at remarkably regular intervals along their lengths. When their several frequencies of ring formation are finally measured and compared, some interesting correlations may be discovered.

What controls the periodicity of these rings? Are they produced in response to some environmental rhythm, or are they in step with an intrinsic physiological periodicity in the animal's system? In the case of the bighorn sheep, it would be tempting to conclude that the thirteen

Fig. 105 **Captured specimens of bighorn sheep from Northwest Territory, Canada. The adult male is in his sixth year, having just begun to deposit a new yearly segment of horn in the early summer. Previously formed annual rings are clearly visible, as are the thirteen minor growth rings laid down in each year.** (*Courtesy of Dr. John Harper, Brown University.*)

Fig. 106 **Measurement of horn growth in the aoudad. Left, a scratch (arrow) was filed on base of the horn in the winter when growth had ceased. Right, same mark as it appeared the following fall at the end of the growing season. The horn had grown some 9 cm in length, and nine new growth rings were added during that year's period of elongation. Horn growth will be slower in subsequent years as the animal ages.** *(Specimen by courtesy of the Roger Williams Park Zoo, Providence, Rhode Island.)*

or so rings produced each year might reflect lunar cycles, except that these horns grow only from April to October. This means that rings must be fabricated at about sixteen-day intervals, which happens to coincide very closely with the duration of the estrous cycle in the domestic sheep. This may or may not be a meaningful correlation, but if it is we must still figure out how such a rhythm could affect rams as well as ewes.

Not even the nineteenth century zoologists, including John James Audubon himself, believed the early tales about the pronghorn antelope, *Antilocapra americana*. The incredible stories of the western pioneers claimed that here was an animal which not only had branched horns, but also shed them and grew new ones each year. Since no other animal in the world did this, it took some persuading before the validity of the first reports was finally established. These graceful inhabitants of our western plains from Canada to Mexico grow horns which may reach lengths of more than a foot in the male. Their branched configuration, so distinctive in external appearance, is a property of the cornified sheath only. The bony core is unbranched, as in the horns of all other animals (Fig. 99). Hence, the shape of the horn is no impediment to the shedding process, which occurs in the late fall shortly after the rutting season. Even before the old sheath has been lost, the new one starts to grow underneath and may well contribute to the loosening of the old attachments. Just before shedding is to occur the sheath may be held on only by the hairs embedded in the horny substance near its base. The new horn, which completes its growth in the spring, develops by the rapid production of keratinized cells from the epidermis covering the horn bone. Cornification is most rapid at the apex where the recurved point is produced. The anterior prong, formed by the heightened rate of epidermal growth on the front of the horn, may be comparable in a sense to the ridges on the horns on other kinds of animals.

Inasmuch as the horn sheaths are shed each year at the end of the breeding season (not unlike the loss of antlers in deer) it is possible that the decline in sex hormone secretion at that time of the year might have something to do with the separation of the old from the new. If a buck is castrated, however, the horns are not shed. In the permanent absence of testosterone the growth of new horn substance is not prevented, but the previous years' unshed increments may be pushed ahead of it in a forward curl (Fig. 107). The retention of several successive annual segments attached together one after another is a freakish condition in the pronghorn antelope, but it closely resembles the way horns normally grow in other species of ungulates.

Fig. 107 **Effects of castration on the pronghorn antelope. In the absence of testosterone the horn sheaths cannot be shed but new ones keep growing each year. The result is an abnormal piling up of cornified annual increments and a grotesquely misshapen pair of horns.** (After Pocock, 1905.)

Anatomy of Antler Regeneration When primitive birds and mammals first evolved from reptilian ancestors, they lost the ability to regenerate amputated appendages. This attribute, so prevalent among fishes, amphibians and reptiles, may have been sacrificed in the course of evolution as a concession to the advantages of becoming warm-blooded.

To maintain an elevated body temperature, an animal must have a heightened metabolic rate, which in turn requires ample nutrition at frequent intervals. Should such a creature lose a limb, chances are it would starve or be eaten before it could regenerate a functional replacement. Hence, there may have been no selective advantage for homeothermic vertebrates to regenerate vitally essential appendages. Nonessential structures, however, might be expected to have acquired regenerative potentialities, especially if they enhanced the reproductive opportunities of their possessors and at the same time were subject to injury. Antlers fulfilled all these qualifications.

Had antler-bearing animals never existed, there might have been some reason for a pessimistic view of the prospects of mammalian appendage regeneration. Yet the ability of antlers to be shed and replaced by new outgrowths each spring and summer testifies to the fact that the regeneration of histologically complex body parts is not necessarily incompatible with the warm-blooded condition. This ex-

Fig. 108 **American elk, or wapiti** (*Cervus canadensis*), **with growing antlers in velvet.** (*Specimen by courtesy of the Southwick Wild Animal Farm, Blackstone, Massachusetts.*)

ceptional potential resides in the pedicles that protrude from the frontal bones of the skull.

What is it about the tissues of these frontal pedicles that enables them to replace lost parts, while other areas of the body lack this capacity? We know that one of the advantages of being a bird or a mammal is that wound healing involves the prompt formation of a thick dermal scar. There is reason to believe, however, that this may constitute a barrier between the overlying epidermis and the tissues beneath. Epidermal-mesodermal contact, it will be recalled, is important to the formation of a blastema from which new appendages develop in lower vertebrates. If precocious scar formation which occurs in warm-blooded vertebrates prevents blastema development on such nonregenerating structures as limbs, digits and tails, why does this not happen on the antler pedicle?

Credit for explaining this paradox goes mostly to the late George B. Wislocki of the Harvard Medical School, who more than any other individual in recent times pioneered in the exploration of how antlers grow. He and his colleagues showed that in the earliest phases of antler growth, the cells in the dermal layer of the pedicle skin give rise to the tissue which subsequently differentiates into the substance of the antler. Thus, the dermis, which elsewhere in the body is responsible for producing the regeneration-inhibiting scar, is the very tissue which makes antler development possible. In this sense, then, we may regard antlers as extraordinarily modified scars, and their regeneration as an exaggerated version of wound healing.

The onset of renewed growth is forecast by the shedding of the previous year's dead antlers. Due to the erosion of bone by osteoclasts, the attachment of the nonliving antler to the living pedicle becomes weakened. This process occurs rather abruptly, for one can drag an anesthetized deer bodily by his antlers only days before they fall off of their own weight. The base of the shed antler (Fig. 109) is studded with many spicules of pure white bone, normally unstained with blood. Not until after the moment of detachment does bleeding commence from the pedicle stump, and this is only enough to produce a scab over the wound. Healing then occurs by the ingrowth of the tumescent skin from around the edges of the pedicle (Fig. 110).

It is this skin which gives rise to the antler bud that pushes up from the stump of the pedicle. Within a couple of weeks there develops a rounded outgrowth enveloped in a layer of smooth, shiny epidermis. It is a "rubbery" structure with an inner consistency about like that of cheese. Such a rudimentary antler feels almost hot to the touch owing to its extremely rich blood supply. If injured at this stage of develop-

Fig. 109 The base of a shed antler. The central portion consists of numerous tiny spicules of bone where the antler had been attached to the pedicle bone before the osteoclasts eroded the connections. Around the edges shreds of epidermis from the pedicle skin still adhere to the antler beneath the burr.

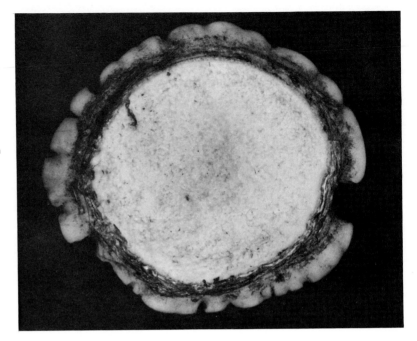

ment it will bleed profusely and may give rise to deformed antlers. Little wonder that the deer so adroitly avoids bumping his sensitive antler buds against anything during this formative period.

The skin of the antler is particularly interesting. Its velvety texture is the result of numerous short hairs standing out at right angles to the surface. Each one is equipped at its root with a large sebaceous gland which secretes an oily liquid onto the epidermis. The follicles from

Fig. 110 Sequence of events in the shedding and regrowth of an antler. A. Erosion of bone at the junction of the live pedicle and the dead antler. B. When antler is shed, pedicle skin has already started to grow. Scab forms on exposed pedicle bone. C. Skin of pedicle migrates inward beneath scab to heal the wound. D. Antler bud is produced by proliferation of scar tissue. (Adapted from Waldo and Wislocki, 1951.)

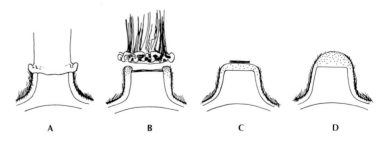

A   B   C   D

which these hairs develop arise at the apex of the antler and are left behind as the growing tip advances beyond them. Dermatologists have long sought in vain for ways to augment the number of hair follicles on the adult human body. Even in healing wounds the induction of new follicles is problematical at best. Yet the ease with which this is achieved by a deer is as encouraging as it is humiliating to man's attempts to do likewise.

At the apex of the young antler bud the epidermis exhibits a very curious and interesting configuration. There are long tongues of epidermis which extend deep into the connective tissue beneath. Whether these are formed by the downward invasion of the basal epidermis into the underlying dermis, or are left behind by the rapid upgrowth of tissues from below, we do not know. Reminiscent of the apical epidermal thickenings seen in amphibian limb blastemas, these transient formations soon disappear as the growing antler continues to elongate.

The role of nerves in antler regeneration is an important facet of the problem originally explored by Wislocki and Singer. They severed the nerves supplying a young antler in a white-tail buck, and discovered that growth was not inhibited as it is in the case of regenerating appendages in lower vertebrates. The denervated antler did not grow to normal dimensions, but this was attributed to injuries sustained as a result of its sensory deprivation. This interesting exception to the rule that nerves are generally required for appendage regeneration may relate to the fact that in their fully developed condition antlers are dead and nerveless anyway. From the utilitarian point of view, therefore, there would seem to be no compelling reason why antlers should be expected to have evolved a dependence upon adequate innervation for their development.

One of the most remarkable attributes of deer antlers is the rapidity with which they elongate (Fig. 111). Once the bud has formed, its rate of growth accelerates as new tissue is added apically. From time to time the soft growing tip bifurcates to put out the tines that branch off the main beam. It may take up to four months to grow a complete rack of antlers, and in larger species of deer (e.g., moose, elk, caribou) their length may increase more than one centimeter per day, a rate of growth probably unequaled anywhere else in the animal kingdom.

The sequence of events by which an antler elongates may be visualized by examining the internal tissues from the apex to the base (Fig. 112). At the very tip there is a mass of rapidly proliferating fibroblasts which produce quantities of collagen fibers just beneath the epidermis. Farther down, cells may be seen to have differentiated into

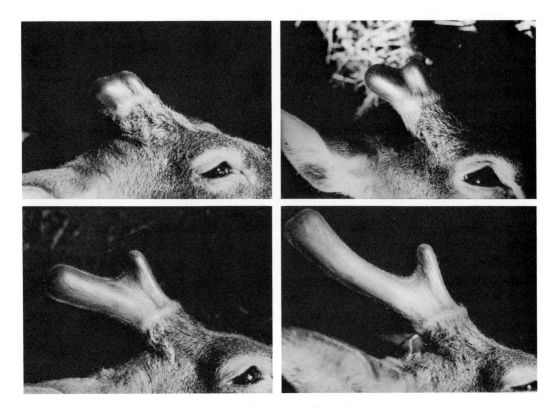

Fig. 111 **The rapid growth of antlers is illustrated in these photographs of a sika deer taken three, four, five and seven weeks after the old antlers were shed. The maximum rate of growth occurred during the fifth week when the rate of elongation exceeded 0.5 cm per day.** (*Specimen by courtesy of the Southwick Wild Animal Farm, Blackstone, Massachusetts.*)

cartilage. Still lower, bone is formed in progressively denser deposits to provide the rigidity necessary to support the weight of the antler. These internal tissues are honeycombed with numerous capillaries carrying away blood delivered to the antler via large arteries in the velvet. Later, as continued ossification solidifies the bone, the inner venous return becomes progressively restricted and the flow of blood is increasingly confined to the velvet. When even the latter circulation is abolished the entire antler dies. The deer then rubs off the tattered fragments of skin exposing the solid bone of the mature, but dead, antlers. This heralds the approach of the mating season.

Before the recurring annual cycle of antler growth can be established, the frontal pedicles from which the antlers sprout must first develop. The precursors of these pedicles may be felt even in the fawn as small bony knobs above and just behind the eyes. The impetus for pedicle growth resides primarily in these bony excrescences, for if they are surgically removed from the fawn's skull no antlers will ever be produced. However, if just the overlying skin is excised, wound healing takes place and subsequent antler growth is not inhibited. In Czechoslovakia, Anton B. Bubenik successfully substituted skin from the back of the head for that normally present in the presumptive antler region. He found that an antler grew just the same. Hence, although skin must participate in pedicle development, apparently any kind of skin will do.

Once pedicles have developed, the stage is set for the production of antlers when the deer is about a year old. This, however, does not

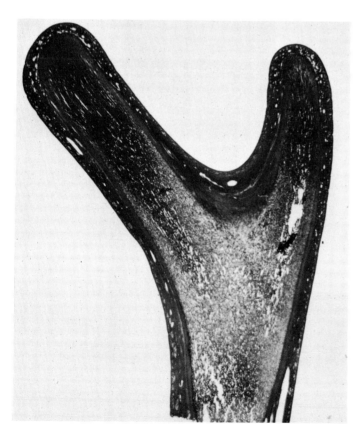

Fig. 112 Longitudinal section through a growing antler. Blood is conveyed to the tips via large arteries in the dermis and returned through veins in the spongy interior. The apex of each growing point is made up of multiplying fibroblasts, which are later destined to become cartilage and then bone cells as reflected in the spatial sequence of tissues along the shaft.

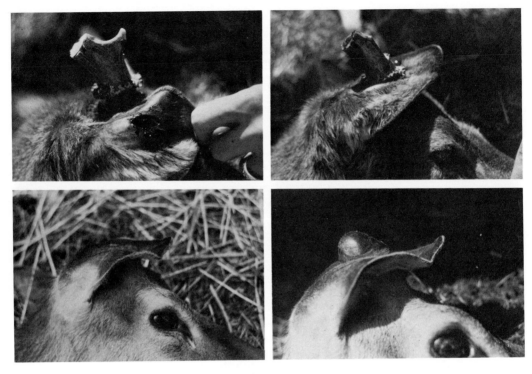

Fig. 113 **Substitution of ear skin for pedicle skin in a sika deer. Most of antler is sawed off, a ring of pedicle skin is removed and a hole cut in the ear** (*top left*). **Ear is pulled over antler and impaled on pedicle** (*top right*). **Inner ear epidermis heals to that of the distal pedicle skin. After old antler is shed, outer ear epidermis heals over end of pedicle** (*bottom left*). **When new antler grows it is covered with epidermis originally belonging to the ear** (*bottom right*). (*From Goss, 1964.*)

depend on the presence of bone as did pedicle formation. Bubenik removed all the bone along with part of the underlying skull from the pedicles without abolishing the capacity for subsequent antler regeneration. This is further evidence that it is the *skin* of the pedicle, not the bone, which now possesses the potentiality for antler genesis.

To determine what role the *epidermal* component of the skin plays in the process of antler development, it was necessary to substitute the epidermis on the pedicle skin with that from somewhere else on the body. The ear is very conveniently located for such an operation, but is far enough removed from the pedicle to lack all antler-forming capacities. A group of sika deer, originally an oriental species now common in zoos around the world, were used for this investigation as depicted in Fig. 113. In the early spring, weeks before the old antlers were due to be shed, such deer were anesthetized with a tranquilizer gun and a ring of skin about a centimeter wide was removed by circumcision from the distal pedicle. Then a hole of appropriate size was cut in the nearby ear. After sawing off most of the old antler, the ear was pulled over onto the pedicle where the inner skin of the ear subsequently healed to the proximal skin of the pedicle. The outer ear skin, however, could not heal to anything, at least not until the old antler was shed about a month later. When this happened, the stump of the pedicle healed over as usual, but the grafted ear constituted the only available source of epidermis. Hence, if an antler were to be produced under these circumstances, it would have to utilize epidermis derived from the ear, not the pedicle.

As it turned out, this experiment yielded positive results. Antlers did grow from such pedicles, and although they were covered with ear epidermis, their skin was indistinguishable from that normally occurring on antlers. Even typical velvety hairs were induced to grow from the newly formed follicles, despite the fact that wounds inflicted on ears heal without replacing their missing hair follicles. It must be concluded that although epidermis is necessary for antler growth, its source is of little or no consequence. Whether it develops ear-type or antler-type characteristics, however, depends on the nature of the underlying tissues.

Fig. 114 **A three-antlered fallow deer produced by grafting an antler bud to the center of the forehead.** (*Courtesy of Dr. Zbigniew Jaczewski, Polish Academy of Science.*)

The foregoing experiment afforded an opportunity to explore still another facet of regeneration. It has long been known that amphibian limbs, for example, can regenerate in either direction. That is, if a leg is grafted backward onto the body, the proximal stump (which is now distal) will regrow a typical leg made up of parts normally located beyond that level of amputation. Much the same thing happens in the case of deer antlers. If the pedicle to which the ear was grafted is cut away from the skull, the severed segment then remains attached only to the ear. The following spring it will grow new antlers from both proximal and distal ends, thus adhering to the laws of polarity governing other regenerating appendages.

These results also demonstrate that antlers can be produced from transplants to other parts of the body, as was first proved by the grafting experiments of Zbigniew Jaczewski in Poland. By cutting off the growing tips of antler buds in fallow deer and red deer, and transplanting them to the middle of the head between the eyes, he was able to create several deer bearing three antlers apiece (Fig. 114). These "third" antlers tended to go through the typical annual cycles of loss and replacement more or less in synchrony with the animal's other two normal ones.

Hormonal Control of Antler Growth

Antlers are secondary sexual characters, and as such they are profoundly influenced by sex hormones. They occur in the males of all species except the musk deer and the Chinese water deer, which have small but formidable tusks instead. Reindeer and caribou, on the other hand, have antlers in both sexes, although those on the males are larger.

The most impressive effect of sex hormones (or rather the lack of same) on deer antlers is demonstrated by castration. These effects were known even by Aristotle, who wrote, "If stags be mutilated when, by reason of their age, they have as yet no horns, they never grow horns at all; if they be mutilated when they have horns, the horns remain unchanged in size and the animal does not lose them." Centuries later, biologists confirmed and amplified what the ancient Greeks had already learned. They showed that castrated fawns fail to grow antlers altogether. In adult bucks, however, the effects of castration depend on the time of year when the operation is performed. In the fall and winter, when antlers are composed of dead bone, castration brings about the premature shedding of the old antlers after several weeks. New antlers may then begin to regenerate even in the middle of winter. If castration is performed in the summer when the antlers are still growing, they cannot thereafter shed their velvet.

In either case, a castrated buck ends up with persistently viable antlers that remain permanently in velvet, and thus incapable of being shed in the normal way. In temperate zones the antlers of such animals tend to freeze in the winter and the necrotic portions are lost. Yet each spring growth is renewed not only to replace the frozen parts but also to thicken that which may have survived the winter. With each succeeding summer new antler tissue is added to the preceding years' accumulations, eventually giving rise to some very grotesque outgrowths.

These outgrowths attain their most bizarre form in the European roe deer. Within a few years after castration, roebucks develop large and extremely amorphous masses of antler tissue. Because such tumorous antlers may grow down over the head like a wig, these deer are called "peruke bucks." An extreme case of this condition is illustrated in Fig. 115. Eventually, such unfortunate animals may be destined to die from infections in their excessively heavy antlers. Their only salvation is to be injected with sex hormones, which induce the velvet to shed and the antlers to ossify. When injections are stopped, these antlers are shed (as in castrated animals), but since they are subsequently replaced, the treatment must be repeated from time to time.

The castrate antlers of the roebuck develop considerably faster and more extensively than do comparable growths in other species. This may be attributed in part to the unique annual cycle of antler growth characteristic of the roe deer. Whereas most deer inhabiting temperate regions grow antlers in the spring and summer, roebucks regularly do so in the winter. Perhaps it is the enriched vascularization during the coldest time of year that protects the viable antlers from freezing and

Fig. 115 **Peruke roebuck. Following castration the antlers remain viable and permanently in velvet. Unlimited growth produces a wiglike mass of amorphous antler tissue which eventually brings about the animal's demise.** (After Tandler and Grosz, 1913.)

Fig. 116 **Excessive antler growth in castrated white-tail deer. When the deer are kept indoors to prevent freezing, the antlers grow new branches each year without having lost the previous years' accumulation. After many years an impressive bouquet of antlers is produced.** (*After Wislocki et al., 1947*).

accounts for the greater annual increment of antler tissue in castrated animals of this species.

In fact, a castrated white-tail deer kept indoors at the Philadelphia Zoo for many years grew a remarkable profusion of antlers while it was protected from freezing weather (Fig. 116). After one injection of testosterone, however, the velvet, and later the antlers, were shed and new antlers regenerated.

The sequence of changes that mark the antler growth cycle in deer is obviously under the control of hormones. The effects of castration indicate that testosterone is necessary if the antler is to become fully ossified and the velvet shed. These events coincide with the onset of the autumn breeding season, when the rising levels of testosterone transform the buck's normally even disposition into one of dangerous aggression.

In the spring, however, the diminished secretion of testosterone somehow triggers the shedding of old antlers and the growth of new ones. At this time of year the males are sterile due to reduced sperm production in their testes. Thus, it is experimentally possible to prevent the loss of antlers in the spring by giving appropriate injections of testosterone in advance of the normal shedding date. If this treatment is continued through the summer, the previous year's antlers are retained until the following spring, when the normal cycle is resumed. Once antler regeneration is under way in the spring or summer, however, testosterone administration brings about an abrupt cessation of growth, followed by the premature shedding of the velvet. Hence, male sex hormone has the general effect of promoting and maintaining antler maturation, while in its absence the antlers remain viable and capable of growth.

Of course, the shedding and regrowth of antlers may not be directly stimulated by reduced testosterone secretion alone. It is posssible that there may be a concomitant rise in some other hormone when testosterone levels are lowered naturally in the spring or artificially by castration. Various pituitary hormones have been suggested to play such a role. Hypophysectomy totally abolishes the capacity for antler production. Since the secretion of gonadotropins is in reciprocal balance with sex steroids, it has often been proposed, but not yet proven, that they might act directly on antlers. This unsolved problem becomes even more intriguing with the fact that female reindeer and caribou regularly shed their antlers within a few days of giving birth in the spring. Barren females, however, lose theirs in the winter, as do the males.

Strangely enough, the female sex hormone, estrogen, has exactly the same effects on antlers as testosterone. It will prevent the shedding of old antlers and induce growing ones to harden and shed their velvet. Since both hormones act alike on antler development, how can we explain the production of antlers in only one sex? Indeed, what accounts for the rare occurrence of antlered does?

Pedicles must develop before antlers can grow. Castrated fawns never grow antlers because they cannot produce pedicles. It is tempting to venture the educated guess that pedicles (unlike antlers) may react differentially to male and female sex hormones. Experiments bear this out. When young male deer are treated with estrogen, their pedicle development is arrested and no antlers grow. Conversely, female fawns have been made to develop small pedicles by repeated injections of testosterone. They do not, however, produce antlers, perhaps because of the inhibitory effects of their own estrogen secretion.

In adult female deer, ovariectomy by itself does not lead to pedicle growth. Testosterone injections however, stimulate pedicle development in spayed females, but even this does not lead to antler growth.

Yet there is a precedent for antler production in does. J. Kenneth Doutt and John C. Donaldson of the Carnegie Museum in Pittsburgh, have analyzed many cases of antlered female white-tail deer mistaken for males by Pennsylvania hunters. They estimate that about one out of every 2300 "male" deer with antlers turns out to be a female. Although one case they studied was due to hermaphroditism, and another was associated with an adrenal tumor which may have exerted a masculinizing influence, the majority of antlered does seem to be otherwise normal females which may even be pregnant or lactating. Their antlers are almost invariably in velvet during the December hunting season. The explanation of such anomalies, however, must remain a matter for conjecture pending further investigation.

Photoperiodism and the Antler Cycle The endocrine control of antler growth is well established, but what is it that regulates the annual cycle of hormone secretion? In temperate regions of the earth, seasonal changes in the environment are responsible for the synchrony with which various physiological events occur in the year of the deer. When New Zealand was stocked with elk, moose and white-tail deer from North America, and with red deer and fallow deer from England, these immigrants converted in due course to the reversed seasons of the southern hemisphere.

For example, in the case of several red deer shipped from England in October of 1907, adaptation was surprisingly prompt. Arriving in mid-November, the stags responded precociously to the "early" New Zealand spring by growing a second, albeit smaller, set of antlers a few months later. They shed the velvet on these antlers by April, 1908, and came into rut in early May, only several weeks after the normal fall breeding season in the southern hemisphere. The females, which were pregnant before they left England, calved in April of 1908. Nevertheless, they mated after a couple of months and gave birth again in February, 1909 (2 months behind the normal New Zealand schedule). By 1910 their reproductive cycles completely coincided with local conditions.

The role of day length in regulating antler cycles was first experimentally investigated in Poland in the early 1950's by Jaczewski. Red deer stags were confined in the dark from 4 P.M. to 8 A.M. each day beginning early in April when their new antlers were just starting to grow. These artificially shortened days accelerated antler maturation. In June or July the velvet was shed, and the belligerent rutting behavior in these deer made them increasingly difficult to handle. Returned to the normal summertime day length, they reacted as if it were spring all over again. Their antlers were shed in July or August, whereupon new ones grew and matured in time for the autumn breeding season. Thus, by interposing a period of foreshortened days during the spring, a second "winter" was artificially created thereby inducing the production of two sets of antlers in one year.

This is reminiscent of what used to occur in Père David's deer (Fig. 117), a species once saved from extinction by a margin of only seven individuals. Originally discovered by Père Armand David, a Catholic

Fig. 117 **Père David's deer.
Now extinct in its native
China, this unique deer
lives on only in captivity.**
(*Specimen by courtesy of
West Berlin Zoo*).

missionary-zoologist living in China in the 1860's, this deer existed
only in the Imperial Park in Peking. The Chinese called it "mi-lou,"
meaning "four-in-one" because it had the tail of a mule, the feet of a
cow, the neck of a camel and the antlers of a stag. Overcoming considerable difficulties, Père David succeeded in sending a pair of these
animals to Paris in 1866. Eventually several zoos in Europe acquired
specimens, but they bred poorly in confinement. To make matters
worse, the Peking herd was slaughtered in 1900 during the Boxer
rebellion. The lone survivor, a female, died in 1920 after a long but
unproductive life. The species was finally rescued from almost certain
extinction by the Duke of Bedford who had quietly bought up enough
animals to establish a breeding herd. Turned loose on his large estate
at Woburn Abbey, north of London, these deer have since multiplied
to several hundred individuals. Today, this magnificent herd may still
be seen thriving on its adopted English countryside.

It was in the early years of their comeback that Père David's deer
were observed occasionally to grow two sets of antlers per year. The
one regularly produced in the spring was sometimes shed in December, after which a second smaller set of antlers grew in the winter.
This phenomenon has never been explained, nor has it been observed
for many years now. But as long as Père David's deer exists we shall

not be denied the chance to investigate this unusual trait in the years to come.

All signs point toward light as the environmental factor most responsible for regulating antler growth cycles in deer. Many experiments on birds have shown that their migratory and reproductive behavior may be controlled by seasonal fluctuations in day length. Only recently it has been learned that in mammals the pineal gland may act as a "physiological clock" responding to the daily rhythms of light and darkness impinging on the brain.

It seemed only logical that some comparable mechanism might be operating in deer. This possibility has been confirmed by a series of long range studies on the effects of light on antler growth cycles. By keeping groups of sika deer indoors under artificial lighting controlled by automatic time switches, it is possible to mimic conditions in different parts of the world, and even to create a few that exist nowhere.

There are several basic ways in which the seasonal fluctuations in day length can be manipulated. The *phase* of the cycle can be reversed, the *amplitude* changed, or the *frequency* altered. If the seasons are reversed to simulate those in the southern hemisphere, the antler cycle likewise shifts six months out of phase (Fig. 118), as had been observed in the deer transported to New Zealand. This still happens even when the temperature cycle remains unchanged. Thus, antlers can be induced to grow during the coldest time of year provided the

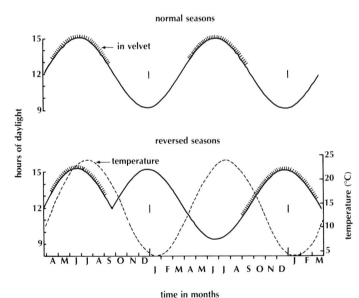

Fig. 118 **Effect of reversal of annual light cycle on growth of antlers in the sika deer. Under normal conditions (above) antlers are in velvet from May to September in the northern hemisphere. When shifted six months out of phase beginning on the autumnal equinox (below), the day length cycle is inverted with respect to the temperature cycle (broken line). Consequently, antlers do not grow until a year later when the days are again increasing in length.**

days are made long in the winter and short in the summer. There can be little doubt that deer program their antler cycles by monitoring the changes in day length between the summer and winter solstices.

At the equator, however, the days are twelve hours long throughout the year. How, then, can the deer native to tropical Asia and South America regulate their antler and reproductive cycles? The answer is that they don't, at least not in unison. Within a given population of deer living near the equator, there are almost always some bucks with antlers in velvet. By the same token, the birth of fawns is similarly irregular, for the does are polyestrous.

These deer remain fertile throughout the year, in contrast to their temperate zone cousins. Regardless of whether their antlers are in velvet or not, active spermatogenesis goes on in their testes. This is taken to indicate that the antlers of tropical deer have declined in importance as secondary sexual characters. Indeed, combat between rival males, although it still occurs in the tropics, tends to be less spirited than among temperate zone species having definite breeding seasons. Perhaps this is because fertile males in velvet are less inclined to lock horns with bucks carrying burnished antlers.

By far, the most puzzling aspect of this problem is the fact that although tropical deer do not all grow antlers synchronously, each individual buck does so at precise yearly intervals. Apparently the months when antler growth typically occurs in a given male are determined by when he happened to have been born. For example, a deer held captive in Caracas was kept under observation since soon after it was born in March, 1957. This buck grew new antlers between January and April of each year from 1958 to 1963, but for unexplained reasons he produced no new antlers in 1964 and 1965. Then, in January of 1966, he again started to grow a new set of antlers right on schedule after waiting exactly thirty-six months from the beginning of the last cycle!

As far as is known, this timing is independent of the environment, for records show that tropical deer transported to zoos in temperate regions still persist in their original rhythms. Yet these deer somehow count off successive twelve-month intervals, each one out of phase from that of his fellows. Perhaps they are entrained as fawns to respond to some recurring environmental cue too subtle to vary with the earth's latitude. More likely, these deer must be relying on some strictly internal physiological rhythm similar to, but much longer than, those responsible for controlling circadian or estrous cycles. In fact, the periodicity of antler growth in tropical deer has much in common with human menstrual rhythms. All women go through cycles of approximately the same duration, but they do not do so in unison. Moreover, such cycles persist for many years without reference to any external timer. Perhaps, as some believe, they were originally synchronized with the lunar month, just as the progenitors of tropical deer once grew antlers in response to seasonal cues in the environment. Yet somewhere along the line the dependence upon external stimuli was lost while the physiological event went on keeping its own time.

Since tropical deer shed their antlers at any time of year, while those in temperate zones do so at definite seasons, there must be an area of transition in between. However, the latitude at which the mutual synchrony of antler cycles is lost has not yet been determined. One way to find the answer would be to gather data on the shedding seasons of deer in their native habitats at various latitudes, say from Mexico to Panama. Such information, unhappily, is not available. A simpler, though indirect, method would be to observe the reactions of temperate species of deer to progressively more tropical climates. It is known that domestic animals, such as sheep and goats, breed throughout the year when moved from northern to equatorial latitudes. But there are no records of deer having been transplanted to the tropics. Experiments on sika deer, however, have shed some light on this mystery. Exposed to twelve hours of light and twelve hours of darkness every day of the year, these deer had no way of knowing what season it was (except for temperature fluctuations, which turned out not to be involved).

Under these simulated equatorial conditions, the deer failed to grow new antlers altogether, at least when put indoors prior to the autumn breeding season. Those started later in the fall or winter usually shed and regenerated antlers on schedule the following spring, but did not do so in succeeding years (Fig. 119). Some of these animals failed to grow new antlers for over three years, with no signs of ever again doing so as long as they remained in an environment without seasons.

Hence, there is a time in the fall when the decreasing lengths of day normally predetermine the events that are to occur months later in the spring. Just as females are destined to give birth seven to eight months after mating season, males are programmed to give rise to new antlers after a similar interval. The roebuck may be an exception that proves this rule. Its anomalous replacement of antlers in the winter is correlated with its equally unusual breeding season in the middle of the summer. Maybe this explains as well the erstwhile production of winter antlers by Père David's deer, a species which also mates in the summer. In any event, the tendency for males to be harmlessly in velvet when fawns are born must have been an important selective advantage in the evolution of deer.

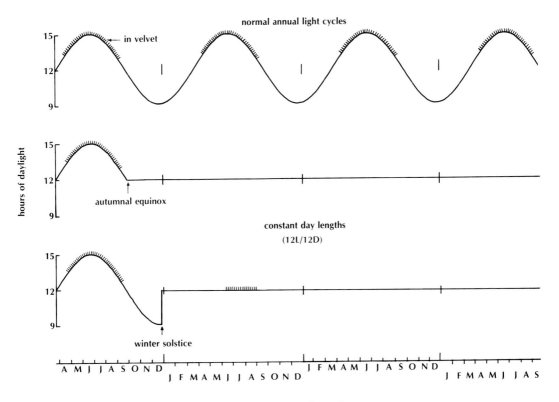

Fig. 119 **When the day length is held constant at twelve hours of light and twelve hours of darkness per day, deer fail to replace their antlers because there are no seasons on the equator. Switched to these conditions at the autumnal equinox, deer neither shed nor regenerate antlers the following spring. If the experiment is started at the winter solstice, antlers are replaced the next spring but not thereafter. Hence, each cycle of antler regeneration is predetermined sometime during the preceding autumn.**

The annual cycle of antler replacement has evolved as an adaptation to the conditions unique to the planet earth. Yet one wonders how this cycle would respond to "years" of different lengths, such as might occur on a hypothetical planet revolving around the sun in less than 365 days.

To test this possibility, sika deer have been maintained under normal cycles of day lengths, except that every other day was omitted. Hence, the year went by twice as fast as it should, and the deer were exposed every six months to antler-inducing changes in photoperiod. Under these unearthly conditions, antlers regenerated twice a year. Moreover, the interval of time from when the old antlers were lost until the velvet was shed spanned only two months, instead of the four-month period

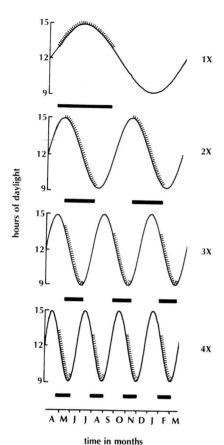

Fig. 120 Changing the frequency of day length fluctuations alters the number of antler growth cycles accordingly. From top to bottom, the number of sets of antlers produced per year can be increased from one (normal) to two, three or four by shortening the light cycle from twelve to six to four to three months, respectively. Note that regardless of how much the "year" is accelerated, the total length of time spent in velvet (black bars) adds up to approximately four to five months in all cases.

normally separating these two events. Since the "growing season" was thus accelerated twofold, these deer grew abnormally short antlers.

How far can this be pushed? The annual light cycle can be experimentally squeezed into ridiculously short periods of time in an effort to learn how frequently a deer can be stimulated to produce antlers (Fig. 120). Animals exposed to four-month cycles, or three-month cycles, grow antlers three or four times as often as normal, but they are truncated stubs hardly more than a few inches high. Six two-month cycles per year, however, do not work. Thus, it is possible to abort the development of antlers by accelerating the passage of "years" and abbreviating the seasons accordingly, but a limit is reached when years are shortened from three to two months.

One naturally wonders if the opposite effect could be achieved by somehow prolonging the growing season. If the length of each day is made to increase indefinitely it is possible to overshoot the summer solstice by many months. This almost endless spring, however, does not stretch the length of time elapsed from the onset of growth to the shedding of the velvet. Because their demise is evidently programmed from the very beginning, antlers cannot be made to grow for longer than normal periods of time. Although their development can be cut short by prematurely reducing day lengths, extra-large antlers apparently cannot be induced to regenerate by artificially preventing the days from shortening.

Antler size is actually a function of body size. Some of the smallest species, such as *Pudella mephistophelis* of South America, have little more than spike antlers a couple of centimeters high. The largest species of deer carry racks of massive dimensions, antlers which are large in relative, as well as absolute terms. Their disproportionate size reached its climax in the case of the Irish elk (*Megaceros*), an extinct

Fig. 121 **The so-called Irish elk** (Megaceros) **was the largest deer ever to live. Neither an elk nor a moose, this magnificent inhabitant of northern Europe during the Pleistocene epoch was a giant descendant of the fallow deer originally native to the Mediterranean region. Stone Age hunters, tempted by his huge dimensions and enormous antlers, probably wiped out the last ones in Neolithic times.**

relative of the fallow deer. The antlers of this gigantic deer grew to lengths of up to two meters with spreads of four meters from tip to tip (Fig. 121). Sometimes their combined weights exceeded that of the rest of the animal's entire skeleton. Yet all antlers, presumably including those of the Irish elk, grow to completion in only three to four months, whether they attain lengths of two meters or two centimeters. The bigger ones simply grow faster.

Since the "normal" size cannot be surpassed by prolonging the growing season, it is the rate of growth which determines how big the antlers shall become. The growth rate is proportional to the initial size of the antler bud, which is in turn related to the dimensions of the pedicle stump. Thus, the deer antler is an object lesson in the principles of growth dynamics, principles as yet undiscovered but of obvious relevance to all regenerating systems.

REFERENCES

ANTHONY, H. E. 1928–29. Horns and antlers. Their evolution, occurrence and function in the Mammalia. *Bull. N.Y. Zool. Soc.* **31:** 179–216; **32:** 3–33.

BILLINGHAM, R. E., R. MANGOLD and W. K. SILVERS. 1959. The neogenesis of skin in the antlers of deer. *Ann. N.Y. Acad. Sci.* **83:** 491–498.

BUBENIK, A. B. 1966. "Das Geweih." Verlag Paul Parey, Hamburg and Berlin.

BUBENIK, A. B. and R. PAVLANSKY. 1965. Trophic responses to trauma in growing antlers. *J. Exptl. Zool.* **159:** 289–302.

COUTURIER, M. A. J. 1962. "Le Bouquetin des Alpes." Imprimerie Allier, Grenoble.

DOVE, W. F. 1935. The physiology of horn growth: A study of the morphogenesis, the interaction of tissues, and the evolutionary processes of a Mendelian recessive character by means of transplantation of tissues. *J. Exptl. Zool.* **69:** 347–405.

DOVE, W. F. 1936. Artificial production of the fabulous unicorn. A modern interpretation of an ancient myth. *Sci. Monthly,* **42:** 431–436.

GADOW, H. 1902. The evolution of horns and antlers. *Proc. Zool. Soc. London* **1:** 206–222.

GOSS, R. J. 1963. The deciduous nature of deer antlers. *In* "Mechanisms of Hard Tissue Destruction" (R. Sognnaes, ed.), pp. 339–369. AAAS Publ. No. 75. Am. Assoc. Advance. Sci., Washington, D.C.

GOSS, R. J. 1964. The role of skin in antler regeneration. *In* "Advances in Biology of Skin. Wound Healing" (W. Montagna and R. E. Billingham, eds.), Vol. 5, pp. 194–207. Pergamon Press, London.

HALL, T. C., W. F. GANONG and E. B. TAFT. 1966. Hypophysectomy in the Virginia deer; technique and physiologic consequences. *Growth* **30:** 382–392.

HUXLEY, J. S. 1931. The relative size of antlers in deer. *Proc. Zool. Soc. London* **1931:** 819–864.

JACZEWSKI, Z. 1954. The effect of changes in length of daylight on the growth of antlers in the deer (Cervus elaphus L.). *Folia Biol. (Warsaw)* **2:** 133–143.

JACZEWSKI, Z. 1961. Observations on the regeneration and transplantation of antlers in deer *Cervidae. Folia Biol. (Warsaw)* **9:** 47–99.

NOBACK, C. V. 1929. The internal structure and seasonal growth-changes of deer antlers. *Bull. N.Y. Zool. Soc.* **32:** 34–40.

NOBACK, C. V. 1932. The deciduous horns of the pronghorn antelope, *Antilocapra americana. Bull. N.Y. Zool. Soc.* **35:** 197–207.

POCOCK, R. I. 1905. The effects of castration on the horns of a prongbuck (*Antilocapra americana*). *Proc. Zool. Soc. London* **1905:** 191–197.

RÖRIG, A. 1907. Gestaltende Correlations zwischen abnormer Körperkonstitution der Cerviden und Geweihbildung derselben. *Arch. Entwicklungsmech. Organ.* **23:** 1–150.

TANDLER, J. and S. GROSZ. 1913. "Die Biologischen Grundlagen der Sekündären Geschlechtscharaktere." Springer, Berlin.

WALDO, C. M. and G. B. WISLOCKI. 1951. Observations on the shedding of the antlers of Virginia deer (Odocoileus virginianus borealis). *Anat. Record* **88:** 351–396.

WISLOCKI, G. B. 1942. Studies on the growth of deer antlers. I. On the structure and histogenesis of the antlers of the Virginia deer (Odocoileus virginianus borealis). *Am. J. Anat.* **71:** 371–416.

WISLOCKI, G. B., J. C. AUB and C. M. WALDO. 1947. The effects of gonadectomy and the administration of testosterone propionate on the growth of antlers in male and female deer. *Endocrinology* **40:** 202–224.

WISLOCKI, G. B. and M. SINGER. 1946. The occurrence and function of nerves in the growing antlers of deer. *J. Comp. Neurol.* **85:** 1–19.

12 Unsolved Problems of Regeneration

THE histologist examines the morphology of a tissue by sectioning it either transversely or longitudinally. Since the same organ cannot be sliced in both directions at once we can see only one dimension at a time. Nevertheless, we can still integrate all the anatomical dimensions of a structure because what the eye perceives separately the mind can interpret comprehensively.

The subject of regeneration has breadth and it has depth. Thus far, it has been explored extensively from unicellular organisms to mammals. Now let us cut through it in other directions, and in so doing hopefully achieve a deeper understanding of the phenomenon in general, an understanding not always appreciated when one's attention is focused only on specific examples.

256

Strategy of Regeneration The capacity to regenerate persists or disappears according to the dictates of natural selection. The mechanism by which regeneration occurs likewise evolves. Of all the many different developmental pathways by which any given structure might have been produced, natural selection has in each case narrowed the alternatives down to a single method. Comparative studies tell us, however, that different kinds of animals do not always regenerate in the same way. To be sure, certain aspects of the process—wound healing, cell migration, differentiation—are evidently so basic that they have changed very little in the course of phylogeny. Others, however, have been modified considerably, because different organisms do not always select equivalent means to the same end.

One of the first problems to be solved if a structure is to regenerate is to decide upon a source of cells. These cells must fulfill two chief prerequisites. They must have some way of moving to the site of amputation, and once there they have to be capable of giving rise to an appropriate regenerate.

Some organisms, if they are not too histologically complex, can manage to regenerate by morphallaxis. That is, older tissues remaining after amputation can sometimes simply reorganize themselves into a replacement of the missing part with a minimum of dedifferentiation and proliferation. No blastema is formed in the process, and this is essentially how sponges and coelenterates repair themselves. Not all animals, however, can replace lost parts of their bodies by such a direct remodeling process.

Higher organisms resort to more complicated mechanisms of development, differing from their predecessors in the production of the regeneration blastema. This cluster of undifferentiated cells which forms at the place of injury has great morphogenetic potentials. Its constituent cells, therefore, must come endowed with some very special properties, including the lack of cytological specializations and the competence to differentiate into appropriate parts of the regenerating structure.

There are two ways to achieve these ends. One is to draw upon local tissues by way of dedifferentiation, and the other is to rely upon various kinds of reserve cells from which to build the blastema. Reserve cells are usually scattered throughout the animal's body and may be required to migrate considerable distances in order to participate in regeneration. The flatworms are believed to regenerate in this way, and annelids often combine this with various degrees of dedifferentiation. In either case, the reserve cells are totally uncommitted at the outset, but have the capacity to turn into whatever they may be called upon to become. Depending on which fragment of the original worm they are in, and the orientation of the cut surface to which they migrate, these cells can take part in either head or tail regeneration with equal facility. The conclusion is inescapable that their original systemic distribution correlates with their equally unrestricted potentialities.

When regenerative competence became increasingly confined to appendages, as opposed to major fractions of the entire body, the histogenesis of blastema cells shifted to local sources. Thus, the cells from which the regenerate is destined to develop reside within the appendage itself, or very nearby. Indeed, it is the distribution of such competent cells which defines the limits of each regeneration territory. No longer can each cell give rise to anything and everything. Now cells can take part in regenerating only their own kind of appendage and no other. What specific role they are to play within these limits remains to be determined. Maybe such cells are restricted to a single histological fate depending on the type of tissue from which they were derived in the first place. Maybe they can switch roles in the course of dedifferentiation and redifferentiation. Either way, the ultimate position of such a cell within a muscle or a skeletal element, for example, must be fortuitously determined (Fig. 122). Hence, a

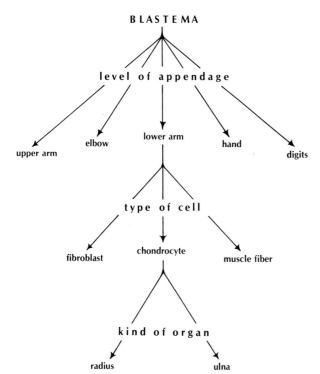

Fig. 122 **The destiny of a blastema cell is partly hereditary and partly circumstantial. In the newt arm, for example, a cell's original information content consists of species specificity and also of membership in its regeneration territory. These attributes are unalterable. In the course of regeneration, the cell and its descendants must first determine at what levels in the new appendage they are to be located. These levels can only be distal to the cell's original position in the limb. If incorporated into the lower arm, for instance, it must next decide what type of cell to become (unless this has already been determined by its former state of differentiation). Should it undergo chondrogenesis, it would have to do so as part of either the radius or the ulna, but whether the cell determines what the skeletal element shall be, or vice versa, we still do not know.**

blastema cell on the arm of a newt may perhaps be programmed to become a chondrocyte, but whether it ends up as part of a humerus or radius or carpal element must be largely a matter of chance.

What we do not know is whether cells from one kind of blastema can actively participate in the morphogenetic expression of a different kind of blastema. Recent evidence by John Oberpriller at Tulane University suggests that maybe they can. He grafted cells from intestinal and tail blastemas, previously labeled with tritiated thymidine, into the limb blastemas of adult newts. The labeled cells were later found to have been incorporated into the differentiating tissues of the limb regenerate. Even intestinal cells, which do not normally undergo chondrogenesis, become chondrocytes within the cartilaginous skeletal elements of the limb. These experiments argue in favor of a greater lability in the potentialities of regenerating cells than was previously suspected. Even if individual cells can be deflected in their pathways of differentiation by inclusion in a different regenerating system, it would be premature to conclude that the same applies to whole blastemas

Thus, from the results of various experiments in which parts may be deleted, grafted or rearranged, we can infer certain things about the information content of regenerating blastemas. Those of amphibians are apparently already determined as to type of appendage, but whether or not their constituent cells are equally determined is problematical. Blastema cells may not be so rigidly controlled as are whole blastemas, for the kind of cell into which they are to differentiate, and the kind of tissue into which they are to be incorporated, may well be dictated by their local surroundings. Thus, some aspects of a cell's destiny may be predetermined while others may be made up as they go along. Hence, regenerating systems tend to evolve toward increasingly rigid control. Regeneration has gradually sacrificed the individual freedom of the flatworm neoblast to the controlled behavior of amphibian appendage cells. In so doing, its accomplishments have diminished for the sake of increased efficiency. Continued to its totalitarian conclusion, this trend would have imposed an excessive inflexibility upon the cells of evolving higher vertebrates, and may well have contributed to the downfall of their regenerative capacities altogether.

Turning now to the problem of growth rates, the developing regenerate is possessed of unknown factors which determine how fast the new structure shall elongate. In general, amputation is followed by a lag phase during which no outgrowth occurs. This is when wound healing, dedifferentiation and general reorganization of the stump are going on preliminary to blastema formation. Elongation of the regenerate commences slowly at first as the blastema takes shape, and then accelerates rapidly during the earlier phases of growth. Later on, the rate of elongation subsides until growth finally comes to a halt.

Naturally, growth curves differ from one regenerating system to another, but they also vary in the same appendage depending upon the circumstances of amputation. Proximal cuts call for more rapid regeneration than do distal ones, whether the amputated structure is a leg, a tail or a fin. This does not mean that regeneration is completed in the same length of time irrespective of how much was cut off. It is not. But the outgrowth from a proximal level almost catches up with a comparable regenerate growing from a more distal level of amputation. And in most respects, the timetable for each is remarkably similar. Except for the extremes, the duration of the lag phase does not differ significantly from one level of amputation to another. Hence, the onset of elongation coincides, as does the time of maximal growth rate. What differs is the magnitude of the rates of elongation and the termination of growth. From more proximal levels, growth is faster and lasts longer than that elicited from more distal levels (Fig. 123).

What accounts for the difference? Lacking any true explanation, all

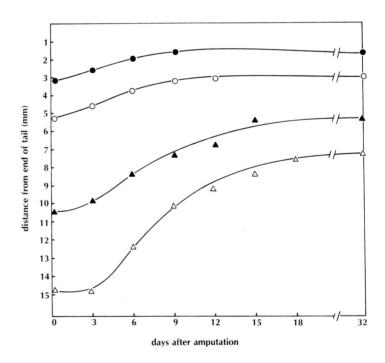

Fig. 123 **Rate of regeneration is a function of level of amputation. In the tadpole tail, the more that is cut off the faster it grows back. Regardless of the level of amputation, the amount regenerated is a constant percentage of the amount lost.** (*From data of Ellis, 1909.*)

we can do is seek correlations between the growth profiles of regenerating appendages and various parameters of the stumps from which they issue. In general, the rate and extent of regeneration relates to how much has been removed, the dimensions of the stump, the size of blastema, and perhaps such other factors as the number of nerve fibers and blood vessels at the level of amputation. Alterations in metabolic rates along the length of an appendage may be involved too. Unhappily, no such correlations have yet been found to apply consistently to all regenerating appendages.

Regeneration is a rebound phenomenon in which the missing part grows back much faster than the original structure developed in the first place. Thus, in a short span of time the accelerated pace of regeneration overtakes the original dimensions of the replaced appendage. The larger the animal, the faster its parts grow, at least in absolute terms. Relative growth rates, however, do not vary a great deal. For example, the curves describing the elongation of a regenerating *Euglena* flagellum and a growing deer antler as a function of time are very nearly the same shape. Only their units of measurement differ.

The eventual size of a regenerated appendage is determined by a combination of the rate and the duration of growth. If one or both of these parameters is inadequate, the final length of the regenerate will fall short of the original. Most appendages capable of regeneration typically attain the full dimensions of the portions being replaced. Some, for unexplained reasons, do not. The tadpole tail is a case in point. It seldom regenerates the total amount cut off regardless of age, level of amputation or temperature.

No matter how much of a structure regenerates, growth must ultimately cease as the rate of elongation decelerates to zero. This seems to result from the failure of the growing tip to keep ahead of the differentiating zone behind it. The regenerate is formed at the expense of the blastema cells, and as long as they can divide faster than their descendants differentiate, then elongation can continue. But it is a losing race because the size of the proliferating tip diminishes during the course of regeneration until all of its cells are used up. Hence, the cessation of regeneration may be attributed to the steady decline in mitosis, but the factors which regulate hyperplasia in the growing tip continue to elude us.

Not all regenerates grow in this way. Most of them, to be sure, possess an apical region of undifferentiated cells (in which case differentiation proceeds in a proximo-distal direction). There are some

Fig. 124 **Regenerates can develop from either proximal or distal growth zones. Proximal ones give rise to distally differentiating structures with no possibility of bifurcation. Distal growth zones can branch dichotomously as differentiated parts are formed behind.**

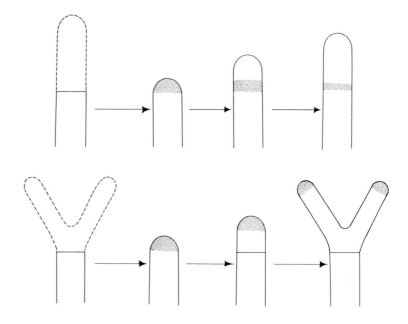

forms, however, which have adopted the opposite mode of development. In flatworms, for example, differentiation in the head blastema commences with the formation of the most anterior portions (brain, eyes), and only later do prepharyngeal and pharyngeal regions develop. Likewise in annelids, in which the terminal segment usually forms first, to be followed by more proximal ones interposed between it and the rest of the worm. Arthropod appendages adhere to a somewhat similar pattern of differentiation. As the regenerate develops, all the segments along its length often appear to be carved out simultaneously. Nevertheless, this case seems to be more closely allied to terminal, rather than to basal, growth.

The strategy which has determined whether the growth zone in regenerating systems shall be proximal or distal, and the general prevalence of the latter, appears to be related to whether or not the possibility for bifurcation of the regenerate must be preserved (Fig. 124). If the growth zone is apically situated, branching can occur by the dichotomous subdivision of the terminal bud. If it is basally located, however, bifurcation is impossible since the most differentiated regions of the regenerate which are formed first are pushed ahead of what develops later. The latter mode of growth is characteristic of organisms capable of regenerating along the body axis. This is the predominant pattern of regeneration in worms. It effectively rules out the undesirable possibility of developing branched heads or tails. The appendages of higher animals, however, retain the obvious advantages of bifurcation by growing at their ends.

Spectrum of Regeneration As interpreted throughout the present account, regeneration has been taken to mean the replacement of amputated structures by the outgrowth *in situ* of new parts equivalent to the original. This kind of regeneration involves a growth zone from which the morphological components of the developing structure are elaborated. At the level of the organism and its appendages, regeneration is achieved by means of a blastema formed at the site of amputation on the surface of the body. At the cellular level of organization, missing parts may also sprout from the surface, as in nerve regeneration. Even certain cytological organelles, such as cilia and flagella, elongate by terminal addition in an apical growth zone. This pattern of regeneration (amputation, formation of growing bud, morphogenesis) is as widespread as it is efficient. But it is limited to those structures in which morphological replacement is imperative if functional recovery is to be achieved.

Wound healing is in much the same category. It completes the interrupted continuity of tissues by means of ingrowth from the edges of what remains. The gap thus becomes filled by immature cells from which new tissues of appropriate kinds differentiate. In the integument, it is the so-called granulation tissue which gives rise to new dermis beneath the regenerated epithelium. In fractured bones it is the callus from which new skeletal tissues take shape. Severed tendons regenerate from the fibroblasts which accumulate between the cut ends and give rise to new collagen fibers. There is scarcely a tissue in the body which will not move to repair an injury. Whether the process is more properly referred to as regeneration or wound healing, however, depends on (a) whether or not the initiating trauma is an amputation or just a lesion, and (b) the extent to which the lost parts in question are replaced. Sometimes it is a moot point where one leaves off and the other begins.

In both regeneration and wound healing there is a distinct growth zone to provide the cells from which new structures can differentiate. This feature is shared also by the various renewing tissues in the body, tissues which must constantly generate a steady stream of new cells to replace their lost predecessors. Characteristic of such tissues as epidermis (and its appendages), the mucosal epithelium of the gut, various blood cells, and gametogenic tissues, this "physiological regeneration" is responsible for a continuous turnover of cells in which the rates of birth and death are carefully balanced. Without this equilibrium the morphology of renewing tissues could not be maintained, nor could their populations of cells be held constant.

Renewing tissues differ from mitotically static tissues (muscles, nerves) and expanding organs (glands) in that they possess a distinct growth zone. That is, the proliferating cells are spatially segregated from their differentiated descendants. For example, hemopoietic tissues are isolated from the circulating blood cells, the crypts of Lieberkühn are separated from the intestinal villi which they supply with epithelial cells, the basal layer of the epidermis is located below the stratum corneum, and primordial germ cells are set aside from the sperm and eggs they produce. The separation of the germinative compartment from the mature and functional one in renewing tissues reflects the incompatibility between mitosis and differentiation in these systems. Yet despite this separation, the input is perfectly adjusted to the output, with the result that a dynamic equilibrium of marvelous precision is established and maintained.

It is not enough, however, to keep a population of cells in equilibrium. The fact that a man may spend as much as he earns does not necessarily determine his salary level. Similarly, the number of cells present in a renewing tissue at any given moment is set at a specific level held constant by homeostatic mechanisms. This level is not predetermined, but is established relative to the physiological demands upon it. It can be raised or lowered as these demands wax and wane. Hence, the thickness of the epidermis or the number of erythrocytes in the blood may vary according to circumstances, for what is normal under one set of conditions may be pathological under another. A "normal" hematocrit at sea level, for example, would be anemic at high altitudes. "Every organism is what it is," wrote C. M. Child, "because of the relation of all its parts to each other and to the rest of the world."

The importance of this interplay between growth and function cannot be exaggerated, for it requires a communication mechanism to activate the generative tissues. Whether this communication is represented by stimulators or inhibitors, the views expressed so well by Michael Abercrombie of University College, London, are very much to the point: "Either the stimulant is systemically distributed by the blood stream, the response being localized only because the sensitive cells are localized; or the stimulant is predominantly local, the responding cells being not so much those sensitive to as those exposed to stimulation." Both of these alternatives have some truth to them because different kinds of tissues do not all adhere to the same rules.

Like appendage regeneration and wound healing, some renewing tissues, such as epidermis, appear to be under local control. That is, loss of tissue in one region does not elicit growth reactions throughout the rest of the epidermis. Conversely, loss of blood promotes heightened rates of hemopoiesis everywhere in the marrow. In the former case, the stimulating agency is locally effective (and may or may not exhibit tissue specificity); in the latter case its distribution is bodywide, but its control applies only to a specific tissue.

To replace exactly what was lost is not the only way to regenerate (Fig. 125). Many of the body's internal organs compensate for losses without bothering to grow back the missing part. Instead, they enlarge what remains. They can afford to react in this way because one part of their mass is as good as another. Liver regeneration, for example, is not achieved by replacing the lobes which may have been removed. To do it this way would have required more effort than was warranted. It is sufficient simply to expand the size of the residual lobes thus restoring the original mass of hepatic tissue as well as its functional capacities.

Compensatory hypertrophy in the liver is accompanied by hyperplasia of its cells and of the histological functional units into which

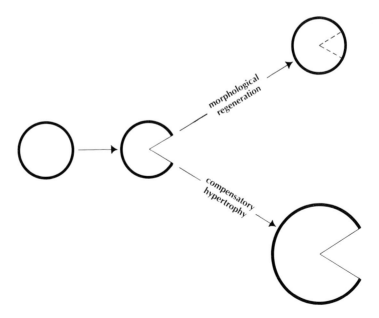

Fig. 125 **Comparison between qualitative and quantitative modes of regeneration. Some structures are replaced** in situ **by morphological regeneration. Others are not regrown, but their residual portions enlarge by compensatory hypertrophy.**

they are organized. Comparable responses are possible in many other endocrine and exocrine glands following surgical depletion or physiological insufficiency. The pancreas, thyroid, adrenals and ovaries are a few examples of organs which may grow back to their original volumes after partial deletions or unilateral extirpations. The way they compensate for such losses is the same way they grew during ontogeny. Here, then, "regeneration" is little more than a continuation of the original development of the organ. Why original development was turned off in the first place, to be reactivated after maturity by experimental or pathological interventions, will be an important part of our story.

Many organs in the body, such as those cited above, are theoretically capable of unlimited expansion because they never lose the capacity to multiply the units of structure upon which their specific physiological activities depend. These functional units may be cells in some cases (e.g., blood, parathyroid cells), but in many others they are represented by histological complexes (e.g., follicles, secretory acini). The important thing is that the population of these units in an organ can be indefinitely augmented under appropriate conditions.

Even more important, however, is the fact that not all organs are able to multiply their functional units in this way. Neurons and muscle fibers, for example, cannot undergo mitosis, thus restricting the growth potential of the adult nervous system, heart, and skeletal muscle. The lungs and kidneys are similarly limited by their inability to make additional pulmonary alveoli or renal nephrons, respectively, beyond early developmental stages.

How can such organs compensate when reduced in mass or overburdened with work? They have no alternative but to resort to hypertrophy when hyperplasia is not possible. That is, they increase the sizes of their remaining functional units rather than their numbers. Hypertrophy is not so physiologically efficient as hyperplasia, but it is better than nothing. Mindful of the fact that wherever hypertrophy of an organ occurs there must be hyperplasia of its constituent cells and organelles, one is impressed that the strategy of growth represented in different organs has not evolved by selecting either hypertrophy or hyperplasia as a *modus operandi* but by determining the levels of organization at which these methods of growth shall take place.

The panorama of regenerative phenomena extends from the replacement of amputated structures at one extreme to the compensatory growth of residual homologous tissues at the other. The mechanism adopted by each system suits its needs optimally, and alternative methods of growth are inefficient, if not ridiculous. Thus, organs composed of numerous functional units need not replace the exact portions which may have been removed when all that is required to restore physiological efficiency is to re-establish the original number of units no matter where they are located in the organ. Conversely, a bodily appendage for obvious reasons does not react to amputation by enlarging the dimensions of the stump or by doubling the size of the contralateral appendage. Neither of these methods would restore the function of the missing structure. Hence, natural selection has favored direct morphogenetic regeneration as the only way to make good the loss of many kinds of appendages. For equally good reasons, compensatory hypertrophy has been favored as the best way to restore internal organs.

Between appendicular regeneration on the one hand and compensatory hypertrophy on the other, is the rare but interesting phenomenon of compensatory regulation. This may occur when paired appendages are asymmetrical in size or degree of development. It sometimes happens that upon removal of the larger or more specialized structure, the contralateral one develops into a replica of its missing opposite partner. This reversal of asymmetry following unilateral amputation was first discovered many years ago by Hans Przibram. He found that in a few species of crustaceans the autotomy of the larger chela brought about at the next molt the transformation of the contralateral smaller one into a new large chela. Meanwhile, the original one is regenerated as a new small chela.

Something comparable was studied in the early years of this century in a serpulid worm by Charles Zeleny of Indiana University. Like so many biologists then and since, Zeleny used to spend his summers at the Marine Biological Laboratory at Woods Hole, Massachusetts. Here his attention was drawn to the curious fact that in *Hydroides dianthus*, a tube-dwelling annelid worm, an operculum with which to close the opening of its tube was developed on only one side. On the opposite side of the head, there is only a very rudimentary outgrowth. When he cut off the large functional operculum, Zeleny discovered that the opposite rudimentary one now began to develop into a large and effective replacement, while the original operculum was succeeded by only a small rudimentary one (Fig. 126). Nearly fifty years later, Marcel Abeloos at the University of Marseille re-examined this curious phenomenon. He discovered that by making an appropriate incision near the base of either the functional or the rudimentary operculum, the latter could be induced to develop into a mature operculum in a worm still in possession of its original functional one. Since the operation interrupts neither the nervous nor the vascular connections

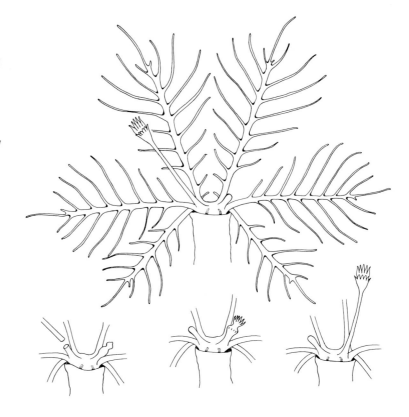

Fig. 126 **Compensatory regulation in the annelid worm** Hydroides dianthus, **which possesses a functional operculum paired with a rudimentary one on the opposite side. When the fully developed operculum is cut off (lower left) the former rudimentary appendage now matures into a functional one.** (After Zeleny, 1905.)

between the two opercula, neural and humoral communications must evidently be ruled out as possible explanations for the inhibitory influence by which the mature operculum dominates the immature one. What does account for the competition, however, remains as deep a mystery as ever.

Parenthetically, one is reminded of comparable examples of compensatory regulation in other systems. In some birds, there is characteristically only one ovary (on the left side). The right gonad remains rudimentary, unless the left ovary is removed, whereupon it now begins to develop. In most cases the new gonad turns out to be a testis, which secondarily brings about a reversal in the overt sex of the bird.

Perhaps still another example may be found in the narwhal. In the males there is a single long tusk which is an overdeveloped canine tooth. Only one canine (the left) develops to the dimensions of a tusk, the other remaining small. Possibly this is also a case of contralateral inhibition. One wonders if the smaller canine tooth would resume growth should the tusk itself be extracted.

In such sundry structures as crustacean chelae, annelid opercula, avian gonads and maybe even narwhal tusks, one member of a pair of organs is normally smaller than the other, but can develop into the larger type if the original one is removed. Compensatory regulation, then, is a kind of "regeneration" stimulated not by direct amputation, but by release from an inhibitory influence presumably emanating from the more dominant member of the pair. What this influence could be, and how it operates to hold development in check, is one of the great unsolved problems in regeneration.

The Utilitarian Imperative What do the diverse modes of regenerative and compensatory growth have in common? Confronted with similar problems, namely, the need to replace lost parts, various organs and tissues arrive at similar solutions by way of very different routes. Their common denominator, however, is not so much the structures to be regenerated as the functions these structures represent.

The process of regeneration restores physiological as well as morphological integrity, for the replaced parts, if they are to be useful, must be the very essence of functional design. Not unexpectedly, factors responsible for stimulating regeneration are time and again the very ones upon which the ultimate function of the new structure will depend. Natural selection operates on the basis of physiological efficiency, so it is no coincidence that nothing ever regenerates unless it is functional. To be sure, structures do not regenerate for the purpose of functioning. They function because all of the less useful alternatives were long since weeded out in the discriminating course of evolution.

Neither regeneration nor compensatory hypertrophy occurs solely as a result of amputation of an appendage or partial ablation of an organ. Something extra is needed, namely, a link with appropriate physiological factors. Regenerative strategy dictates that the wherewithal for functional competence shall develop coextensively with the structural machinery for implementing that function. Indeed, so intimately related are these two components of the system that neither can develop without the other. Of the two, however, it is significant that the physiological factor plays the role of stimulator upon which morphological regeneration depends, which may be taken to indicate that function is of greater fundamental importance than structure in regenerating or compensating systems.

This is undeniably evident in the case of compensatory hypertrophy. The growth of adult organs can be stimulated not only by their partial resection, but equally well by functional overload. Indeed, the reason that growth is promoted when the mass of an organ is reduced is because the residual portion is now subjected to greater demands for physiological output. If such demands are bypassed by various forms of replacement therapy, then a partially excised organ will not grow, and may even atrophy. For example, unilateral adrenalectomy fails to elicit hypertrophy of the opposite organ if cortical steroids are administered. Similarly, the loss of blood can enhance erythropoiesis only if the body's demands for oxygen are raised, as they usually are. But if a bled animal is exposed to elevated atmospheric pressure or increased amounts of oxygen, the rate of red cell production may be depressed instead of stimulated.

Thus, the growth of each organ or tissue is susceptible to influences which regulate its physiological activities, and these are as varied as the jobs to be performed. Many of the endocrine glands respond both functionally and developmentally to appropriate trophic hormones. Others are affected by electrolyte levels in the blood, such as calcium in the case of the parathyroid and sodium in the case of the zona glomerulosa of the adrenal cortex. In each case, a deficiency of these ions in the blood stream promotes growth as it stimulates secretion in the corresponding glands. What altitude is to the lungs, so also is hypertension to the heart, testosterone to the prostate, autonomic innervation to the salivary glands, and exercise to skeletal muscle. We do not pretend to know in the case of each and every organ what controls its growth, but the pattern is inescapable: one looks for the factors which regulate function, and there are to be found the keys to growth. It is no coincidence, therefore, that the organs whose growth is most poorly understood, namely, liver and kidney, happen to be the ones which are physiologically most complicated.

Clearly, what works for one organ does not work for another. When seeking unified explanations for diverse phenomena it is futile to take the specific details too literally. Rather, each must be looked upon as a special case of a more general concept. In compensatory hypertrophy, it is unimportant whether growth is controlled by hormones, electrolytes, nerves, or oxygen levels. The salient point is that each agent is pertinent to the functional competence of an appropriate organ or tissue. We must now ask if the same rule applies to the regeneration of amputated structures.

In view of the prevalence of the trophic effect of nerves on regeneration, and sometimes the very maintenance of so many structures in the invertebrates as well as the vertebrates, one is tempted to regard neural relationships as essential to all kinds of regeneration. Not only do many appendages, such as limbs, fins and barbels, require nerves for their structural regeneration, but most tails depend upon the spinal cord, annelid regeneration is absent or abnormal without the ventral nerve cord, eyes fail to regenerate in flatworms unless the brain is present, the newt lens is not replaced if the neural retina is lacking, and taste buds degenerate following denervation. These and many other examples testify to the widespread role played by neural tissues in regeneration. Yet the overwhelming importance of the trophic effects of nerves in so many regenerating systems must not blind us to the fact that not everything depends upon innervation in order to grow and regenerate. For unexplained reasons, tadpole tails can regenerate without a spinal cord, and the regenerates of *Xenopus* legs, if reamputated and denervated, can grow out again despite the absence of a nerve supply. In the case of deer antlers, which also regenerate independently of their innervation, the explanation is easier to grasp. Although antlers are richly supplied with nerves while growing, their mature ossified form is skinless, nerveless and dead. It is hardly surprising, that for these secondary sexual characters the gonads, not nerves, should be significantly involved in their growth.

Nerves, therefore, are not universally necessary for regeneration. They are more widely required than other factors only because of their major importance in mediating function in such a large variety of organs and tissues. Consequently, the regeneration of an inordinate number of structures is bound up with innervation. But the trophic influence of nerves is not to be regarded as the only stimulus to regenerative growth. It has its counterparts in all other pathways for regulating physiological activities in many of the body's internal organs, organs which can grow and function even in the absence of a nerve supply but not in the absence of their own specific forms of physiological stimuli.

Hence growth in adult organisms depends upon a broad spectrum of function demands, a prominent segment of which embraces the trophic influences of neural tissues. In this perspective, the common denominator of regeneration and compensatory growth lies in the utilitarian imperative that the parts of mature animals may grow only on the condition that the end product of development shall be physiologically meaningful.

Embryology and Regeneration

What applies to the adult does not necessarily apply to the immature organism. Adults function, embryos do not. One of the major differences between regeneration and generation, therefore, is that regeneration depends on physiological stimuli while embryos develop autonomously. The utilitarian imperative cannot logically be applied to prefunctional systems in the sense that no physiological deficiency is fulfilled by embryonic development. You cannot lose anything until you have it to lose, and the embryo rarely misses what it never had. It follows that embryos ought not to be able to regenerate. In most cases they cannot, although the distinction between regeneration and regulation is admittedly hazy.

In flatworms, for example, regeneration can occur in embryos but it is delayed until a sufficient degree of maturity has been attained. Not only must neoblasts have developed, which they do early in embryonic life, but the nervous system must also have differentiated. If the embryo is cut in half prior to these stages, blastema formation is held in abeyance until nerve trunks develop. Only then will regeneration commence.

If part of the tail bud is cut off an amphibian embryo, there is little or no regeneration and the resulting tail turns out to be correspondingly deficient. The missing parts are not restored in the larva unless the whole tail is amputated proximal to the defective region, whereupon normal regeneration ensues. Presumably the absent portions are not replaced at the time they are removed due to the lack of sufficient maturity on the part of the tissues in the developing tail bud. Once these tissues attain an appropriate level of maturity they still fail to regenerate spontaneously because there is no injury of amputation.

A similar example is encountered in the case of the lizard tail. Amputation is seldom followed by regeneration in the embryo unless performed soon before hatching. At best only small abortive outgrowths, destined for regression, are produced. Such tails do not resume their growth belatedly even after hatching, unless, of course, they are reamputated.

A somewhat different situation obtains in the eyes of newts capable of regenerating lenses. Here it will be recalled that neither injury nor wound healing is a factor in initiating the development of a new lens from the dorsal iris after the original one has been removed. Hence, it would be interesting to learn if the iris can regenerate a lens when there was never any lens there to begin with. These circumstances can be set up experimentally by removing the presumptive lens ectoderm from the embryo before it has been induced to form a lens, or by lentectomy at various later stages of development. In both cases, the eye eventually does regenerate a new lens from the dorsal iris, but only after a considerable delay (Fig. 127). Not until early larval stages does the pigmented iris epithelium acquire the competence to react to the lensless condition by "replacing" what was never there in the first place. Here again it seems that regeneration cannot proceed until a

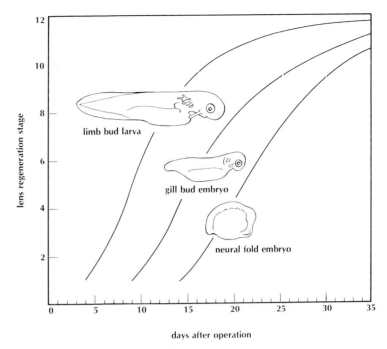

Fig. 127 **Regeneration from the dorsal iris of lenses in lensless embryonic salamander eyes. Lentectomized larvae (left curve) replace lenses at normal rate. Advanced embryos (middle curve) from which the incipient lens rudiments have been removed, regenerate new lenses only after several days' delay. Early embryos (right curve), deprived of presumptive lens ectoderm before lens differentiation has begun, grow lenses from the dorsal iris following a lag of about two weeks. The length of delay is proportional to the time required for the iris to mature enough to be able to give rise to a lens.** *(Adapted from Reyer, 1948 and 1950).*

sufficient degree of maturity has been reached, but what qualities must be acquired before the tissues of an embryo become regeneratively competent time alone will tell.

Apropos of the elusive distinction between embryogenesis and regeneration, a major breakthrough was achieved in the studies of amphibian arms allowed to develop from the limb bud stage in the permanent absence of nerves. These aneurogenic limbs regenerate despite their lack of innervation. One might say that they never became dependent upon the nerves which never invaded them. Is this remarkable phenomenon one of a kind, or does it represent a more general situation lying undiscovered in many other regenerating systems? Perhaps the multitude of organs and tissues elsewhere in the body, each in its own way, arrive at a crucial period in their ontogenies when their future growth becomes inseparably bound to those regulatory mechanisms upon which functional activity depends. If so, could they continue to grow and regenerate on their own as do nerveless limbs in amphibians? This improbable possibility has yet to be subjected to experimental tests. It deserves to be explored, however, for the clues it might provide toward the solution of such urgent problems as how tissues grow, regenerate, and at times become cancerous.

New Parts for Old There are two ways to replace missing parts of the body. One is to grow new ones; the other is to graft them. Regeneration is nature's way of making good a deficit; transplantation is man's solution to the problem. Seldom has nature resorted to transplantation; rarer still has man successfully contrived to induce regeneration where nature did not intend.

Regenerative powers are inconveniently deficient in higher vertebrates. Worse still, our immunological defenses insure that foreign tissue grafts shall be efficiently rejected. With the odds stacked heavily against us, the problem of how to repair the depreciation of the body's organs is as formidable as it is intriguing. And even if we cannot do much about the situation yet, perhaps some consolation is to be found in understanding why such a state of affairs should have evolved in the first place.

Regeneration is a negative phenomenon in the sense that it presupposes a vulnerability on the part of all organisms. The fact that the phenomenon exists at all testifies to the prevalence of this susceptibility to the hazrads of life. Nature has invented no end of ingenious ways to provide for the replacement of or compensation for lost parts. Yet the very existence of such mechanisms is in inverse proportion to the progress that organisms have made toward reducing their liability to injury. This is not surprising since evolution itself operates on the principle of competition, which is by definition a dangerous sport.

Nevertheless, the absence of regeneration in certain forms may sometimes be taken to indicate that the problem of vulnerability may have been solved by preventive measures rather than remedial ones. In other words, regeneration is a good thing when an organism has failed to insure its own security from injury. But it is far better not to be injured in the first place, thus making regeneration superfluous. Hence, the phylogenetic reduction in regenerative potential signifies not so much a loss of developmental versatility as the successful evolution of self-protective adaptations. This may be regarded as an encouraging trend.

Of one thing there can be no doubt, that regeneration was originally universal and synonymous with development and reproduction. From the beginning, the potential to regenerate has been sacrificed as other advantages have evolved. Yet, regenerative capacities have not been abandoned lightly. Indeed, the remarkable thing is how cleverly organisms have contrived to retain the ability to regenerate while evolving ever more complex strategies to avoid extinction. Only as a last resort has regeneration been forfeited in order to secure the advantages of attributes with which regeneration proved to be incompatible. Admittedly, nature can achieve almost anything if the stakes are high enough, provided the laws of chemistry and physics are not violated. Thus, in some instances regeneration manifests itself in extraordinarily unexpected places. In other cases, its unaccountable absence might never have been predicted.

In the course of evolution, the pros and cons have been weighed by each group of animals. Some have found regeneration to be indispensable, and have devised all manner of mechanisms to insure its retention. Others have opted to get along without it, and have derived the benefits of investing their energies in other directions. Most animals have struck a compromise by keeping the ability to regenerate some parts of the body, but not others.

It is generally accepted, with some important reservations, that regenerative ability has tended to decline during the course of evolution. Yet this notion must be qualified with reference to the level of organization at which structures are replaceable, a perspective graphically represented in Fig. 128. At the molecular and ultrastructural levels, regeneration is equally efficient in all organisms throughout the phylogenetic scale. It is at the higher levels of organization, where histologically complex body parts are involved, that the ability to grow

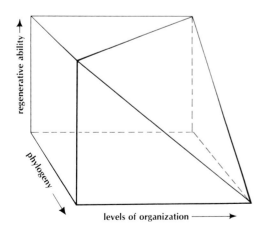

Fig. 128 **Regenerative ability declines in two dimensions at once. At lower phylogenetic levels, regeneration is possible at all levels of structural organization. Higher organisms regenerate cells, organelles and molecules as well as lower ones do, but not appendages or major fractions of their bodies.**

replacements has been curtailed in the course of evolution. Thus, higher animals are less capable of regenerating heads, tails or appendages than lower ones, but their molecular and cellular turnover is just as good as it ever was. Therefore, it is not regeneration *per se* which has been selected against during phylogeny, but the level of organization at which it occurs.

There is, in addition, more than one way to regenerate. The most direct, of course, is to grow back what was lost in exactly the same form and location as the original. The new thus becomes a replica of the old, indistinguishable in every detail from the structure it replaces. Yet sometimes a given body part is not so individually important that its loss cannot just as well be made good in ways other than by reproducing a faithful copy of itself. Homologous structures, for example, may be increased in size or number to compensate for missing parts, and thereby achieve the ultimate goal of regeneration, namely, the recovery of function through replacement of structure. To expect organisms always to regenerate precisely what was lost is to deny the evolution of the most efficient way of achieving an end. Evolution is not that rigid. It has no loyalty to one mode of development over another. All that counts is whether or not the method which evolves is the one that works best.

Man is in no position to dispute the dogma that what evolves is by definition that which is the fittest. Our very existence on earth testifies to the fitness of our progenitors, and hopefully of ourselves. This, despite the inability of most of us to regenerate parts of ourselves we might often wish to replace. Yet we have eluded extinction despite such shortcomings. Nature may indeed be capable of achieving virtually anything so long as it is within the rules of the game, but in the final reckoning the advantages of such achievements must be weighed against the costs. He who spends money on luxuries at the expense of necessities is not a very good financial risk. Thus, if we lack certain attributes that other animals possess, let us not lament the unfairness of things, for what we do not have would probably have cost too much anyway.

REFERENCES

ABELOOS, M. 1952. La "régénération compensatrice" chez *Hydroides norvegica* (Gunn) et les mécanismes de la morphogenèse. *Bull. Soc. Zool. France* **77**: 462–470.

ABERCROMBIE, M. 1957. Localized formation of new tissue in an adult mammal. *Symp. Soc. Exptl. Biol.* **11**: 235–254.

BRYANT, S. V. and A. D'A. BELLAIRS. 1967. Amnio-allantoic constriction bands in lizard embryos and their effects on tail regeneration. *J. Zool.* **152:** 155–161.

BULLOUGH, W. S. 1967. "The Evolution of Differentiation." Academic Press, New York.

BULLOUGH, W. S. and E. B. LAURENCE. 1967. Epigenetic mitotic control. *In* "Control of Cellular Growth in Adult Organisms" (H. Teir and T. Rytömaa, eds.), pp. 28–40. Academic Press, New York.

CHILD, C. M. 1902. Studies on regulation. I. Fission and regulation in Stenostoma. *Arch. Entwicklungsmech. Organ.* **15:** 187–237.

ELLIS, M. M. 1909. The relation of the amount of tail regenerated to the amount removed in tadpoles of *Rana clamitans. J. Exptl. Zool.* **7:** 421–455.

GOSS, R. J. 1965a. "Adaptive Growth." Academic Press, New York.

GOSS, R. J. 1965b. Kinetics of compensatory growth. *Quart. Rev. Biol.* **40:** 123–146.

GOSS, R. J. 1965c. Mammalian regeneration and its phylogenetic relationships. *In* "Regeneration in Animals and Related Problems" (V. Kiortsis and H. A. L. Trampusch, eds.), pp. 33–37. North-Holland Publ. Co., Amsterdam.

GOSS, R. J. 1965d. The functional demand theory of growth regulation. *In* "Regeneration in Animals and Related Problems" (V. Kiortsis and H. A. L. Trampusch, eds.), pp. 444–451. North-Holland Publ. Co., Amsterdam.

GOSS, R. J. 1966. Hypertrophy versus hyperplasia. *Science* **153:** 1615–1620.

GOSS, R. J. 1967. The strategy of growth. *In* "Control of Cellular Growth in Adult Organisms" (H. Teir and T. Rytömaa, eds.), pp. 3–27. Academic Press, New York.

LE MOIGNE, A. 1965. Mise en évidence d'un pouvoir de régénération chez l'embryon de *Polycelis nigra* (Turbellarié-Triclade) *Bull. Soc. Zool. France* **90:** 355–361.

OBERPRILLER, J. 1967. A radioautographic analysis of the potency of blastemal cells in the adult newt. *Diemictylus viridescens. Growth* **31:** 251–296.

PRZIBRAM, H. 1907. Equilibrium of animal form. *J. Exptl. Zool.* **5:** 259–264.

REYER, R. 1948. An experimental study of lens regeneration in Triturus viridescens viridescens. I. Regeneration of a lens after lens extirpation in embryos and larvae of different ages. *J. Exptl. Zool.* **107:** 217–267.

REYER, R. 1950. An experimental study of lens regeneration in Triturus viridescens viridescens. II. Lens development from the dorsal iris in the absence of the embryonic lens. *J. Exptl. Zool.* **113:** 317–353.

ROSE, S. M. 1967. The aging of the system for the transmission of information controlling differentiation. *J. Gerontol.* **22:** 28–41.

TASSAVA, R. and R. J. GOSS. 1966. Regeneration rate and amputation level in fish fins and lizard tails. *Growth* **30:** 9–21.

WILSON, E. B. 1903. Notes on the reversal of asymmetry in the regeneration of the chelæ in Alpheus heterochelis. *Biol. Bull.* **4:** 197–210.

ZELENY, C. 1905. Compensatory regulation. *J. Exptl. Zool.* **2:** 1–102.

ZELENY, C. 1907. The direction of differentiation in development. *Arch. Entwicklungsmech. Organ.* **23:** 324–343.

Index